£2.80

Last copy offers.

AUTHOR	CLASS X
MILLIKAN, R. A.	539.72112
TITLE	No.
Electron.	491157800

ROBERT ANDREWS MILLIKAN

THE ELECTRON

ITS ISOLATION AND MEASUREMENT
AND THE DETERMINATION OF SOME
OF ITS PROPERTIES

ROBERT ANDREWS MILLIKAN

Edited with an introduction by
JESSE W. M. DuMond

THE UNIVERSITY OF CHICAGO PRESS
CHICAGO AND LONDON

This is a facsimile of the original 1917 edition,
and in the interests of bibliographical integrity
errors rectified in the second edition here stand
uncorrected.

Library of Congress Catalog Card Number: 63-20910

THE UNIVERSITY OF CHICAGO PRESS, CHICAGO 60637
The University of Chicago Press, Ltd., London W.C.1

© *1917 and 1924 by The University of Chicago. All rights
reserved. Published 1917. Second Edition 1924. Tenth
Impression 1968. Printed in the United States of America*

TO

ALBERT A. MICHELSON

AND

MARTIN A. RYERSON

THIS SMALL OUTGROWTH OF THEIR

INSPIRATION AND GENEROSITY

IS RESPECTFULLY DEDICATED

PREFACE TO THE FIRST EDITION

It is hoped that this volume may be of some interest both to the physicist and to the reader of somewhat less technical training. It has been thought desirable for the sake of both classes of readers, not to break the thread of the discussion in the body of the book with the detailed analyses which the careful student demands. It is for this reason that all mathematical proofs have been thrown into appendixes. If, in spite of this, the general student finds certain chapters, such as vii and viii, unintelligible, it is hoped that without them he may yet gain some idea of certain phases at least of the progress of modern physics.

R. A. MILLIKAN

CONTENTS

EDITOR'S INTRODUCTION

There were giants in the earth in those days.

GEN. 6:4

The life of Robert Andrews Millikan covered the period from March 22, 1868, to December 19, 1953. Assuming his career as a physicist to have started in 1895, the year he received his Ph.D. at Columbia University, he was active as a physicist for fifty-eight years up to a few months before his death.

This particular fifty-eight-year span may well be said to have been the golden age of pure physics. A few examples of the progress made in this period should serve to justify this statement.

W. C. Roentgen discovered X-rays in 1895, the year Millikan's career as a physicist began. The next year Henri Becquerel discovered nuclear radioactivity (in potassium uranium double sulfate), and this was rapidly followed by the isolation of the radioactive substances—radium, thorium, and polonium—by the Curies in 1898.

The famous experiment of Michelson and Morley demonstrating that the speed of light propagation relative to the terrestrial frame of reference is independent of the motion of that frame relative to the fixed star system had been performed only eight years earlier, in 1887. This experiment was the chief foundation stone upon which Albert Einstein, in 1905, constructed his earliest (or "special") theory of relativity, with its astonishingly far-reaching consequences.

In 1901 Max Planck proposed a new formula which described, far more successfully than any other up to that time, the curve of the spectral distribution of intensity of so-called "black body radiation," the equilibrium state of electromagnetic radiation when exchanging energy with the material walls inside an inclosure held at a definite temperature, T. The theory upon which this formula was based required the supposition that radiant energy must be emitted from the atoms of the walls or absorbed by them only in discrete amounts ("quanta") proportional to the frequency of the radiation, and Planck was able to give a numerical estimate for

xi

the constant of proportionality, h. Thus the quantum theory was born, although no direct observation of the discontinuous processes of emission and absorption of radiation by atoms had as yet been made.

The photoelectric effect may be said to have been first discovered by Heinrich Hertz and by Hallwachs in 1887 and 1888. In 1905 Einstein proposed the quantum law describing the photoelectric effect, the discontinuous process just referred to. It was reserved for R. A. Millikan in 1916 to verify experimentally the correctness of this law and to use it to make a quantitative determination of the above-mentioned universal constant, h.

In 1897 J. J. Thomson's measurements of the specific charge-to-mass ratio of cathode rays and Townsend's estimates of the electronic charge, e (by observing rates of fall of clouds consisting of charged droplets), were the forerunners which stimulated Millikan in 1909 to perform the famous oil-drop experiment (described in this volume), which clearly demonstrated the discrete or "unitary" nature of electricity and which made Millikan world-famous.

In order to see R. A. Millikan's contribution more clearly in relationship to the rapid general evolution of physical science in this exciting period, the Calendar following this Introduction lists in chronological order some of the outstanding events, discoveries, and inventions between 1887 and 1953. It is worthy of note that in the fifty-eight-year period, 1895–1953, which covered Millikan's career, there were more than seventy outstanding events of scientific significance, advances in knowledge of physical laws or inventions of new scientific techniques or apparatus.

The vitality, zest, enthusiasm, excitement, and creativity of this period were enormous. It is difficult to convey adequately to one who has not lived through such an experience how deeply its participants were involved. Millikan was very much a part of this intensely stimulating activity and his name was closely linked with those of many of the other outstanding scientific men of the period, A. A. Michelson, H. A. Lorentz, Albert Einstein, Ernest Rutherford, Niels Bohr, Arthur Compton, W. Pauli, Carl D. Anderson, George E. Hale, and many more.

One of the qualities that characterized the period and which in the United States set it apart rather distinctly from the post-World

War II scientific epoch was a direct result of the paucity of financial support for research in the physical sciences. Physics had not yet been overfed with money. There was no incentive other than a devouring interest in the subject for itself. Purity of motivation on the part of workers in the physical sciences was thus almost automatically guaranteed. Scientific curiosity, the attraction of the unknown, the challenge of the unexplained were necessarily the most powerful and indeed virtually the only stimuli. The word *physicist* was almost meaningless to the man in the street. The career of physicist was by and large so ill-compensated that nothing but the inherent attraction of the subject itself could account for its selection as a life work by a man with Millikan's well-rounded gifts of personality.

Millikan's first inclination was to a career as an instructor in physical training, and friends from his early days recall seeing him doing exhibition performances on the parallel bars with a flaming orange-colored sash pendant from his waist. If he had stayed in that profession, his income might indeed for a decade or more have been superior to his actual compensation as a physicist!

Fortunately, fate ordained that Millikan early in his life would be bitten by the research bug and acquire a thirst for scientific knowledge. These never deserted him. His life was full of turning points ("forks in the road," he called them), at which major choices had to be made between personal security, ease, wealth, even luxury on the one hand, and on the other the challenge of the difficult, the uncertain, the untried in the search for knowledge and for what he believed would make a better world. In these choices he never failed to accept the challenge and to reject the easeful temptation. Thus he was not only a great teacher by precept but in the noblest and most convincing of all ways—by example.

Mrs. Millikan as late as the 1920's was wont to tell a story of the days at the University of Chicago when the young couple were living on a salary whose initial figure at the time of their marriage was $1,800 a year. (Millikan states in his autobiography that he "started at the bottom of the many-runged ladder at Chicago University" on a salary of $900 per year.) The famous oil-drop experiment on which her husband was working at the time required him to sit for long hours continuously observing the rise and fall of a tiny droplet of oil suspended in air between the opposing forces of gravity and the balancing upward pull of an electrical field furnished by a source of electrical potential under his control, changing the field as needed to maintain balance if the droplet accidentally captured or lost a unit or more of charge. Since the atoms of the electrically charged droplet were said to be "ionized," the droplets themselves were frequently loosely referred to as "ions." On many occasions, when Millikan, preoccupied with research, worked late into the evenings in the laboratory after a long day of teaching, it was his wife who took his place at parties and University social functions. To get complete data on one particular oil droplet sometimes involved hours of patient watching in the microscope. One night the Millikans were to have guests to dinner. At six o'clock Dr. Millikan was only halfway through with his observations on a droplet, so he told Mrs. Millikan on the telephone (to quote from his autobiography): "I had watched an ion for an hour and a half and had to finish the job." He asked her to go ahead with dinner without him. When the wife of a well-to-do friend of the University inquired at the table why Dr. Millikan was absent, the reason was given verbatim. Later the lady spoke to her husband, saying in a shocked tone, "I think it's scandalous that they underpay these poor young professors so cruelly! I always heard their salaries were small but I was really astonished when Mrs. Millikan told me her husband had to miss his dinner because he had 'washed and ironed for an hour and a half and had to finish the job.'"

Another condition peculiar to this time was the relatively small number of practicing physicists. They formed a very limited coterie of initiates who understood each other's enthusiasms, interests, and hopes, and who by and large helped and stimulated each other in the midst of a philistine world. This was true to a large extent even in Europe, but it was most emphatically so in the United States. Up to the year 1893 no specialized American journals in the physical sciences existed. The *Physical Review*, founded by E. L. Nichols of Cornell, and the *Astrophysical Journal*, founded by George E. Hale of the University of Chicago in that year, were the first publications.

DEVELOPMENT OF OUR KNOWLEDGE OF THE ELECTRON
FROM 1897 TO 1947

Undoubtedly the most important factor contributing to the vitality and productivity of this epoch in American science was the intrinsic fascination and excitement of the subject itself. To try to visualize this, consider the evolution of knowledge concerning just one of the entities which early twentieth-century research brought to light and with which Millikan's name is so closely linked—the electron. The very *meaning* of the word has changed radically from the one it had when Millikan and others first used it. In that earlier sense the word did not refer, as it does today, to a particle or entity of some kind possessed of a number of measurable properties such as a magnetic moment, an angular momentum with a spin direction, a wave length, an intrinsic self-energy, etc. The word electron implied simply *a quantity of electricity*, the fundamental unit in fact, of either positive or negative sign. However, Millikan and other early writers at times seem to use the word electron almost synonymously with proton. It is the "quantity of electricity" about which they are speaking, wholly dissociated from the other characteristics of mass, energy, linear momentum, angular momentum, magnetic moment, or the like, which a particular charged particle may happen to possess. And indeed the fact that this fundamental unit of charge is, as far as we know, precisely the same in absolute magnitude whether it is associated with an electron, a proton, a π- or a μ-meson, or with a large number of other particles, gives us good reason to justify the use of a word to describe it independently of the other properties of the entity with which it is associated. Nevertheless, the word *electron* has long since ceased to mean simply the natural indivisible unit of electrical charge.

The idea that electricity is not an infinitely subdivisible continuous fluid but consists of discrete particles of some kind, an idea entertained by British physicists such as Sir William Crookes but opposed by the Germans such as Philipp Lenard, was rendered much more tenable by the work of J. J. Thomson in 1897. He deflected a beam of cathode rays, as they were then called, by projecting them through the electrical field between two condenser plates in a vacuum tube. By also providing a magnetic field of strength and direction suitable to restore the beam to its original undeflected course, Thomson was able to compute the velocity of the postulated charged particles. The measurement of the deflection suffered by the beam under the influence of the electric field alone then served to give sufficient information to compute the specific charge-to-mass ratio, e/m, of the particles. This ratio turned out to be very close to that inferred by Zeeman in 1896 for the charged particles which he postulated as taking part in light emission from atoms under the influence of an externally applied magnetic field.

Next, Townsend, working in J. J. Thomson's laboratory, observed the rate of fall of the clouds of water droplets that form about the ions in saturated air. From the observed rate of fall of the cloud, he was able to determine the average size of the droplets by applying Stokes' law for the terminal velocity of free fall of spheres through a viscous medium. By a measurement of the total quantity of water in the cloud, he could then estimate the number of droplets in the cloud. Assuming that each droplet had condensed around just one ion and that that ion carried one, and only one, of the fundamental unit charges, he was able to estimate the magnitude of the unit charge. This estimate yielded 6.5×10^{-10} esu, a value which later proved to be only about 30 per cent too high.

Twelve years elapsed before Millikan developed a more reliable method of studying ionic charges, the single oil-drop method, which constitutes the principal subject of this volume. The lucidity and simplicity of his own explanation cannot be improved upon. The reader of this book will surely find it stimulating.

Millikan arrived at the value for the electronic charge

$$e = 4.774 \times 10^{-10} \text{ esu .}$$

This value of e was accepted for the next twenty years, but in 1928 Erik Bäcklin's measurements of the absolute wave lengths of certain X-ray spectral lines by means of an artificial ruled grating yielded an indirect but more accurate way of calculating e. For if the wave length of the X-ray line is known, the absolute size of the atomic lattice spacings in crystals can be determined by the methods of X-ray crystal diffraction discovered and developed in 1912 and 1913 by Laue, Friedrich, and Knipping in Germany, and by Sir

William Bragg in England. The absolute volume of the "unit cell" of the crystal can thus be calculated, and multiplying this by the macroscopically measured density of the crystal gives the absolute mass of the unit cell. The quotient of the molecular weight of the unit cell by the absolute mass then gives the Avogadro number, N. Dividing the Faraday (the electrical charge carried by a monovalent gram atom of any substance, a quantity accurately determinable by electrochemical methods) by N then yields e. Bäcklin in this way obtained a value of e substantially larger than Millikan's. The discrepancy was later traced to Millikan's having used too low a value for the viscosity of air in reducing his oil-drop data. The accepted value of e is now in the neighborhood of

$$e = 4.8033 \pm 0.0002 \times 10^{-10} \text{ esu}.$$

The accurate determination of the numerical value of the electronic charge was not Millikan's greatest achievement, however. Certainly to have determined it correctly with an error of less than 1 per cent was a great advance on the earlier, far less accurate information obtained from Townsend's clouds of water droplets. But the outstanding achievement of Millikan's oil-drop studies was, to use his own term, the demonstration beyond any manner of doubt of the "unitary nature of electricity." What could be more exciting or more awe-inspiring for a physicist than to watch the speed of rise or fall of that tiny oil droplet and realize that the figures proved that the charge on it never changed save in discrete steps, and that all of these steps could be accounted for as small whole multiples of a single unit! Imagine Millikan in those lonely midnight vigils when he was watching the droplet, the first to be *certain* of this tremendous piece of evidence about one of the fundamental building blocks of the world.

Others at the time attacked Millikan's conclusion, in particular the Viennese physicist Ehrenhaft, who tried to adduce evidence that he had observed "sub-electrons," that is to say, increments of electrical charge substantially smaller than Millikan's e, but Millikan's achievement has withstood the test of time and the natural unit of electrical charge is a universal constant which constitutes one of the cornerstones of physical theory.

Other very important by-products resulted from the oil-drop

work, such as Millikan's studies of the Brownian motion from which the Avogadro number can be estimated, and his correction to Stokes's law of terminal velocity of fall of spheres in a viscous medium for the case of low gaseous pressures. Each is a classical example of careful research. The latter work Millikan lovingly referred to as "the oil drop falling down through the holes between the atoms," when their mean free paths became long relative to the diameter of the drop.

Let us proceed however with the story of the evolution of knowledge concerning electrons. J. J. Thomson had proposed an atom model in which the mass and positive electricity were more or less uniformly and continuously distributed throughout a small spherical region. The electrons were supposed elastically imbedded in this sphere "like plums in a pudding," occupying positions of equilibrium about which they might vibrate when excited—for instance by electromagnetic radiation. In 1909 and 1910 Geiger and Marsden in England performed experiments in which alpha particles (helium nuclei) were projected through thin foils of gold and other materials. They found that, whereas most of the particles passed nearly straight through the foil, some of them (more than would be predicted on the Thomson model) were scattered violently in the backward direction. In 1911 Ernest Rutherford proposed a new type of atom model which successfully explained the distribution of the scattering of Geiger and Marsden's alpha particles. Rutherford assumed that in an atom the positive charge and most of the mass are concentrated in a small central region, later called the nucleus, about which the electrons are grouped in an extended and much less dense configuration. Rutherford likened the scattering of alpha particles by the gold foil to the bombardment by a barrage of tennis balls of a hedge consisting of hop-vines supported on poles hidden among the foliage. Most of the tennis balls pass through the foliage with little or no deflection by the light, leafy structure of the vines, but once in a great while a ball hits a pole in approximately head-on collision and is thrown violently backward by this heavy obstacle. At the time, however, this essentially correct picture was faced with one difficulty. The Reverend Samuel Earnshaw had shown on the basis of the known properties of electromagnetism that no arrangement of positive and negative point charges can ever be in static stable equilibrium. If the electrons were to remain bound in the inverse-square-law field of force of the nucleus (the so-called Coulomb field), they must execute some sort of orbit around the nucleus as center. But if they did this, the electromagnetic laws of Maxwell would require them to radiate energy so that they would execute spiral paths of diminishing radius and eventually fall into the positive nucleus. It was impossible to understand how such an atom model could emit spectral lines of constant frequency characteristic of each atom.

Clearly something radically new had to be injected into the picture, and this came in 1913 with Niels Bohr's proposal of a quantum condition which determines certain orbits for the electrons as non-radiating states. This condition was at first invented *ad hoc* to fit the observations regarding the characteristic spectral lines of hydrogen which form an orderly series of frequencies, the so-called Balmer series. Bohr's proposed quantum condition required that the angular momentum of the electron in its orbital motion about the nucleus be an integral multiple of a natural unit, $h/2\pi$, where h was the quantum of action of Max Planck. The success of this theory in explaining *quantitatively* not only the hydrogen spectrum line series but also other series, notably the lines in the X-ray spectrum which had just been discovered and studied by Moseley, was nothing less than sensational. About eleven years elapsed, however, before the meaning of Bohr's quantum condition began to be appreciated in terms of a new property of the electron. The wave-aspect of the electron was first proposed by Louis de Broglie in France, followed soon after by Schrödinger's equation and then by the Davisson and Germer experiment in which electron waves were clearly shown to be diffracted by the periodic lattice structure of a monocrystal (a crystal of nickel in the first experiment) in a way completely analogous to the diffraction of X-rays by crystal lattices. These developments clarified the meaning of Bohr's "stationary states" or non-radiating electron orbits in terms of the electron waves. Just as the length of a violin string, the size and shape of a drum head, or the geometry of a cavity define natural periods of vibration for sound waves or electromagnetic waves which, by repeated reflection from the boundaries, interfere to form stationary nodes and loops, so the Coulomb field of the nucleus, boxing in the bound electrons, defines natural modes of vibration of the electron waves. The Coulomb field does not constitute a sharply defined boundary like the walls of a cavity, but this merely complicates somewhat the spatial distribution of the stationary nodes and loops. It is as though the waves were reflected by a long shelving beach instead of by a vertical sea wall. Thus we see that the experiments of physicists have forced them to endow the electrons with a wavelike character.

But this was not the only new property which it was found necessary to assign to the electron. In 1925 Uhlenbeck and Goudsmit pointed out that certain features in atomic spectra could be explained if a model for the atomic electrons were assumed in which each electron spins around its center of mass and, as a consequence, has both an intrinsic angular momentum (like a gyroscope) *and a magnetic moment*. The atomic electrons also were shown to exhibit angular momentum and magnetic moments associated with their orbital motions about the nucleus, and it was possible to study the interaction between the spin magnetic moments and the orbital magnetic moments by spectroscopic methods.

In the same year, 1925, Wolfgang Pauli enunciated his famous "exclusion principle" as a generalization from the observed properties of the "electron shells" in the structures of the electron configurations clustered about the nuclei of atoms. An electron could be characterized by such properties as its energy of attachment, its orbital and angular momentum (a vector quantity having both magnitude and direction), and its spin (a similar vector quantity). All these properties were found to be *"quantized,"* to be capable of assuming only discrete, well-defined values described by "quantum numbers," and to each electron of an atom a set of these quantum numbers would be assigned. The Pauli exclusion principle in its earliest and simplest form asserted that no two electrons in an atom can have identical sets of quantum numbers. The significance of the Pauli principle is clearer perhaps if stated in a more general form. Suppose the electrons are inclosed in a box with perfectly reflecting walls, in which no forces act on the electrons save when they are reflected at the walls. The electron waves must now be stationary states, i.e., normal modes of vibration within such an inclosure such that the walls of the box become nodes of the standing wave pattern. The Pauli exclusion principle asserts that in the lowest energy state of such an assemblage, no more than two electrons can be associated with any particular standing wave mode and these two electrons must have their spins in opposite directions. Now the wave lengths of free electron De Broglie waves, it had been found, were inversely proportional to their velocities (more strictly to their momenta). When these conditions are analyzed mathematically, it can be seen that associated with each pair of oppositely spinning electrons, when the assemblage is in its lowest energy state, there must be a finite volume of the interior of the box and also a finite volume in momentum space (a space in which the linear momentum of each electron is plotted as a vector in magnitude and direction from a common origin point), and the product of these two finite volumes cannot be less than h^3 (the cube of Planck's constant). Thus if the box is fitted with one movable wall like a piston and we squeeze the geometrical volume down, the momentum volume of the electrons must expand to maintain the product of the two types of volume constant. This implies that some of the electrons must move faster, which in turn implies that energy must be supplied. The electron clouds that form the outer cloaks of atoms therefore strongly oppose the close approach of other atoms by demanding additional energy through the operation of the Pauli exclusion principle. Thus, although the electronic outer structure of atoms is tenuous and contains usually less than 0.03 per cent of the total atomic mass, it is nevertheless this cloak of electrons which determines the "size" of the atom and the volume it occupies in solid matter. This is indeed a very strange property of the electrons but one essential in determining the structure of the world as we know it.

The interaction between electrons and light (indeed electromagnetic radiation in general) was intensely studied during the epoch of which we are speaking. The photoelectric effect, already mentioned as discovered by Hertz and by Hallwachs in 1887 and 1888, was studied with great care in 1916 by R. A. Millikan in a highly successful effort to verify the simple quantum law which governs it, proposed by Einstein in 1905. Millikan designed what he humorously called a "barber shop in a vacuum tube," which permitted him to shave off all traces of contamination from the surfaces of metal electrodes inclosed in a highly evacuated glass envelope so as to study the ejection of electrons from these surfaces when they were illuminated with monochromatic light of known wave length. He showed that the kinetic energy imparted to the most energetic of these photoelectrically ejected electrons (those coming from the immediate metallic surface) was a linear function of the frequency of the light used and, with due allowance for the constant energy required to extract the electrons from the surface atoms, the total work done by the light was shown to be precisely $h\nu$ where h is Planck's constant and ν the frequency of the light. Millikan's verification of Einstein's proposed quantum law of photoelectric emission was of immense importance for the quantum theory.

The next mode of interaction of light with electrons was discovered and explained in terms of a famous billiard-ball model proposed by Arthur H. Compton in 1923. Compton pictured a free, stationary electron as being hit by a "photon" of light (conceived no longer as a wave but as a particle!), in a way analogous to a billiard ball being hit by a cue ball, the electron recoiling under the impact and thereby carrying away in the form of kinetic energy some of the original energy, $h\nu$, of the photon. If the photon were deflected through a large angle from its original direction in such a process, it would deliver a large impulse to the electron and hence would lose a large amount of energy. Applying the simple well-known laws of conservation of energy and momentum to such a collision process, Compton showed that the wave length, λ', of the scattered photon should be shifted to a value longer than its initial wave length, λ, following the simple equation

$$\lambda' - \lambda = [h/(m_0 c)] \, (1 - \cos \varphi) \, ,$$

wherein φ is the angle through which the photon is deflected in the scattering process. Compton's experiments with X-rays as the photons scattered by the weakly bound electrons in solids of low atomic number showed the existence and the essential correctness of the above law of shift in wave length. The constant, $h/(m_0 c)$, itself, wherein h is Planck's constant, m_0 the rest-mass of the electron; and c the velocity of light, has come to be known as "the Compton wave length for an electron." In a series of beautiful experiments with a Wilson cloud chamber fitted with an array of parallel copper partitions, Compton and Simon were able to give concrete evidence of the correlation between the direction of recoil of the electron and the direction of scattering of the photon. This experiment seemed at the time to ring the death knell of the spreading-wave concept of light and to establish the extreme picture of light energy as being transported in the form of small localized packets or particles. The present interpretation of these paradoxical experiments, however, is that both light and matter present the dual aspects of wave and particle, depending on the experiments we do to investigate them.

Compton's unusual billiard-ball picture of the interaction between a particulate "photon" and a particulate electron is, in fact, only one aspect or "explanation" of the process which bears his name. It can be understood equally well using a model proposed by Schrödinger (1927) in which both electrons and photons are waves. According to this picture the De Broglie wave trains of the free electron in its initial and final states (before and after the scattering process) interfere so as to form a stationary standing wave pattern of "matter waves" (if the process is observed from an appropriately chosen frame of reference) and the photon's waves are diffracted from the set of equidistant parallel planes of these matter waves according to the same conditions of selective reflection as obtain when X-rays are selectively reflected from the atom planes of a crystal. This model serves clearly to explain why the scattered light direction and the direction of the recoil of the electron are correlated as Compton and Simon showed that they are. Studies by Heisenberg, by Schrödinger, and by Bohr of a wealth of experimental evidence have led to the present conviction that the dual aspect of wave and particle is a very general property of both matter and radiation, in fact of energy in all its forms. Such studies are also closely related to the famous principle of indeterminacy first enunciated by Heisenberg. It appears to be useless to ask whether the electron is "really" a wave or "really" a particle. Its wave properties and its particulate properties are apparently two indissoluble aspects of the same entity which obscure each other so that both cannot be observed simultaneously in the same elementary process.

How large is an electron? One answer to this is called "the classical radius of the electron," namely, $e^2/(m_0c^2) = r_0 = 2.8178 \times 10^{-13}$ cm. This is the radius of a circle whose area is a measure of the cross-section which a simple free electron presents for scattering radiation of quantum energy, small compared with the electron's rest-mass energy. It is also a radius such that the work required to charge a small sphere of that radius with a charge equal to one electron shall be just equal to the relativistic value, m_0c^2, of the total energy associated with the electron's mass. This length magnitude, r_0, therefore clearly has important physical significance but, for many purposes involving the interaction of electrons with radiation, the Compton wave length, $h/(m_0c) = 2.4262 \times 10^{-10}$ cm., has at least an equally important significance. It is the wave length of a quantum of electromagnetic radiation whose energy, $h\nu = hc/\lambda$, is just equal to the relativistic rest-mass energy, m_0c^2, of the electron. The electron is indeed a thing of many aspects, both a wave and a particle, and it is unsafe to picture it in terms of macroscopically familiar physical objects.

Compton's simple theory of the scattering of radiation by a free, initially stationary electron is an oversimplification of the mechanism which is actually observed. The scattering electrons, to be sufficient in number density to give any observable scattering, have of necessity always been atomic electrons in one of the three states of matter: solid, liquid, or gaseous. Thus it has been possible to show by a study of the breadth and structure of the shifted Compton line that the atomic electrons possess linear orbital momentum. From the particle point of view, the moving atomic electrons, depending on the direction of their motion, can deliver blows or "pull their punches" given to the radiation quanta that are being scattered by them. From the wave point of view, the initial orbital motion of the electron approaching the radiation or receding from it produces an observable Doppler broadening of the Compton-shifted line.

This effect was brought to light and explained in 1930 by H. A. Kirkpatrick and J. W. M. DuMond. It has served to study the distributions of electron momenta both in gaseous atoms and in solid bodies.

The fact that the electron is in reality not free but bound to an atom also causes the Compton shift to be in fact slightly less than the simple formula for a free electron predicts. In the case of the bound electron set free from the atom at the expense of some of the recoil energy it has received, a small part of the momentum change associated with the scattering of the radiation is imparted to the nucleus and to the other electrons, i.e., to the remainder of the atom from which the electron has been ejected. Because of the far greater mass of the latter, this momentum gives negligible kinetic energy to the residual atom. As a result the recoil electron, deprived of some of the momentum it would have received if it had been initially free, abstracts a little less energy from the radiation and the shift in wave length is rendered smaller. This effect was quantitatively observed by P. A. Ross and P. Kirkpatrick in 1931.

About 1928 R. A. Millikan, who had left the University of Chicago in 1921 to lead the California Institute of Technology, made important studies in collaboration with one of his graduate students, G. H. Cameron, of a new type of radiation to which Millikan had in 1925 given the name "cosmic rays." Millikan and Cameron lowered sensitive electroscopes into water, deep below the surfaces of mountain lakes such as Gem Lake in the High Sierras. The effect had been discovered and studied earlier in Europe (*ca.* 1911) by V. F. Hess and by W. Kohlhorster. It had been observed ever since 1900 by Elster and Geital and by C. T. R. Wilson that no matter what precautions were taken to insulate the support of a sensitive electroscope, the insulated system, if charged electrically, always gradually lost its charge through ionization of the air which thereby became an electrical conductor. Hess and Kohlhorster showed that when electroscopes were sent up to high altitudes in balloons the charge on the electroscope leaked away much more rapidly. To explain this effect, Hess proposed that the ionization of the air was caused by a penetrating radiation coming from outer space. These postulated radiations were known in Germany as *Höhenstrahlung* or *Ultrastrahlung*, but their extra-terrestrial origin and their enormous penetrating power were not immediately universally accepted. Millikan and Cameron's experiments with electroscopes submerged in snow-fed mountain lakes (which should contain particularly pure water free from radioactivity) showed that the leakage of charge through air ionization inside the sub-merged electroscopes did indeed decrease with increasing depth below water level. A comparison of the curves of leakage rate versus depth for two lakes, Gem Lake at altitude 9,080 feet and Arrowhead Lake at altitude 5,100 feet, showed that the two curves agreed perfectly if one compared points on the Gem Lake curve, all of which were six feet deeper beneath the water surface than those on the Arrowhead Lake curve. This six-foot depth of water turned out to be just the equivalent in mass of the column of air com-prised between the altitude of the surface of Arrowhead Lake and the altitude of the surface of Gem Lake. It was therefore concluded that the apparently great penetrating power of the rays was real and that their source was extra-terrestrial.

Millikan's cosmic ray studies lasted over a period of two decades and took him with his collaborators to many far off regions of the earth. Not all of his conclusions proved to be correct. Through an unfortunate fluke he missed the discovery of the latitude effect, a significant dip in the intensity of cosmic rays in the equatorial regions together with a nearly level value over a range of order 60° measured from each geomagnetic pole toward the equator. Out of a series of points on the earth's surface surveyed for cosmic rays by one of Millikan's early expeditions, all but one at Lima, Peru, were in the nearly level region north of geomagnetic latitude 35°. The observations at Lima would have given evidence of the lower effect, but the electroscope had been damaged in its transfer from ship to shore. Two years later the effect was established by J. Clay, though at that time he overestimated its magnitude.

Undoubtedly, the most important result of Millikan's interest in the cosmic rays was that it led him to start a program of work with the Wilson cloud chamber which was performed by a series of his graduate students at the California Institute of Technology, notably by Dr. Carl D. Anderson and Anderson's first graduate student, Seth Neddermeyer.

To investigate the composition of the cosmic ray particles (their energy distribution), Anderson had set up a cloud chamber in a vertical plane and provided a horizontal magnetic field of 15,000 gauss with the lines of force directed normal to the plane of the chamber to deflect the particles. A charged particle crossing the lines of force of a magnetic field at right angles to them is deflected so as to execute a circular path whose radius of curvature, r, is proportional to the momentum, p, of the particle according to the equation $r = p/(He)$, wherein H is the strength of the field and e the charge on the particle. They provided a horizontal lead partition 6 mm. thick, diametrically crossing the interior of the chamber. Among several thousand exposures with this apparatus, in several cases tracks appeared, which could only be interpreted as being particles of positive charge, but much lighter than protons—in fact positive electrons. From the direction of curvature of the track, the direction of the magnetic field, and the direction of motion of the particle, its sign of charge was established as undoubtedly positive. The direction of motion was established by the fact that the particle had passed through the lead partition and was more sharply bent by the magnetic field on what therefore could only be interpreted as the exit side because of retardation in the lead. In a later cloud chamber photograph, *two* particles of opposite sign of curvature appeared, emerging from the same side of the lead plate. This was correctly interpreted as the "creation" or "materialization" of an electron-positron pair in the lead plate by high energy cosmic rays.

Five years earlier, in 1930, P. A. M. Dirac, the British theoretical physicist, had improved upon the famous Schrödinger wave equation in his successful attempt to construct a theory of the mechanics of the electron, describing both its wave and particulate aspects, which would also be in conformity with the known facts expressed in Einstein's restricted theory of relativity. Schrödinger's wave equation had been less ambitious in that it merely attempted to describe the mechanics of an electron, in both its wave and particulate aspects, for such low electron velocities that Newtonian mechanics could be considered a valid approximation.

The relativistic behavior of a free electron can be summarized in the statement

$$E^2 = P^2 + \mu^2 ,$$

wherein $E = T + m_0c^2$ is the total energy of a free electron (its kinetic energy of motion, T, plus its intrinsic rest-mass-energy, m_0c^2), $P = pc$ is the ordinary momentum of the electron multiplied by the velocity of light (sometimes called the Heitlerian momentum), and $\mu = m_0c^2$ is the electron rest-mass-energy, an energy of about 511 electron-kilovolts. The momentum, P, is a vector with components along the three cartesian axes, P_x, P_y, and P_z so that $P^2 = P_x{}^2 + P_y{}^2 + P_z{}^2$, and we have therefore the relativistic equation for a free electron connecting total electron energy (including rest-energy) with momentum

$$E = \pm \sqrt{P_x^2 + P_y^2 + P_z^2 + \mu^2}\,.$$

Dirac took seriously the sign of ambiguity and concluded that relativity must require that both positive and negative values of total energy, E, be considered as having a real interpretation. Inspection of the radicand in the above expression shows that it is not, as it stands, a perfect square. Most mortals would give up, therefore, any attempt to find its square root, but not Dirac! Clearly, if the expression had in addition six cross-product terms— $2P_xP_y$; $2P_xP_z$; $2P_x\mu$; $2P_yP_z$; $2P_y\mu$; $2P_z\mu$—all would be well; the operation of taking the square root could be explicitly carried out. Dirac conceived of four coefficients, a_x, a_y, a_z, a_μ, by which to multiply each of the four quantities, P_x, P_y, P_z, μ, respectively. These coefficients were not ordinary numbers, however, but *operators* having the form of four-by-four matrices and so chosen that the product of any pair of *different* a's, a_ia_j, was of opposite algebraic sign to the product of the same pair of a's taken in reverse order, a_ja_i,

$$a_ia_j = -\, a_ja_i\,,$$

while the squares of all the a's were equivalent to unity.* (Obviously no set of four ordinary numbers can be found with such a property, but the rules of matrix multiplication *do* permit choices of this sort.) Thus when the expression, $a_xP_x + a_yP_y + a_zP_z + a_\mu\mu$, is squared, the operation of the a's upon each other causes all the cross-product terms to vanish by cancellation in pairs and causes all of the coefficients of the squared terms to be unity, so that we see that Dirac *has* indeed extracted the square root and

$$E = \pm \left[a_xP_x + a_yP_y + a_zP_z + a_\mu\mu\right].$$

---

* Since the a's are in fact matrix operators, the product, a_ia_i, gives the identity operator, I, such that its application leaves the operand unchanged, in complete analogy to multiplication of ordinary numbers by unity.

Now it turns out that these matrices, a_i, which are invisible in the preceding radicand because of the special properties just described, actually contain by implication the secret of the spin and magnetic moment of the electron. Schrödinger's wave equation, in its most general form containing the time, described the probability of observing the electron in a given space-time element in terms of the square of a probability amplitude, ψ, the dependent variable in the above-mentioned second order differential wave equation. It was notable that that equation contained the imaginary unit, $i = \sqrt{-1}$, explicitly in one of its coefficients, and as a consequence the probability amplitude, ψ, had in general necessarily to consist of two components, one real, the other imaginary. Dirac's wave equations, on the other hand, which are differential equations of the *first* order, describe the probability of finding the electron in terms of four-component instead of two-component probability amplitudes. Dirac also introduced the strange idea of states of negative total energy for the electron, states which are completely occupied with electrons as densely as the Pauli exclusion principle will permit.

According to Dirac's picture, a free electron would have available to it not only a continuum of states of total energy, E, extending upward from $+ m_0c^2$ to plus infinity but also a continuum of negative energy states, $-E$, extending downward from $- m_0c^2$ to minus infinity. The negative energy states constituted the Dirac densely filled sea. As far as we know even today, this sea is bottomless, i.e., without any limiting lower value of negative energy. Dirac got around the difficulty of the infinite charge which must be associated with such a bottomless sea of electrons by pointing out that "empty" space as we know it has always been just this. What it would be like if this infinite constant charge density were removed no one knows, but we may disregard its presence just as we disregard the pressure of the atmosphere in which we live and breathe. The "creation" or "materialization" of an electron-positron pair would then correspond to the ejection of one of the electrons in the sea of negative energy electrons across the gap of width $2m_0c^2$ (1,022,000 electron volts) which separates the permitted negative energy states of an electron from its permitted positive energy states. The hole left behind in the negative energy sea is the positron. As long as it remains in the already otherwise densely filled sea, its neighboring negative electrons cannot "annihilate" it, for when one of them "falls" into the empty space (which is the hole) a new empty state is created in the place left by the electron which fell. This is indistinguishable from saying that the positron has moved into the newly emptied energy state.

At the time Dirac first conceived these ideas, the discovery of the positron of Anderson was still four years in the future and, knowing of no other particle with a single positive charge of magnitude, e, Dirac at first felt forced to suppose that the hole in the negative energy sea must be a proton. The far greater mass of the real proton, 1,836 times as great as the electron mass, remained therefore a severe difficulty. Carl D. Anderson's discovery of the positive electron cleared up this mystery very neatly and convinced the scientific world that Dirac's theory contained important elements of truth in spite of its seeming improbability.

This brief and rough thumbnail sketch in a sense completes the story of the evolution of our knowledge about the electron save for one more step, the discovery by Anderson and Neddermeyer in 1937 of the muon. Because the muon, also called the mu-meson, is a particle of mass about 207 times the electron mass, it might have been objected up until 1961 that the muon is an independent particle from the electron and has nothing to do with the evolution of our knowledge of the latter. However, experiments on the spin, magnetic moment, and magnetic moment anomaly have shown that, except for its much greater mass, the muon apparently possesses identical characteristics with the electron. Moreover the muon, which occurs with both positive and negative signs of charge (of magnitude plus or minus one "electron" in the early sense of the term), actually decays spontaneously with mean life of about two microseconds into an electron (of the same sign of charge) and two neutrinos. Of the neutrino, an evanescent chargeless form of energy first postulated by W. Pauli in 1930 in order to explain bookkeeping deficits in the energy and momentum balance of beta decay and other nuclear reactions, we only have space to remark that clear evidence of its presence was finally obtained by Reines and Cowan in 1953, a short time before Pauli's death. Pauli was informed of this important result by telegram, to which he replied, also by wire, "Everything comes to him who waits."

Negatively charged muons can substitute for electrons in atoms, which are then called mu-mesonic atoms; the radiation emitted when the muon executes transitions between quantized energy levels in such atoms has given important information concerning the sizes and structure of their nuclei, since the greater mass of the muon, compared to that of the electron, and its consequent shorter De Broglie wave length imply that the muon approaches much closer to the nucleus and is a much sharper probe for exploring nuclear structure. It appears highly likely that the muon is simply a heavy counterpart of the electron. The interesting possibility of discovering further family relationships between the so-called fundamental particles of high energy physics is thus greatly encouraged.

The last step we shall describe then, in the evolution of our ideas about the electron, was taken by Carl D. Anderson and Seth Neddermeyer. These young men had been studying the losses of kinetic energy sustained by cosmic ray particles which penetrated partitions (usually of lead) placed in Wilson cloud expansion chambers in the presence of strong magnetic fields, as explained above, in connection with their discovery of the positive electron. Extensive measurements of this sort were begun in 1932 in spite of the fact that Millikan was convinced that the cosmic rays were electromagnetic radiation, the "birth cries of atoms" in outer space. These were continued in the Norman Bridge Laboratory for a considerable period of years and notably in one summer vacation in 1935 on Pikes Peak.

No research was as lavishly financed in those days as it is today! Fortunately, the cosmic ray work carried on by Millikan and his students was done under grants in the form of annual appropriations from the Carnegie Corporation of New York averaging, over a twenty-year period, about $15,000 annually. This sum, which in these days of multimillion-dollar research projects sounds so small, was made to go a long way by the devotion of Millikan and the young men whom he inspired by his precept and example. Those years of the Great Depression following the 1929 stock market crash were very difficult indeed, and some of the storms that besieged Caltech and its "Chief" and threatened them with bankruptcy and disaster are described in more detail below. The picture of Anderson and Neddermeyer working with their homemade cloud chamber in the Caltech Aeronautics Laboratory, the only place where there was an adequate d.c. power supply, is unforgettable. The cycle of operations necessary for repeated expansions and photography of the cloud chamber picture was accomplished automatically by means of switching, timing, and programming equipment built by themselves out of cast-off parts picked up in junk yards and second-hand stores and assembled on a wooden table of about 4×7 feet. But it was with this equipment that the first evidence for the positron was obtained as well as a large part of the evidence for the muon (not of course so called at that time).

To get nearer to the top of the earth's atmosphere and thus, as they hoped, to obtain better and more evidence on the nature of particles constituting the original cosmic rays entering the earth's atmosphere from outer space, particles which might indeed be completely absorbed in the atmosphere and therefore unobservable at the level of the Norman Bridge Laboratory in Pasadena, Anderson and Neddermeyer decided to take their complete magnetic cloud chamber equipment to the top of Pikes Peak, an elevation of 14,100 feet.

The departure from the Caltech campus of the strange caravan which these two young physicists had prepared for the trip to the mountaintop is a precious memory for the present writer. It consisted of an asthmatic $1\frac{1}{2}$-ton panel truck and a flat-bed trailer, each of very ancient vintage, which they had procured with their slender means and rigged up themselves with the homemade, water-cooled electromagnet and cloud chamber weighing *2 tons*. These were mounted on the flat-bed trailer and a housing was built over the bed out of old packing cases given to them by the Bekins Van and Storage Co. through the courtesy of a Bekins executive, Mr. Herbert Holt, a Caltech graduate. There were several large steel tanks which would be needed on the mountaintop to contain the supply of cooling water for the magnet; a gasoline-driven motor-generator set for the electrical power to operate the magnet, the controls for the cloud chamber, and the vacuum and hydraulic pumping equipment; the camera and photographic paraphernalia for photographing the tracks in the cloud chamber and for developing the 35 mm. movie film on the mountain. Camping equipment was dispensed with, and when Anderson and Ned-dermeyer reached the mountaintop they found that the rental of the little shelter provided there totaled $5.00 per day for the two of them. This was more than their budget permitted, but they were welcomed as guests by a construction gang which shared their housing with them. Time, space, and money were at a premium on this trip and, to economize on all three, Anderson and Neddermeyer had removed the legs from their laboratory table and had installed the 4 × 7 foot wooden table top, with its entire complement of intricate home-built switching relays and control equipment, in a vertical position like a switchboard on the inside wall of the trailer carrying the cloud chamber and magnet. This traveling junk shop reminded one of the Tenniel illustration of the white knight from *Alice in Wonderland*.

Those of us who bade them goodbye and watched the departure of the two ancient vehicles chugging at a snail's pace in second gear up the slight grade, first on California Street, then along Lake Avenue to reach Colorado Boulevard, the main highway and the beginning of the week-long grind of 900 miles to Pikes Peak, believed they had hardly an even chance of success! But, in spite of many mishaps and adventures, some of them amusing, they reached the top and managed to return with all their equipment and with a wealth of precious information in the form of pictures of particles penetrating the 1-centimeter-thick platinum plate which they had installed in the cloud chamber.

When the data on energy losses of some ninety-three particles, taken both in Pasadena and on Pikes Peak, had been reduced and plotted on a now famous graph in which the energy loss of a particle in traversing the centimeter of platinum was plotted as a function of the particle's incident energy, it became amply evident that the particles grouped themselves into two fairly distinct categories: nearly seventy out of the total of ninety-three particles sustained considerably less energy loss in traversing the platinum than the remainder.

All the energies, initial and final, were computed from the magnetic curvature of the tracks, on the assumption that the particles were of electronic charge-to-mass ratio. It was further observed that the class which sustained heavy retardation in the plate consisted of those associated with "showers" (in which a number of particles appeared simultaneously in the chamber as though originating simultaneously from some single event), whereas the particles which traversed the plate with little loss of energy were almost invariably single particles. The penetrating power of the single particles could most readily be explained by assuming their masses to be greater than those of electrons, for the radiative energy loss decreases rapidly with increasing mass, but it was reasoned that they could hardly be as heavy as protons because a proton with the same "magnetic rigidity" (resistance to magnetic deflection) as a 200 MeV electron (the general order of rigidity these particles exhibited) would show in the chamber a track of ionization *much heavier* than those actually observed. Earlier, and with commendable caution, Anderson and Neddermeyer had stuck to describing as electrons both the penetrating single particles and the more readily retarded particles. In their private conversation, to distinguish the two types, they spoke jokingly of the first category as "green" and the second as "red" electrons. The experiments with the platinum partition, however, gave convincing evidence that the two groups were quite distinct and that the distinction was probably a difference of mass. Neddermeyer and Anderson thereupon wrote a report in which they named the heavy particles mesotons, but on Millikan's insistence a wire was sent to the editors changing the name to mesotron.

Meanwhile, in 1935, the Japanese theoretical physicist Yukawa proposed a new type of particle to explain the short-range nuclear forces which bind together nucleons, the constituent protons and neutrons in nuclei, and from the general range of action of nuclear forces he concluded these particles must have masses about two hundred times that of the electron. Contrary to the assertion in some textbooks, it was not on account of this but on the strength of their own experimental evidence that the experimental physicists screwed up the courage to assign a name and an independent energy to the "green electron." In fact, two years elapsed after Neddermeyer and Anderson's suggestion of the name mesotron before R. Oppenheimer called their attention to the Yukawa paper. Eventually the name mesotron was shortened to meson, and later it was found that there are in fact two kinds of mesons, at first distinguished as pi-mesons and mu-mesons, later abbreviated to pions and muons, and that the Yukawa particle accounting for nuclear binding is in fact of the pi-variety which spontaneously decays into the mu-variety and a neutrino.

A further continuation of this story would lead us into the fascinating field of high energy and strange particle physics, but this would not be relevant to the purpose at hand which has been only to paint a picture of what research was like in the golden age of physics, the period during which Millikan lived and before physics became a paying business.

THE CHAIRMAN OF THE EXECUTIVE COUNCIL OF CALTECH

Perhaps the best way to convey an idea of Millikan's personality is to describe him in action during the years that he was building Caltech. How a man behaves, under both ordinary and extraordinary circumstances, is what he is. This writer's first memories of Millikan date back to 1921, Millikan's first year of permanency at the California Institute of Technology. The faculty and graduate students were still a small enough group so that at the first faculty dinner we could all sit around a single long table in the basement of the Crown Hotel. Professor Millikan gave the after-dinner speech and got off to a good start by announcing that his wife Greta, seated beside him, had that day told him a story. "It takes the form of a conundrum," he announced with a twinkle in his eye. Then, with a characteristic gesture by which we were to remember him affectionately, he hooked his thumbs into the armholes of his vest, rocked gently back and forth on his heels and toes, and said, "Why is a novel by Sir Walter Scott like an old-fashioned bustle?" The answer: "Because each is a fictitious tale based upon a stern reality." Before the laughter had subsided, Mrs. Millikan rose without the shadow of a smile. The bunch of little artificial cherries on her hat vibrated, unmistakable evidence of her deep emotion. "Ladies and gentlemen," she said firmly, "I never heard that disreputable story before in my life!"

It was at this same dinner that Millikan told us something of his philosophy of university organization and administration. He made it clear that his mind was made up to continue to be, first and foremost, a physicist. Indeed, he told us that the written contract that he had signed with the trustees of the Institute provided explicitly that he was not to be required to take its presidency; that he was not expected to spend any time raising funds; that his first and most pressing job was to build the best department of physics of which he was capable with the aid of funds up to some $90,000 per year if required. Throughout his thirty-year leadership at Caltech, he consistently refused the title of president and would accept none other than that of Professor of Physics and Chairman of the Executive Council.

In Millikan's younger days at Chicago he, along with George Vincent and James Angell, had led something of a revolt (and a successful one at that) against the system originally set up by President Harper who, to quote from Millikan's autobiography, "appointed some dozen or more head professors, paid them the princely salaries (for those days) of $7,000.00 each, made them essentially czars in their departments, and gave them much power, also, in the University at large." The younger men (to continue the above quotation) "urged that the highest rank and the highest salaries obtainable in the University of Chicago be associated with its most distinguished and outstanding teachers and scholars, rather than with its deans or administrative officers, administration being in general subordinated to distinguished intellectual accomplishment for [and Millikan emphasized this] example is the best of all teachers."

Millikan's philosophy as given in his after-dinner speech was substantially equivalent to what he wrote in his autobiography some thirty years later:

... beginning with the unsupported assertion that, in general, the American college or university president has or may assume more power than is good either for him or for his institution. I attribute most of the academic rows about which I have known during the past sixty years to that situation. . . . What, then, is the origin of the American system in which the college president is given so much power and stands to such an extent for the university? I suspect that the system has been transplanted from American business in which, especially because of the newness of the country, aggressiveness and activity being the indispensable qualities for success, there has developed, quite logically too, a semi-military form of organization with lines of authority and responsibility clearly marked. Let me call it the Pentagon philosophy of organization, and let me recognize the fact that wherever *action* is more important than *wisdom*, as in military operations [*sic!*] and to a lesser extent in American business, it represents at any rate a natural, if not a necessary, mode of organization. Also, since the trustees of most of our higher educational institutions are nearly all businessmen, a president and a hierarchy of deans was the natural basis about which the whole institution became organized and managed. . . . At the time I came to the Institute with a well-formulated scientific program, which it was my purpose to carry out, the Pentagon philosophy obviously represented an impossible mode of organization for me to fit into.

Accordingly, the scheme of organization set up for the Institute was

. . . based on the postulate that the field of higher education differed radically from the field of military operations or the field of business in that in it *wisdom* was vastly more important than *action* and that *wisdom only comes from the joint, independent judgements* of a group of able and informed men.

Millikan recounts that they

. . . therefore set up, to take the place of president, an executive council consisting of four of the most interested and active trustees (an educating device for them) and four members of the faculty, all of large experience in educational matters.

It was as chairman of this governing group that Millikan led the Institute throughout his active career. He goes on:

As a result of some fifteen years of participation by Dr. Thomas Hunt Morgan in the plan here outlined, shortly after his retirement he took me aside on purpose, as he said, to register the statement that in his long career in American universities he had never seen any plan of organization that worked anything like as well as this one.

But, in spite of the promise Millikan had exacted as the price of his coming to Caltech, the promise "not to be required to spend any time raising funds," circumstances sooner or later forced all of these manifold cares and responsibilities and many others upon his broad and capable shoulders and he accepted them ungrudgingly because the challenge that was presented to him was of the sort that a man of his character had no choice but to accept.

Quoting again from his autobiography:

For the first three years I took the trustees at their word and put in nearly all my time and my energies on the work connected with the building and expansion of the Norman Bridge Laboratory of Physics.

But one Saturday in the spring of 1924 Henry Robinson, than whom no man deserves more credit for the creation of the California Institute of Technology, came to my office in Throop Hall, and as we stood looking out of my East window at the sad wreck of what had once been a thriving orange orchard stretching 300 yards eastward—I suddenly said, "Henry, this community is growing very rapidly and if we don't soon find or make a way to move forward with it, we are going to miss the boat. I am getting scared. Do you think we could find a hundred men in Southern California who would be both able and eager to put in a thousand dollars apiece each year for a period of ten years in order to push this enterprise along before it is too late?" His answer was, "I think we can do it, and I fully agree that we have no time to lose. Indeed, we ought to have been at it at least a year ago."

From that moment I knew that the idea, stated in my contract, that I was to be relieved of the money-raising job, was out of the window, willy-nilly, I had to take on that job in addition to physics, which I was determined not to ditch.

He was as good as his word. This was the beginning of one of Millikan's strokes of genius as a fund-raiser—the institution of the group which came to be known as the "Institute Associates."

Any cultured person of means, who felt he or she could afford to shoulder the responsibility, could be invited to become an Associate of the California Institute of Technology, for which privilege he promised to pay dues of one thousand dollars a year. In return he was given many privileges on the campus where, if he wished, he could attend lectures and seminars and to which he would be periodically invited to dinners and luncheons at which he might meet prominent scientists and listen to lectures by them.

Through the generosity of Mr. and Mrs. Allan C. Balch "The Athenaeum" was built "as the hearthstone of the Associates," to quote Mr. Henry O'Melveney, and as their meeting place with the staffs of the Institute, the Huntington Library, and the Mount Wilson Observatory. The Athenaeum had to be designed with an elegance appropriate to its use as "hearthstone" for its wealthy supporters; at the same time its more frequent function as a faculty club and hostelry for visiting professors required that its operation be sufficiently economical to place it within their means. This was indeed a wide chasm to straddle, and many said it could not be done. But Millikan made it work.

The idea of the Athenaeum and the Associates was in reality an extremely shrewd one, characteristic of Millikan's vision. The Athenaeum was built in the painful beginning of the severe depression in 1929 and 1930 for a total cost in money which today would scarcely suffice to pay for the beautifully sculptured woodwork and paneling in its dining room! Millikan's conversation with Henry Robinson in 1924 and his realization then that he must "willy-nilly" shoulder the additional burden of money-raising had come none too soon! Though neither of these men could foresee it in the "roaring twenties," the Great Depression of the thirties was just around the corner. The storm was very rough and Caltech came perilously close to bankruptcy. To quote again from the autobiography:

This was due, in the first instance, to the fact that the great depression beginning 1929 swept away all, save some $250,000 of the original Fleming endowment fortune (estimated by him at $4,200,000) which in 1921 he [Fleming] had turned over, as agreed, to the Institute in the form of an irrevocable trust. This trust he, a lumber man, had to manage, since the bulk of the trust's estimated assets was in the Sugar Pine Lumber Co., of which he was president and which in the early twenties had paid large dividends, but which in the early thirties went into liquidation.

Millikan modestly refrains in his autobiography from mentioning the most frightening feature of the situation the Institute now found itself in. Our benefactor, Arthur Fleming, to expand his successful lumber business in the twenties, had obtained additional financing through the sale of debenture bonds to the public which were guaranteed only by his personal note. According to the indenture of these bonds the bondholders could claim repayment of the entire principal if the company defaulted on the interest. Thus the Institute, as the legatee of the Fleming trust, found itself not only without any income from the Fleming endowment but, in addition, heavily in debt to the bondholders. No one and nothing but the depression itself could be blamed. Mr. Fleming had given the Institute everything in good faith. A more devoted friend

.

cannot be imagined. I clearly remember seeing him weeding the lawn (which he had himself planted) to the east of the Norman Bridge Laboratory. To quote again from the autobiography:

The Institute was . . . faced with an intolerable deficit. In determining to restore balance to the budget, which we succeeded in doing, every employee of Caltech took a ten per cent salary cut and, without a word of complaint, too. Mr. Allan C. Balch replaced Mr. Fleming as President of the Board of Trustees, and committed himself for a large annual contribution ($35,000.00).

Here Millikan's autobiography is completely silent about a fact which brings out that really great man's character better than anything else! At this juncture, with the blackest imaginable outlook for the financial future of the Institute, the United States Steel Company approached Millikan with an offer of a salary of $100,000 per annum, and any budget he wanted to name, to organize for them a laboratory of pure and applied research of which he would become the director. Think what a temptation this must have been. He hesitated long enough to have everyone connected with Caltech shaking in his shoes and expecting the doors to close for good! Then Robert Andrews Millikan made one of his truly great decisions. He accepted the challenge of making the Institute he believed in a success and refused the tempting offer. How many men are there today, out of our population of 180 million, who would have the courage to make such a choice?

Millikan undoubtedly understood the nature of the nearly superhuman task that lay ahead of him. Fortunately, he had a constitution of iron and boundless energy, and he needed every ounce of both for he was as good as his word in remaining first and foremost a physicist and a teacher; but he was also a father to his children and students, a writer, fund-raiser, administrator, an organizer of vision, and an inspiration, by his example of dedication and energy, to all who knew him.

During his leadership and, as we have seen, with less than no finances, the Caltech campus grew from its first nucleus of Throop Hall and the Gates Chemistry Laboratory to include the two Norman Bridge Laboratories of Physics; the High Tension Laboratory with its million-volt transformers designed by Professor Royal Sorensen; the Athenaeum; the Dabney Hall of the Humanities; the Kerckhoff Laboratories of the Biological Sciences; the Seeley Mudd and Charles Arms Laboratories of the Geological Sciences; the Henry M. Robinson Laboratory of Astrophysics; the Crellin Laboratory of Chemistry; the Guggenheim Laboratory of Aeronautics; the four undergraduate student houses named after their donors, Ricketts, Blacker, Dabney, and Fleming; the Keith Spalding Mechanical Engineering Laboratory; the remarkable Earhart Plant Research Laboratory (facetiously known on the campus as the "phytotron") for the study of plant growth under completely and accurately controlled environmental conditions of every kind. Off campus must be mentioned the two enormously important developments of the Seismological Laboratory and the Palomar Observatory with its 200-inch telescope. In all of this growth Millikan was very much the leader. The Institute ran during this period of immense and rapid growth with a minimum of administrative help. This was partly because Millikan was everywhere planning, pushing, deciding, admonishing, and partly because he did not believe in running an organization like a huge automatic juggernaut with relentless rules. He made the rules, he made them flexible, and, when reason and common sense dictated that they be modified or broken, he modified or broke them. He, who in his youth had rebelled against the dictatorship of professors and administrators, became by the irony of fate the most dictatorial of all dictators—though a benevolent one beloved of his subjects even when they chafed under his yoke.

In fact, the Institute ran well and smoothly with little help, largely because of the excellent *esprit de corps* which his example and his enthusiasm had imparted to all of its faculty and permanent staff. Everyone *wanted* to see it succeed and every shoulder pushed energetically at the wheel. The energy Millikan displayed in this era would be beyond belief save to those who witnessed it. His day at the Institute, starting at eight o'clock in the morning, frequently did not terminate until long after midnight. At that late hour he was a well-known sight under a certain old live-oak tree west of the Norman Bridge Laboratory, reading his cosmic ray ionization electroscope. His three sons complained resignedly because he awoke them so early every morning to play tennis with him before breakfast, to give him his only chance for routine exercise. He treasured opportunities to travel by train across the continent because these gave him an uninterrupted interval for writing his books and papers. In later years, he had a pulpit or lectern installed, at which he did most of his writing *standing erect*. I learned from Millikan's faithful secretary, Miss Inga Howard, and verified it from some of his most intimate younger associates, that he wrote standing up because if he sat down he would frequently be so fatigued as to fall asleep in spite of his best efforts. Yet, with time at such a premium he never forgot his graduate students or refused an opportunity to talk over their work and encourage them. I recall clearly an occasion one Sunday when the Chief had made an appointment to visit my research room in the west wing of the Norman Bridge Laboratory to discuss the interpretation of some results, because no other time was available. True to his word, Millikan came on time and became deeply interested in the discussion which lasted longer than either participant realized, until suddenly the militant clicking sound of feminine heels was heard through the open door rapidly coming down the "padre tile" paved hall. (Millikan loved to refer to the Norman Bridge Laboratory with its Spanish cloistered style of architecture as a Monastery of Science.) Mrs. Greta Millikan, who had clearly been searching for her husband "from Dan to Beersheba," hearing and recognizing his voice, exclaimed in righteous and high-pitched indignation, "Now Robert, you *know* we are supposed to attend that wedding at eleven o'clock, and you *know* how rude it is to be late at a wedding!"

Millikan could turn his hand to any job that had to be done. He would have been a success no matter what role Fate might have cast for him. He was especially fond of the histories of such men as Tycho Brahe, Galileo Galilei, Isaac Newton, Benjamin Franklin, and George Washington, and it is perfectly clear that what he admired in them was the combination of character with high purpose and undeflectable will, exactly his own qualities. So, when it became evident that he must make a salesman of himself for the sake of science and the development of Caltech, he embraced the necessary task warmly without disdain or flinching.

The launching of the Athenaeum with the first dinner to be held for the Institute Associates was a most memorable affair. For this purpose Millikan succeeded in inducing no less a celebrity than

Albert Einstein to come from Princeton and to lend his fame to the occasion. Einstein, who hated formality and detested wearing even simple business clothing, being much happier when in his sailboat smoking his pipe and wearing an old sweater, nevertheless (*O mirabile visu*) came to the dinner dressed in conventional evening attire! When the cigars had been passed around, it chanced that an immediate neighbor of Einstein at the dinner table that evening was a very successful businessman from New York City, Dr. Leon L. Watters, who had earlier been a research chemist and held a Doctor's degree in chemistry from Columbia University. During the speeches, Dr. Watters, apparently sensing that Einstein might temporarily have taken mental refuge from the dignified entourage and pompous atmosphere of the Athenaeum dinner table to cogitate on the unified field theory, wrote a bit of verse on a slip of paper, folded it, and passed it on to Einstein. It read somewhat like this:

> Though lost amid a host of unknown faces
> With all the world a-jangle and a-jar,
> I meditate on interstellar spaces
> And smoke a mild cigar.

As a result of this incident, which apparently pleased Einstein tremendously, these two became warm friends. Dr. Watters, whose admiration for the famous scientist was unbounded, was deeply gratified to have made this friendship, which continued for many years. During this same visit of Einstein to Pasadena, having received my doctorate in the previous year, I had asked the Chief to find some financial solution, if possible, for the continued support of my X-ray research work in the study of the momentum distributions of atomic electrons by means of the breadth and structure of the Compton shifted line. Millikan turned to Einstein, who suggested Dr. Watters as a possible benefactor. As a result, my work was financed for a period of more than a decade, the difficult decade of the Great Depression, through that kindly gentleman's generosity. At his request the funds, which were used chiefly to purchase equipment, were set up as the Frances Hayes Watters Memorial Research Fund, in memory of his first wife. Dr. Watters' interest in the work has continued, and a warm friendship and mutual affection have lasted over a period of thirty years, long after the period of need for this financing ceased. This is presented as a clear example of the immediate results of Millikan's idea of providing a meeting place for people of means and culture with men actively engaged in scientific research. There were, of course, countless other and more important examples of the benefits derived from the Athenaeum and the Associates of the Institute.

Two other incidents illustrative of Millikan's character occurred in the early years at Caltech. The first of these was in 1923, the year Millikan was awarded the Nobel Prize for his oil-drop work demonstrating the unitary nature of electricity and for his work on the photoelectric effect. I was then a graduate student and registered for a course given by Millikan himself in electron theory. On this particular morning, the class of some fifteen to twenty students had heard the good news about the Prize before Millikan entered the room and had decided to greet his entrance with congratulatory applause and the shuffling of feet traditionally practiced in Germany. When Millikan came in, he appeared at first quite startled by the unusual commotion, then a look of comprehension came into his face. He said not a word, however, but merely walked over to the open window and looked out westward waiting for our greeting to subside. Then, as though nothing had happened, he turned to the blackboard and started the lecture in a perfectly controlled and even voice. But many of us had seen the tears glistening in his eyes. Millikan, unlike most Nobel Prize winners, did not go to Stockholm to participate in the festivities and in the glory of his award. Instead, he wrote the Nobel Prize Committee apologetically that he could not afford the loss of time from his research and from his students and responsibilities at Caltech, and the American ambassador to Sweden was delegated to receive the award for him. It must be recalled that in 1923 one did not fly overnight from California to Sweden. The expedition would have taken more than a month.

About this same time, the earliest group of graduate students in physics was distressed to see what appeared to be the original oil-drop equipment down in "the morgue," as it was called. This was a space in the sub-basement of the Norman Bridge Laboratory where abandoned apparatus and equipment were stored waiting either to be resurrected and adapted to some new application or else eventually to be sold as junk. There was a strong feeling among the students that this famous piece of apparatus should be resurrected, refurbished, and used to form the initial nucleus of a museum of historical scientific equipment such as one sees in famous universities like Cambridge or Glasgow. Since I happened to be about ten years older than the other graduate students of this group, I was selected as the spokesman to propose the idea to Millikan. He listened patiently and when all the favorable arguments had been aired he looked very severely at me. "Jesse," he said, "once the experiment has been performed and the conclusions have been reached and published so that anyone can repeat and check them, the apparatus with which the work was done is *just so much junk*. I don't believe in glorifying or worshipping junk."

I understood what he meant and the occasion left a deep impression. It is said that of Tycho Brahe's beautiful observatory at Uraniborg (where the observational data were taken on the motions of the planets from which Kepler deduced his famous laws of planetary motion and on which, in his turn, Isaac Newton founded the science of mechanics), there remains today but one stone. This stone was once the lintel over the main entrance door. The old King of Sweden, Frederick II, had supported Tycho's astronomical studies and his observatory enthusiastically and generously, but when he died in 1588, his young successor could see no use in this drain on the royal treasury and he banished Tycho and had the observatory of Uraniborg razed.

Fortunately, Tycho had had the foresight to realize that it is not enough to *do* research. It is also a duty to *publish* it, so as to give it to the world, because every scientist, no matter how great, can only contribute a few stitches to the beautiful and ever growing tapestry which represents man's knowledge of the world in which he lives; and, no matter how great or how humble the contribution may be, it may be just the missing piece without which a large part of the whole will fail to make sense. Tycho, therefore, had set up a printing establishment at Uraniborg at which his results were duplicated and sent to many learned centers, and thus they were not lost, even though Uraniborg was destroyed. By a strange irony of fate the surviving lintel stone bears an inscription (in Latin) which translated reads: "Eternal only are the things of the spirit."

This is what Millikan meant by his resolute refusal to glorify his oil-drop apparatus in a museum exhibit.

It was at about this same time in the early years of Millikan's leadership at Caltech that he (more or less accidentally) committed himself to the dictum that science and religion are not antithetical but complementary, a pronouncement which he found himself, perhaps somewhat to his own surprise, obliged to defend for almost all the rest of his life! As nearly as I can recall, the dictum arose through the circumstance that he had been asked to give an after-dinner address at one of the local service leagues, Lions Club, Kiwanis, or the like. By chance he happened in his extempore speech to mention that he felt no incompatibility between religion and science and, as chance would have it, representatives of the press were present who pounced upon this statement, which the next day appeared in headlines in the local newspapers. There is not the slightest doubt in my mind that Millikan was simply giving voice to a deeply held conviction, without cautious reflection as to the electrifying effect it might have on the lay public. The incident grew to be such a *cause célèbre*, however, to which agnostics and atheists reacted with nothing less than "religious fervor," to use Millikan's own phrase, that a group of fifteen scientists, sixteen religious leaders, and fourteen men of affairs signed a "Joint Statement" prepared by Millikan with the critical advice of Arthur Amos Noyes. The explicit purpose was: ". . . to assist in correcting two erroneous impressions which seem to be current among certain groups of persons. The first is that religion today stands for medieval theology; the second, that science is materialistic and irreligious."

The official draft of the "Joint Statement" consisted of three very dignified and carefully worded paragraphs. It is interesting that a first draft, which appears among the papers left by Dr. Millikan, has *five* paragraphs. All of the second, and the bulk of the fourth paragraphs were, however, deleted in pencil with marginal notes to the effect, "Noyes thinks this might be omitted." Some of the fourth paragraph was retained and became the last sentence of the second paragraph in the definitive version. There is an eloquent lesson here in the interchange between two first-class minds of completely different quality, each to the great benefit of the other: Millikan, outgoing, positive, warm-hearted, energetic, and intensely active; Noyes, a deeply reflective, quiet thinker. The "Joint Statement" was reproduced in Millikan's autobiography and since, unfortunately, that is out of print, it is reproduced here:

A JOINT STATEMENT UPON THE RELATIONS OF SCIENCE AND RELIGION

We, the undersigned, deeply regret that in recent controversies there has been a tendency to present science and religion as irreconcilable and antagonistic domains of thought, for in fact they meet distinct human needs, and in the rounding out of human life they supplement rather than oppose each other.

The purpose of science is to develop, without prejudice or preconception of any kind, a knowledge of the facts, the laws, and the processes of nature. The even more important task of religion, on the other hand, is to develop the consciences, the ideals, and the aspirations of mankind. Each of these two activities represents a deep and vital function of the soul of man, and both are necessary for the life, the progress, and the happiness of the human race.

It is a sublime conception of God which is furnished by science, and one wholly consonant with the highest ideals of religion, when it represents Him as revealing Himself through countless ages in the development of the earth as an abode for man and in the age-long inbreathing of life into its constituent matter, culminating in man with his spiritual nature and all his Godlike powers. June 1923.

The only possible weakness in this statement, if weakness it be, is the flavor of homocentricity which is conveyed in the last paragraph. Clearly, the "Joint Statement" is an effort to define what these men thought both religion and science *ought ideally to aim to be* (with tacit recognition that both, as we all know, have frequently fallen short of this goal). It is clearly the statement of men who "accentuate the positive."

Actually, the material chosen for deletion tells an even more eloquent story of the interplay of character between Noyes and Millikan than does the material of the final version. The deletions were clearly made for the purpose of enhancing the objectivity of the statement and removing, as far as possible, any elements of sectarianism or emotionalism.

It seems to the present writer of some importance in forming a picture of Millikan's character to note that in his public statements of his religious views the uppermost element is concerned with *human behavior here and now*, and not with puerile ideas of heavenly rewards in an afterlife. He admitted that no one can be sure which, if any, of the multitude of religions of mankind is the true one, and he sought, therefore, to find the one element common to all religions which seemed to him the most indispensable. To quote from his autobiography:

That common element is found, I think, simply in the life and teachings of Jesus—*the attitude of altruistic idealism* which was the sum and substance of His message. . . . "Whatsoever ye would that men should do to you, do ye even so to them." *You* are the sole judge of what you *ought* to do. . . . But this raises another very important question, namely, what guide has man to enable him to determine what is the good and what the evil way? Listen to how the great French political philosopher Montesquieu in 1747 answered that question for himself: "If I knew something beneficial to myself but harmful to my family, I would drive it out of my mind. If I knew something advantageous to my family but injurious to my country, I would try to forget it. If I knew something profitable to my country but detrimental to Europe or profitable to Europe and detrimental to the human race, I would consider it a crime." . . . This means that my personal job is to develop an *attitude* of willingness—better, determination—to subordinate my own immediate personal impulses, appetites, desires and short-range interests to the larger good of my fellow man, *as I see it*, in cases in which there seems to me upon careful consideration to be conflict between the two. Otherwise I am free to follow my inclinations. Further, that kind of altruistic idealism is certainly the very essence of the teachings of Jesus. From my point of view, *this attitude is the essence of religion*. . . . It necessarily involves faith in the existence of an ultimate Good (Einstein calls it "The intelligence manifested in Nature") which is worth living or dying for.

Later in the same chapter of his autobiography Millikan says: "But I wish to go a step farther, for someone asks, 'Where does the idea of God come in? Isn't it a part of religion?'" And Millikan's first and best answer is taken directly from Holy Writ and reads: "No man hath seen God at any time. . . . If a man says I love God and hateth his brother, he is a liar: for he that loveth not his brother whom he hath seen, how can he love God whom he hath not seen?" In other words, one's attitude toward God is revealed by and reflected in his attitude toward his fellow men.

Millikan made plain that, in his system of values, *behavior* is the test of a man's religion, not belief or disbelief in any theological or philosophical system. This was what he meant when he said he saw no antithesis between religion and science. The effect of the scientific method on his thinking is nowhere clearer than here, for it is precisely the approach of the physicist in his attempts to study natural phenomena. The physicist does not ask: "What *is* matter? What *is* energy in its different manifestations? What *is* electricity?" Rather he asks: "How do these things which I observe around me behave? If I do this or that, how do they react?" The test of a hypothesis to the physicist is "Does it work? Does it explain my observations? Does it predict correctly and quantitatively the results of further new observations?" The physicist does not ask for ultimate truth, no matter how attractive its attainment may appear, because he knows that it is beyond reach. He contents himself with the next best variety, the approximate kind of truth which works. He is always ready to abandon or revise it, when more searching tests show wherein it fails and how it must be replaced with a closer approximation to the facts of observation. He neither asserts nor denies that about which he has no evidence, for to do so would be to deceive and the scientist knows that deception does not work. His faith, if faith it be, is in the reasonableness, the reproducibility, the reliability of nature, without which his efforts to study natural phenomena would be vain. The fact that those efforts have already been rewarded with so many successes is his best reassurance.

If Millikan had been asked, "What is the reason for preferring the altruistic behavior recommended by Montesquieu rather, let us say, than the egoistic behavior extolled by Nietzsche?" I believe he would have replied, "Because I think it will tend to make this world more nearly like the kind of place we would all prefer to live in." However, I believe even this answer would have been to some extent a rationalization on Millikan's part and an answer even closer to the truth would have been, "I choose altruism because that is how I am constructed."

For Millikan the years slipped rapidly by, crowded with work as scientist, world traveler in the exploration of cosmic ray phenomena, lecturer and teacher on both scientific and ethical subjects, planner, administrator, and promoter and fund-raiser for the California Institute of Technology. His hair gradually changed from black to gray and then to a snowy white. With many greatly successful men who have won the respect and recognition of their fellows, whose shoulders have been heavy with responsibilities discharged brilliantly and without failure, and whose judgments in many vital matters have proven sound, the "habit of success" breeds a subconscious conviction that they cannot be wrong. This traps such a man the more easily, the more he has become accustomed to having others agree with him. With the growth of his success and power, an inevitable number of sycophants and seekers of personal advantage swell the ranks of the "yes-men" crowding about him, until nothing less than a superhuman being could resist becoming somewhat opinionated, convinced of the inevitability of his own rightness, and immune to revising his viewpoint. Nevertheless, it is part and parcel of the scientific method that the scientist must be always alert to the need for revision as newly discovered facts make their appearance, for he is never in possession of ultimate truth, only pragmatic truth—that which successfully explains and codifies the present state of knowledge.

Millikan fell into this trap. From the time of his earliest work with Cameron (1928) on the cosmic rays, he was deeply impressed with their very great penetrating power and since at that time electromagnetic radiation of very high frequency (or short wave length), i.e., the so-called nuclear gamma rays such as had been observed coming from radioactive substances like radium or thorium, was the most penetrating sort known, he started with the assumption that the cosmic radiation coming into our atmosphere from outer space was of this nature. It later became clear to him, however, from his work and that of his collaborators, that the cosmic rays were not all of one homogeneous penetrating power but consisted of a whole spectrum of different degrees of absorbability, a fact which by itself he felt did not contradict his assumption as to their original electromagnetic character. That the rays were *charged particles*, deflectable by the magnetic field of the earth, began to be evident with the latitude effect, the work of Clay (1927, which Millikan at first ignored, then doubted) and later with the work of Compton (1933), about whose results he was also at first skeptical. We must remember the unfortunate injury to his electroscope in Peru, at the one point where he might with better luck have observed the dip in cosmic ray intensity.

At some point in his thinking he was taken with the idea that matter is created in the outer vastness of space by some unknown process and that in this act of creation the cosmic rays (electromagnetic radiation) are emitted. He thenceforth referred to them as "the birth cries of atoms." (The idea of the spontaneous creation of matter in the depths of outer space was lately revived by Fred Hoyle but in connection with a very different set of ideas than Millikan's.)

There may have been a certain element of mysticism in Millikan's thinking in connection with his idea expressed in the phrase "birth cries of atoms." He may have felt (how consciously we cannot know) that this concept savored of a divine revelation or inspiration. He has even referred to the cosmic rays as the "music of the spheres." In spite of the contrary views of his own collaborators and many others, he clung very stubbornly and for a long while to his ideas of the cosmic radiation as purely electromagnetic in original character. In his latest (1935) revision of the volume, whose first title in 1917 had been simply *The Electron* but which in 1935 became *Electrons* (+ *and* −), *Protons, Photons, Neutrons, and Cosmic Rays*, there is no indication that he had revised this belief. (This last published version of the book was the one of which E. U. Condon, in a review, facetiously said should have been entitled "Happy Days and Nights in the Norman Bridge Laboratory," to such a great extent did it ignore work done anywhere else.) Carl Anderson and Seth Neddermeyer had great difficulty convincing the Chief of the reality, first, of the evidence for very high primary cosmic ray energies from the particles they were observing with their magnetic cloud chamber work, and, second, of the presence of other particles of mass intermediate between that of electrons and that of protons, the mesons. It must be recalled, however, that he was nearly seventy years old at this time. It is greatly to his credit that he *did* come around, soon after, to recognition of these new phenomena, and once he comprehended the evidence he lost no time in admitting his mistake and apologizing to "his boys," Anderson and Neddermeyer.

The great debate between R. A. Millikan and Sir James Jeans occurred during the period when Millikan still entertained many of his earlier erroneous notions about the nature of the cosmic rays. These two prominent scientists had already shown evidence of marked disagreement in their pronouncements in scientific publications concerning the character and origin of the cosmic rays. Thus, when the lecture hall of the Norman Bridge Laboratory of Physics was thrown open to any of the public who might wish to witness a debate on this subject between these two great authorities, it is not surprising that it was packed to the last bit of standing room. One exchange of intellectual swordplay between the two contestants will suffice to convey an idea of the tenor of this occasion. In his speech, Jeans asserted that he knew of no form of electromagnetic radiation which under any circumstances when interacting with (i.e., passing through) matter became "harder," that is to say more penetrating. All processes which he knew of either left the radiation unmodified in this respect or else rendered it "softer," or less penetrating. (Jeans had in mind initially spectrally homogeneous radiation in making this statement, but he neglected to say so explicitly.) When it was Millikan's turn for rebuttal, he pounced upon this statement, eagerly saying that, on the contrary, he knew of no case in which radiation filtering through matter did not become harder rather than softer. (He meant, of course, that spectrally heterogeneous radiation would, upon passage through material screens, dissipate in the screening matter its more absorbable components first and the remainder would as a result consist, on the average, of the more penetrating components.) Finally, Jeans had his turn at rebuttal and he rose to say that obviously there could be no real fundamental disagreement about the facts of physical science between two authorities such as himself and his eminent colleague. It was all a semantic misunderstanding. "Of course, if you kill off all the old men in a community, the average age of the community grows younger, but this does not imply that any of its individual members are growing younger with passage of time." When the debate terminated, though no one knew any more about the true nature and origin of cosmic rays than before, it is certain that all felt highly edified and contented with having witnessed a very significant event. I congratulated

Millikan, as he was leaving the lecture hall, upon the adroitness and aplomb with which he had parried the attacks of his adversary, and Millikan replied with a chuckle, "Jesse, neither of us knew anything about what we were speaking of." That was over three decades ago, but though we know a great deal more about the cosmic rays now than we did then, the question as to their origin and process of generation is still almost as great a mystery as ever.

Shortly after this incident, the correctness of Millikan's value of e (4.774 $\times$ 10^{-10} esu) began to be questioned, as a result of the work of Erik Bäcklin in Sweden in determining the absolute wave lengths of X-ray emission line spectra, the work already alluded to above as done in 1928. Actually, in the decade after 1928 there was much questioning and investigation of the apparent "discrepancy" between the so-called oil-drop and X-ray values of e, and many hypotheses to reconcile the two differing results were considered, put to the test of experiment, and rejected one after the other when found untenable. Millikan's prestige was so great that people were most reluctant to doubt his correctness in this case, and many efforts were made to search for the fault elsewhere, namely, in the chain of reasoning and experiment whereby e was evaluated from the X-ray measurements on crystals. One suggestion, the most difficult of all to refute, was that the crystal lattice spacing measured with the X-rays might not be the same as the spacing prevailing throughout the bulk of the crystal sample whose mean density, macroscopically measured, was used in the calculation. Up to that time, most precise X-ray measurements made on crystals were made *by reflection from the surfaces*, a very special region which, therefore, could not strictly be regarded as safely sampling the microscopic lattice dimensions of the crystal as a whole. The plausibility of this criterion was greatly weakened in 1932 by Yuching Tu, who showed that the measured densities and X-ray values of grating constants combined with unit-cell molecular weights gave, for many different species of crystals, substantially consistent values of the Avogadro number, N. It seemed unlikely that all these species should exhibit, by accident, the same difference between surface and interior grating spacings. Doubts persisted for a time, nevertheless, because of a suggestion by F. Zwicky that a superlattice structure, consisting of periodic local deviations of the lattice from the average grating spacing, might be a general property of all crystal lattices because of some very fundamental far-reaching and general co-operative effect of the interatomic forces extending over wide domains of the crystal. Zwicky suggested that the boundary surface of a crystal might, by certain considerations of minimum energy, be invariably the site of one of these abnormal grating constant regions. For a considerable time the proponents of the correctness of Millikan's value of e, including Millikan himself, clung to this criticism of the X-ray value of e as the explanation of the discrepancy.

In collaboration with V. L. Bollman, V. A. Brown, and later P. H. Miller, however, I eventually succeeded in eliminating this uncertainty completely: (1) by showing that when X-rays are reflected *from the internal planes* of crystals of the "perfect" type, crystals such as had been used in the X-ray determination of N and e, precisely the same value of the grating constant of these planes is obtained as had been found by the surface reflection; (2) by powdering crystals so finely that "primary extinction," as it is called, could not prevent the entire volume of every crystallite from being uniformly bathed in the X-rays. The grating constant and the density of such powdered crystallites were then measured, the first by X-ray powder diffraction methods, the second with a pycnometer, and no significant difference was observed in the inferred value of N from that obtained with macroscopic crystals. As a result of answering this last criticism of the X-ray approach to evaluating e, all the input data which had been used in Millikan's determination began to be much more carefully scrutinized and soon thereafter experimenters showed that the one element in Millikan's reduction of his data which had not been re-examined critically, namely, the viscosity of air, was the chief cause of the trouble. Millikan, with his many responsibilities, overlooked the evidence from internal X-ray reflection and powdered crystals until it was called to his attention by R. T. Birge. When he had completely understood the unimpeachability of the evidence and the inevitability of the conclusions, he called me to his office for the express purpose of acknowledging his recognition of the significance of these results. Millikan was often wrong, just as everyone else has been who has attempted much, and in his later years he became opinionated and unreceptive to what was new, but his basic intellectual honesty when he finally recognized his mistakes was always admirable and beyond question.

Millikan died in 1953 at the age of eighty-five, seven years after his replacement as chairman of the Executive Council of the California Institute of Technology by Lee A. DuBridge. His health, both physical and mental, had been excellent until a few months before his death. The decline of his faculties in the last months was precipitate, and in the opinion of this writer it is unlikely that he had any awareness of his decline, so painful to those of us who had loved and admired him so long. Fate was kind to him and spared him even any knowledge that a similar end was approaching concurrently for his faithful wife, Greta. He died shortly before Christmas. I was absent on a brief visit to Stanford University, so that the following account of his funeral ceremony is not that of an eyewitness. The circumstances surrounding it are worthy of recitation, however, since they have a special significance and interpretation in terms of this great man's character.

Millikan was buried on the twenty-third of December in the Court of Honor in Forest Lawn Memorial-Park with great pomp and circumstance. Friends, personnel of the California Institute of Technology, and even members of his immediate family, were astonished to learn that the Forest Lawn Memorial-Park Association had obtained a written authorization over Dr. Millikan's signature, granting them the exclusive privilege to inter his body in their Court of Honor as one of those whom they had "elected as an Immortal."

Friends and associates at the California Institute of Technology received invitations to the ceremony delivered, not by mail, but in person by messengers. The solemnities have been reported to the writer as follows: After the speeches, the Roger Wagner Chorale furnished several vocal numbers and finally executed the solemn "March Past" (the casket of the deceased), singing as they did so. Two of the speakers, in long robes suggestive of ancient academic rites, then received, one a scroll of parchment, the other a laurel wreath of gold. These were carried to them on velvet cushions by two page boys in Louis XIV costume. This "Pronouncement" was then read from the parchment scroll:

> The Council of Regents of Memorial Court of
> Honor in Forest Lawn Memorial-Park has elected
> Robert Andrews Millikan an Immortal of the Court
> of Honor with all the rights and privileges which
> accompany this selection, among which is the right
> of entombment within the Court of Honor, where all
> crypts are reserved as gifts for great Americans who
> have contributed outstanding service to humanity.

Another principal in this dramatic performance then lifted the
golden laurel wreath from the cushion and placed it upon the
flower-decked coffin.

There are those who regard this astonishing and unexpected
finale to the great man's life as an undoubted indication of his
innermost vanity, a weakness to which they suppose he finally
gave way after having been several times importuned by the
Forest Lawn Memorial-Park Association. I do not believe it for
one instant. Consider the facts in Millikan's own life. This was the
man who had refused the title of "college president"; the man
who had refused the security and prestige of a princely salary and
a research directorship with the United States Steel Corporation to
accept the challenge of resuscitating Caltech and building it into
its uniquely superior position; the same man who chose not to
mention in his autobiography the decision just cited, a decision
which I regard as the finest tribute to his character; the same man
who would not have his oil-drop apparatus preserved for posterity
in a museum; the same man who could not spare the time from his
research to go to Stockholm to receive a Nobel Prize. He had been
showered with *genuine* honors during his life. How can anyone
believe he would value such a pinchbeck performance as this over
his dead body!

No—the clue to Millikan's last gesture lies in the fact that a
part of the bargain which he had signed with the Forest Lawn
Association was that it was to contribute a sum of money to his
beloved Caltech *for the support of research* in return for the privilege.
The sum shall not be named here, but it is of great significance
that the sum was indeed modest. What Millikan was saying, with
his last gesture, was:

"The experiment is finished. The apparatus with which it was done is just so much junk. Let those who worship material things pay for it whatever they think it worth so long as it may contribute to the advancement of knowledge."

J. W. M .D.

April 9, 1963

The original of this cartoon is a mural drawing in pastels by Arthur Cahill. It now occupies one entire wall of the billiard room of the Athenaeum at Caltech.

CALENDAR OF SOME EVENTS IN RESEARCH
IN PHYSICS WHICH OCCURRED
BETWEEN 1883 AND 1953

1883   Edison observes thermoelectrically emitted current from incandescent lamp filaments.

1887   Michelson and Morley experiment.

1887–88   Photoelectric effect first observed (but not understood). Hertz, Hallwachs.

1889–96   J. A. Fleming develops the vacuum tube rectifying diode valve.

1895   Discovery of X-rays by W. C. Roentgen.

1896   Discovery of radioactivity (in uranium salts) by Becquerel.

1896   Zeeman discovers the splitting of spectral lines from light sources placed in a magnetic field.

1897   J. J. Thomson's measurements of e/m and with Townsend an estimate of the electronic charge, e, by the rate of fall of charged clouds.

1898   Discovery (isolation) of the elements, radium, thorium, and polonium by the Curies.

1900   Hyperfine structure splitting of spectral lines first observed.

1901   Max Planck's black body radiation formula. Birth of the quantum theory.

1902–8   Millikan's early work on "cold emission" or "field emission" (of electrons) serves as beginning of study eventually resolved between 1919 and 1927 by his students, Shackelford, Eyring, Mackeown, Lauritsen, and explained theoretically by Oppenheimer.

1905   Restricted theory of relativity adumbrated by Einstein.

1905   Quantum theory of photoelectric emission stated by Einstein.

1906   Discovery of isotopes by J. J. Thomson.

1906   C. G. Barkla demonstrates that X-rays are a "transverse" electromagnetic wave propagation phenomenon by showing how they are polarized by scattering at 90° scattering angle.

1908   Rutherford and Geiger's studies of alpha particles from radium. Invention of the Geiger counter.

1908–12   Barkla demonstrates and studies the "K-series" and "L-series" in fluorescent X-rays, characteristic of different atomic species, using purely absorption methods before X-ray spectroscopy by crystal diffraction had been discovered.

1909   R. A. Millikan's oil-drop experiment conclusively demon-
       strates unitary nature of electricity.

1909   Barkla determines, by measuring the intensity of X-ray
       scattering, the number of electrons in carbon.

1909–10 Geiger and Marsden's experiments with alpha particle scatter-
       ing in gold foil.

1911   E. Rutherford, as a result of preceding alpha particle scattering
       experiments, proposes his atom model consisting of a heavy
       central nucleus surrounded by electrons.

1911   Hess and Kohlhorster's discovery of cosmic rays.

1912   Invention by C. T. R. Wilson of the cloud expansion chamber.

1912   The Laue, Friedrich and Knipping experiment opens up the
       field of study of X-ray crystallography.

1912   W. Bragg and his son, L. Bragg, start work in X-ray spectros-
       copy by means of crystal diffraction.

1913   Niels Bohr's theory explaining the spectrum of atomic hydro-
       gen and postulating his stable "non-radiating" electron
       orbits.

1914   Moseley's first comparative studies of X-ray spectra of the
       elements lead him to the concept of "atomic number" and
       Moseley's law.

1914   Frank and Hertz's experiments demonstrate reality of discrete
       atomic energy levels.

1915   "Inverse photoelectric effect" (short wave length limit of the
       continuous X-ray spectrum) studied by Ulrey, Webster,
       Duane, and Hunt.

1916   Millikan (with his "barber shop in a vacuum tube") verifies
       Einstein's law of the photoelectric effect and determines
       Planck's constant, h.

1919   Rutherford with Marsden observes the first case of artificial
       transmutation of the elements: $_7N^{14} + {}_2He^4 \rightarrow {}_8O^{17} + {}_1H^1$.

1920   J. A. Gray discovers modified scattering of X-rays later ex-
       plained by A. H. Compton.

1921   The Stern and Gerlach experiment. Space quantization.

1921–26 Millikan and Bowen develop "hot" spark spectroscopy of the
       extreme ultraviolet. Schrödinger is said to have attributed
       his acceptance of the spinning electron model to this work.

1922   Aston's precision study of isotopic masses leads to his mass-
       defect curve.

1923   A. H. Compton discovers the effect bearing his name.

1924   L. de Broglie conceives of his electron "matter waves."

1925   Uhlenbeck and Goudsmit propose the concept of the spinning electron.

1925   P. Auger discovers the "composite photoelectric effect" which usually goes by his name as the Auger effect.

1926   Schrödinger's equation is evolved.

1927   Davisson and Germer experiment gives first demonstration of electron diffraction by crystal lattices.

1927   Heisenberg proposes the "principle of indeterminacy."

1927–28 Sommerfeld proposes his simple picture of the conduction electrons in an electrical conductor as a degenerate electron gas. Beginnings of solid state physics.

1928   Millikan and Cameron's studies of cosmic rays by means of ionization chamber electroscopes submerged under the water of snow-fed mountain lakes.

1928   Raman effect discovered.

1928   P. A. M. Dirac's relativistically invariant formulation of wave-mechanics.

1928   Erik Bäcklin makes a determination of the absolute wave length of an X-ray line which leads eventually to a more accurate value of e than that of Millikan's oil-drop work.

1930   Dirac's theory of the positron as a hole in the sea of negative electrons in negative energy states.

1930   W. Pauli proposes the neutrino.

1930   Kirkpatrick and DuMond's evidence for the broadening of the Compton shifted line as a Doppler effect of the orbital motion of atomic electrons.

1931   P. A. Ross and P. Kirkpatrick demonstrate "Defect in the Compton Shift" as a result of electron binding.

1931   Van de Graaff, then at Princeton, invents his belt generator.

1931   H. C. Urey, F. G. Brickwedde, and G. M. Murphy separate heavy water (deuterium).

1932   Discovery of the neutron by Chadwick as an interpretation of the experimental results of Curie and Joliot.

1932   E. O. Lawrence invents the cyclotron.

1932–33 C. Anderson discovers the positron.

1933   Studies of electron-positron pair formation and annihilation. Blackett and Occhialini.

1933–39 Work on atomic beams and atomic resonance started by Stern and Estermann at Carnegie Tech. and brilliantly continued and perfected at Columbia by Rabi, Zacharias, Kusch, and others.

1935   Yukawa proposes his theory of the meson to explain nuclear forces.

1937   Neddermeyer and Anderson's discovery of the mu-meson.

1939   Discovery of nuclear fission. Hahn and Strassman, also Meitner and Frisch.

1940   Kerst perfects the "Betatron."

1941   The "Calutron": beginnings of large scale magnetic separation
(ca.)   of isotopes.

1942   E. Fermi's first graphite pile chain reactor at Chicago.

1945   McMillan in U.S.A. and, independently, Veksler in Russia invent the synchrotron.

1946   Beginnings of studies of nuclear magnetic resonance at Stanford and at Harvard.

1946   L. Alvarez and W. Panofsky build thirty-two MeV linear accelerator for protons, an outgrowth of an idea of Lawrence, Sloan, Beams, Livingston, and Alvarez in 1935.

1947   Discovery of pi-meson by Lattes, Muirhead, Occhialini, and Powell.

1947   Lind and DuMond make the 2-meter bent crystal gamma-ray spectrometer work for the first time with a source of Au^{198}, thus opening up a new field of high precision in the direct spectroscopy of nuclear gamma-rays by means of crystal diffraction.

1948   Quantum-electrodynamics is born. Feynman, Schwinger, and others.

1948–50   Willis Lamb's studies with Retherford and others of hydrogen and deuterium spectra by atomic beam resonance methods reveal the "Lamb shift" and give important information on the fine structure constant.

1950–53   Existence and properties of the π^0 meson studied by Panofsky, Steinberger, Steller, et al. at Berkeley.

1953   Reines and Cowan demonstrate effects caused by neutrinos after their emission from nuclear reactors.

INTRODUCTION

Perhaps it is merely a coincidence that the man who first noticed that the rubbing of amber would induce in it a new and remarkable state now known as the state of *electrification* was also the man who first gave expression to the conviction that there must be some great unifying principle which links together all phenomena and is capable of making them rationally intelligible; that behind all the apparent variety and change of things there is some primordial element, out of which all things are made and the search for which must be the ultimate aim of all natural science. Yet if this be merely a coincidence, at any rate to Thales of Miletus must belong a double honor. For he first correctly conceived and correctly stated, as far back as 600 B.C., the spirit which has actually guided the development of physics in all ages, and he also first described, though in a crude and imperfect way, the very phenomenon the study of which has already linked together several of the erstwhile isolated departments of physics, such as radiant heat, light, magnetism, and electricity, and has very recently brought us nearer to the primordial element than we have ever been before.

Whether this perpetual effort to reduce the complexities of the world to simpler terms, and to build up the infinite variety of objects which present themselves to our senses out of different arrangements or motions of the least possible number of elementary substances, is a modern heritage from Greek thought, or whether it is a native instinct of the human mind may be left for the philosopher and the historian to determine. Certain it is, however, that the greatest of the Greeks aimed at nothing less than the complete banishment of caprice from nature and the ultimate reduction of all her processes to a rationally intelligible and unified system. And certain it is also that the periods of greatest progress in the history of physics have been the periods in which this effort has been most active and most successful.

Thus the first half of the nineteenth century is unquestionably a period of extraordinary fruitfulness. It is at the same time a period in which for the first time men, under Dalton's lead, began to get direct, experimental, quantitative proof that the atomic world which the Greeks had bequeathed to us, the world of Leucippus and Democritus and Lucretius, consisting as it did of an infinite number and variety of atoms, was far more complex than it needed to be, and that by introducing the idea of molecules built up out of different combinations and groupings of atoms the number of necessary elements could be reduced to but about seventy. The importance of this step is borne witness to by the fact that out of it sprang in a very few years the whole science of modern chemistry.

And now this twentieth century, though but sixteen years old, has already attempted to take a still bigger and more significant step. By superposing upon the molecular and the atomic worlds of the nineteenth century a third electronic world, it has sought to reduce the number of primordial elements to not more than two, namely, positive and negative electrical charges. Along with this effort has come the present period of most extraordinary development and fertility—a period in which new viewpoints and indeed wholly new phenomena follow one another so rapidly across the stage of physics that the actors themselves scarcely know what is happening—a period too in which the commercial and industrial world is adopting and adapting to its own uses with a rapidity hitherto altogether unparalleled the latest products of the laboratory of the physicist and the chemist. As a consequence, the results of yesterday's researches, designed for no other purpose than to add a little more to our knowledge of the ultimate structure of matter, are today seized upon by the practical business world and made to multiply tenfold the effectiveness of the telephone or to extract six times as much light as was formerly obtained from a given amount of electric power.

It is then not merely a matter of academic interest that electricity has been proved to be atomic or granular in structure, that the elementary electrical charge has been isolated and accurately measured, and that it has been found to enter as a constitutent into the making of all the seventy-odd atoms of chemistry. These are indeed matters of fundamental and absorbing interest to the man who is seeking to unveil nature's inmost secrets, but they are also events which are pregnant with meaning for the man of commerce and for the worker in the factory. For it usually happens that when nature's inner workings have once been laid bare, man sooner or later finds a way to put his brains inside the machine and to drive it whither he wills. Every increase in man's knowledge of the way in which nature works must, in the long run, increase by just so much man's ability to control nature and to turn her hidden forces to his own account.

The purpose of this volume is to present the evidence for the atomic structure of electricity, to describe some of the most significant properties of the elementary electrical unit, the electron, and to discuss the bearing of these properties upon the two most important problems of modern physics: the structure of the atom and the nature of electromagnetic radiation. In this presentation I shall not shun the discussion of exact quantitative experiments, for it is only upon such a basis, as Pythagoras asserted more than two thousand years ago, that any real scientific treatment of physical phenomena is possible. Indeed, from the point of view of that ancient philosopher, the problem of all natural philosophy is to drive out qualitative conceptions and to replace them by quantitative relations. And this point of view has been emphasized by the farseeing throughout all the history of physics clear down to the present. One of the greatest of modern physicists, Lord Kelvin, writes:

> When you can measure what you are speaking about and express it in numbers, you know something about it, and when you cannot measure it, when you cannot express it in numbers, your knowledge is of a meagre and unsatisfactory kind. It may be the beginning of knowledge, but you have scarcely in your thought advanced to the stage of a science.

Although my purpose is to deal mostly with the researches of which I have had most direct and intimate knowledge, namely, those which have been carried on during the past ten years in this general field in the Ryerson Laboratory, I shall hope to be able to give a correct and just review of the preceding work out of which these researches grew, as well as of parallel work carried on in other laboratories. In popular writing it seems to be necessary to link every great discovery, every new theory, every important principle, with the name of a single individual. But it is an almost universal rule that developments in physics actually come about in a very different way. A science, like a planet, grows in the main by a process of infinitesimal accretion. Each research is usually a modification of a preceding one; each new theory is built like a cathedral through the addition by many builders of many different elements. This is preeminently true of the electron theory. It has been a growth, and I shall endeavor in every case to trace the pedigree of each research connected with it.

CHAPTER I

EARLY VIEWS OF ELECTRICITY

I.   GROWTH OF THE ATOMIC THEORY OF MATTER

There is an interesting and instructive parallelism between the histories of the atomic conception of matter and the atomic theory of electricity, for in both cases the ideas themselves go back to the very beginnings of the subject. In both cases too these ideas remained absolutely sterile until the development of precise quantitative methods of measurement touched them and gave them fecundity. It took two thousand years for this to happen in the case of the theory of matter and one hundred and fifty years for it to happen in the case of electricity; and no sooner had it happened in the case of both than the two domains hitherto thought of as distinct began to move together and to appear as perhaps but different aspects of one and the same phenomenon, thus recalling again Thales' ancient belief in the essential unity of nature. How this attempt at union has come about can best be seen by a brief review of the histories of the two ideas.

The conception of a world made up of atoms which are in incessant motion was almost as clearly developed in the minds of the Greek philosophers of the School of Democritus (420 B.C.), Epicurus (370 B.C.), and Lucretius (Roman, 50 B.C.) as it is in the mind of the modern physicist, but the idea had its roots in one case in a mere speculative philosophy; in the other case, like most of our twentieth-century knowledge, it rests upon direct, exact, quantitative observations and measurement. Not that the human eye has ever seen or indeed can ever see an individual atom or molecule. This is forever impossible, and for the simple reason that the limitations on our ability to see small objects are imposed, not by the imperfections of our instruments, but by the nature of the eye itself, or by the nature of the light-wave to which the eye is sensitive. If we are to see molecules our biological friends must develop wholly new types of eyes, viz., eyes which are sensitive to waves one thousand times shorter than those to which our present optic nerves can respond.

But after all, the evidence of our eyes is about the least reliable kind of evidence which we have. We are continually seeing things which do not exist, even though our habits are unimpeachable. It is the relations which are seen by the mind's eye to be the logical consequences of exact measurement which are for the most part dependable. So far as the atomic theory of matter is concerned, these relations have all been developed since 1800, so that both the modern atomic and the modern kinetic theories of matter, in spite of their great antiquity, are in a sense less than one hundred years old. Indeed, nearly all of our definite knowledge about molecules and atoms has come since 1851, when Joule[1] in England made the first absolute determination of a molecular magnitude, namely, the average speed with which gaseous molecules of a given kind are darting hither and thither at ordinary temperatures. This

[1] *Mem. of the Manchester Lit. and Phil. Soc.* (1851; 2d series), 107; *Phil. Mag.*, XIV (1857), 211.

result was as surprising as many others which have followed in the field of molecular physics, for it showed that this speed, in the case of the hydrogen molecule, has the stupendous value of about a mile a second. The second molecular magnitude to be found was the mean distance a molecule of a gas moves between collisions, technically called the mean free path of a molecule. This was computed first in 1860 by Clerk Maxwell.[1] It was also 1860 before anyone had succeeded in making any sort of an estimate of the number of molecules in a cubic centimeter of a gas. When we reflect that we can now count this number with probably greater precision than we can attain in determining the number of people living in New York, in spite of the fact that it has the huge value of 27.05 billion billion, one gains some idea of how great has been our progress in mastering some at least of the secrets of the molecular and atomic worlds. The wonder is that we got at it so late. Nothing is more surprising to the student brought up in the atmosphere of the scientific thought of the present than the fact that the relatively complex and intricate phenomena of light and electromagnetism had been built together into moderately consistent and satisfactory theories long before the much simpler phenomena of heat and molecular physics had begun to be correctly understood. And yet almost all the qualitative conceptions of the atomic and kinetic theories were developed thousands of years ago. Tyndall's statement of the principles of Democritus, whom Bacon considered to be "a man of mightier metal than

[1] *Phil. Mag.*, XIX (1860; 4th series), 28. Clausius had discussed some of the relations of this quantity in 1858 (*Pogg. Ann.*, CV [1858], 239), but Maxwell's magnificent work on the viscosity of gases first made possible its evaluation.

Plato or Aristotle, though their philosophy was noised and celebrated in the schools amid the din and pomp of professors," will show how complete an atomic philosophy had arisen 400 years B.C. "That it was entirely destroyed later was not so much due to the attacks upon it of the idealistic school, whose chief representatives were Plato and Aristotle, as to the attacks upon all civilization of Genseric, Attila, and the barbarians." That the Aristotelian philosophy lasted throughout this period is explained by Bacon thus: "At a time when all human learning had suffered shipwreck these planks of Aristotelian and Platonic Philosophy, as being of a lighter and more inflated substance, were preserved and came down to us, while things more solid sank and almost passed into oblivion."

Democritus' principles, as quoted by Tyndall, are as follows:

1. From nothing comes nothing. Nothing that exists can be destroyed. All changes are due to the combination and separation of molecules.

2. Nothing happens by chance. Every occurrence has its cause from which it follows by necessity.

3. The only existing things are the atoms and empty space; all else is mere opinion.

4. The atoms are infinite in number and infinitely various in form; they strike together and the lateral motions and whirlings which thus arise are the beginnings of worlds.

5. The varieties of all things depend upon the varieties of their atoms, in number, size, and aggregation.

6. The soul consists of fine, smooth, round atoms like those of fire. These are the most mobile of all. They interpenetrate the whole body and in their motions the phenomena of life arise.

These principles with a few modifications and omissions might almost pass muster today. The great advance which has been made in modern times is not so much in the conceptions themselves as in the kind of foundation upon which the conceptions rest. The principles enumerated above were simply the opinions of one man or of a school of men. There were scores of other rival opinions, and no one could say which was the better. Today there is absolutely no philosophy in the field other than the atomic philosophy, at least among physicists. Yet this statement could not have been made even as much as ten years ago. For in spite of all the multiple relationships between combining powers of the elements, and in spite of all the other evidences of chemistry and nineteenth-century physics, a group of the foremost of modern thinkers, until quite recently, withheld their allegiance from these theories. The most distinguished of this group was the German chemist and philosopher, Wilhelm Ostwald. However, in the preface to a new edition of his *Outlines of Chemistry* he now makes the following clear and frank avowal of his present position. He says:

I am now convinced that we have recently become possessed of experimental evidence of the discrete or grained nature of matter for which the atomic hypothesis sought in vain for hundreds and thousands of years. The isolation and counting of gaseous ions on the one hand . . . . and on the other the agreement of the Brownian movements with the requirements of the kinetic hypothesis . . . . justify the most cautious scientist in now speaking of the experimental proof of the atomic theory of matter. The atomic hypothesis is thus raised to the position of a scientifically well-founded theory.

II.   GROWTH OF ELECTRICAL THEORIES

The granular theory of electricity, while unlike the atomic and kinetic theories of matter in that it can boast no great antiquity in any form, is like them in that the first man who speculated upon the nature of electricity at all conceived of it as having an atomic structure.   Yet it is only within very recent years—twenty at the most—that the modern electron theory has been developed. There are no electrical theories of any kind which go back of Benjamin Franklin (1750).   Aside from the discovery of the Greeks that rubbed amber had the power of attracting to itself light objects, there was no knowledge at all earlier than 1600 A.D., when Gilbert, Queen Elizabeth's surgeon, and a scientist of great genius and insight, found that a glass rod and some twenty other bodies, when rubbed with silk, act like the rubbed amber of the Greeks, and he consequently decided to describe the phenomenon by saying that the glass rod had become electrified (amberized, electron being the Greek word for amber), or, as we now say, had acquired a charge of electricity.   In 1733 Dufay, a French physicist, further found that sealing wax, when rubbed with cat's fur, was also electrified, but that it differed from the electrified glass rod, in that it strongly attracted any electrified body which was repelled by the glass, while it repelled any electrified body which was attracted by the glass.   He was thus led to recognize two kinds of electricity, which he termed "vitreous" and "resinous."   About 1747 Benjamin Franklin, also recognizing these two kinds of electrification, introduced the terms "positive" and "negative," to distinguish them.   Thus, he said, we will arbitrarily call any body positively electrified if it is repelled by a glass rod which has been rubbed with silk, and we will call any body negatively electrified if it is repelled by sealing wax which has been rubbed with cat's

fur. *These are today our definitions of positive and negative electrical charges*. Notice that in setting them up we
propose no theory whatever of electrification, but content ourselves simply with describing the phenomena.

In the next place it was surmised by Franklin and
indeed asserted by him in the very use of the terms
"positive" and "negative," although the accurate proof
of the relation was not made until the time of Faraday's
ice-pail experiment in 1837, that when glass is positively
electrified by rubbing it with silk, the silk itself takes up
a negative charge of exactly the same amount as the
positive charge received by the glass, and, in general,
that *positive and negative electrical charges always appear
simultaneously and in exactly equal amounts*.

So far, still no theory. But in order to have a
rational explanation of the phenomena so far considered,
particularly this last one, Franklin now made the assumption that something which he chose to call the electrical
fluid or "electrical fire" exists in normal amount as a constituent of all matter in the neutral, or unelectrified state,
and that more than the normal amount in any body is
manifested as a positive electrical charge, and less than
the normal amount as a negative charge. Aepinus, professor of physics at St. Petersburg and an admirer of
Franklin's theory, pointed out that, in order to account
for the repulsion of two negatively electrified bodies, it
was necessary to assume that matter, when divorced from
Franklin's electrical fluid, was self-repellent, i.e., that it
possessed properties quite different from those which are
found in ordinary unelectrified matter. In order, however, to leave matter, whose independent existence was
thus threatened, endowed with its familiar old properties,

and in order to get electrical phenomena into a class by themselves, other physicists of the day, led by Symmer, 1759, preferred to assume that *matter in a neutral state shows no electrical properties because it contains as constituents equal amounts of two weightless fluids which they called positive and negative electricity, respectively*. From this point of view a positively charged body is one in which there is more of the positive fluid than of the negative, and a negatively charged body is one in which the negative fluid is in excess.

Thus arose the so-called two-fluid theory—a theory which divorced again the notions of electricity and matter after Franklin had taken a step toward bringing them together.   This theory, in spite of its intrinsic difficulties, dominated the development of electrical science for one hundred years and more.   This was because, if one did not bother himself much with the underlying physical conception, the theory lent itself admirably to the description of electrical phenomena and also to mathematical formulation.   Further, it was convenient for the purposes of classification.   It made it possible to treat electrical phenomena in a category entirely by themselves, without raising any troublesome questions as to the relation, for example, between electrical and gravitational or cohesive forces.   But in spite of these advantages it was obviously a makeshift.   For the notion of two fluids which could exert powerful forces and yet which were absolutely without weight—the most fundamental of physical properties—and the further notion of two fluids which had no physical properties whatever, that is, which disappeared entirely when they were mixed in equal proportions—these notions were in a

high degree non-physical. Indeed, J. J. Thomson
remarked in his Silliman Lectures in 1903 that—

the physicists and mathematicians who did most to develop the
fluid theories confined their attention to questions which involved
only the law of forces between electrified bodies and the simultaneous production of equal quantities of plus and minus electricity,
and refined and idealized their conception of the fluids themselves
until any reference to their physical properties was considered
almost indelicate.

From the point of view of economy in hypothesis,
Franklin's one-fluid theory, as modified by Aepinus, was
the better.   Mathematically the two theories were identical.   The differences may be summed up thus.   The
modified one-fluid theory required that matter, when
divorced from the electrical fluid, have exactly the same
properties which the two-fluid theory ascribed to negative electricity, barring only the property of fluidity.
So that the most important distinction between the
theories was that the two-fluid theory assumed the existence of three distinct entities, named positive electricity,
negative electricity, and matter, while the one-fluid
theory reduced these three entities to two, which Franklin
called matter and electricity, but which might perhaps as
well have been called positive electricity and negative
electricity, unelectrified matter being reduced to a mere
combination of these two.

Of course, the idea of a granular structure for electricity was foreign to the two-fluid theory, and since this
dominated the development of electrical science, there
was seldom any mention in connection with it of an electrical atom, even as a speculative entity.   But with
Franklin the case was different.   His theory was essen-

tially a material one, and he unquestionably believed in the existence of an electrical particle or atom, for he says: "The electrical matter consists of particles extremely subtle, since it can permeate common matter, even the densest, with such freedom and ease as not to receive any appreciable resistance." When Franklin wrote that, however, he could scarcely have dreamed that it would ever be possible to isolate and study by itself one of the ultimate particles of the electrical fluid. The atomic theory of electricity was to him what the atomic theory of matter was to Democritus, a pure speculation.

The first bit of experimental evidence which appeared in its favor came in 1833, when Faraday found that the passage of a given quantity of electricity through a solution containing a compound of hydrogen, for example, would always cause the appearance at the negative terminal of the same amount of hydrogen gas irrespective of the kind of hydrogen compound which had been dissolved, and irrespective also of the strength of the solution; that, further, the quantity of electricity required to cause the appearance of one gram of hydrogen would always deposit from a solution containing silver exactly 107.1 grams of silver. This meant, since the weight of the silver atom is exactly 107.1 times the weight of the hydrogen atom, that the hydrogen atom and the silver atom are associated in the solution with exactly the same quantity of electricity. When it was further found in this way that all atoms which are univalent in chemistry, that is, which combine with one atom of hydrogen, carry precisely the same quantity of electricity, and all atoms which are bivalent carry twice this amount, and, in general, that valency, in chemistry, is always exactly proportional to the quantity of electricity carried by the atom in question, it was obvious that the atomic theory of electricity had been given very strong support.

But striking and significant as were these discoveries, they did not serve at all to establish the atomic hypothesis of the nature of electricity. They were made at the very time when attention began to be directed strongly away from the conception of electricity as a substance of any kind, and it was no other than Faraday himself who, in spite of the brilliant discoveries just mentioned, started this second period in the development of electrical theory, a period lasting from 1840 to about 1900. In this period electrical phenomena are almost exclusively thought of in terms of stresses and strains in the medium which surrounds the electrified body. Up to this time a more or less definite something called a charge of electricity had been thought of as existing *on* a charged body and had been imagined to exert forces on other charged bodies at a distance from it in quite the same way in which the gravitational force of the earth acts on the moon or that of the sun on the earth. This notion of action at a distance was repugnant to Faraday, and he found in the case of electrical forces experimental reasons for discarding it which had not then, nor have they as yet, been found in the case of gravitational forces. These reasons are summed up in the statement that the electrical force between two charged bodies is found to depend on the nature of the intervening medium, while gravitational pulls are, so far as is known, independent of intervening bodies. Faraday, therefore, pictured to himself the intervening medium as transmitting electrical force in quite the same way in which an elastic deformation started at one end of a rod is transmitted by the rod. Further, since electrical forces act through a vacuum, Faraday had to assume that it is the ether which acts as the transmitter of these electrical stresses and strains. The properties of the ether were then conceived of as modified by the presence of matter in order to account for the fact that the same two charges attract each other with different forces according as the intervening medium is, for example, glass, or ebonite, or air, or merely ether. These views, conceived by Faraday and put into mathematical form by Maxwell, called attention away from the electrical phenomena in or on a conductor carrying electricity and focused it upon the stresses and strains taking place in the medium about the conductor. When in 1886 Heinrich Hertz in Bonn, Germany, proved by direct experiment that electrical forces are indeed transmitted in the form of electric waves, which travel through space with the speed of light exactly as the Faraday-Maxwell theory had predicted, the triumph of the ether-stress point of view was complete. Thereupon textbooks were written by enthusiastic, but none too cautious, physicists in which it was asserted that an electric charge is nothing more than a "state of strain in the ether," and an electric current, instead of representing the passage of anything definite along the wire, corresponds merely to a continuous "slip" or "breakdown of a strain" in the medium within the wire. Lodge's book, *Modern Views of Electricity*, has been the most influential disseminator and expounder of this point of view.

Now what had actually been proved was not that electricity is a state of strain, but that when any electrical charge appears upon a body the medium about the body does indeed become the seat of new forces which are transmitted through the medium, like any elastic forces, with a definite speed. Hence it is entirely proper to say that the medium about a charged body is in a state of strain. But it is one thing to say that the electrical charge on the body *produces* a state of strain in the surrounding medium, and quite another thing to say that the electrical charge *is nothing but* a state of strain in the surrounding medium, just as it is one thing to say that when a man stands on a bridge he produces a mechanical strain in the timbers of the bridge, and another thing to say that the man is nothing more than a mechanical strain in the bridge. The practical difference between the two points of view is that in the one case you look for other attributes of the man besides the ability to produce a strain in the bridge, and in the other case you do not look for other attributes. So the strain theory, although not irreconcilable with the atomic hypothesis, was actually antagonistic to it, because it led men to think of the strain as distributed continuously about the surface of the charged body, rather than as radiating from definite spots or centers peppered over the surface of the body. Between 1833 and 1900, then, the physicist was in this peculiar position: when he was thinking of the passage of electricity through a solution, he for the most part, following Faraday, pictured to himself definite specks or atoms of electricity as traveling through the solution, each atom of matter carrying an exact multiple, which might be anywhere between one and eight, of a definite elementary electrical atom, while, when he was thinking of the passage of a current through a metallic conductor, he gave up altogether the atomic hypothesis, and attempted to picture the phenomenon to himself as a continuous "slip" or "breakdown of a strain" in the material of the wire. In other words, he recognized two types of electrical conduction which were wholly distinct in kind—electrolytic conduction and metallic conduction; and since more of the problems of the physicist dealt with metallic than with electrolytic conduction, the atomic conception, as a general hypothesis, was almost, though not quite, unheard of. Of course it would be unjust to the thinkers of this period to say that they failed to recognize and appreciate this gulf between current views as to the nature of electrolytic and metallic conduction, and simply ignored the difficulty. This they did not do, but they had all sorts of opinions as to the causes. Maxwell himself in his text on *Electricity and Magnetism*, published in 1873, recognizes, in the chapter on "Electrolysis,"[1] the significance of Faraday's laws, and even goes so far as to say that "for convenience in description we may call this constant molecular charge (revealed by Faraday's experiments) one molecule of electricity." Nevertheless, a little farther on he repudiates the idea that this term can have any physical significance by saying that "it is extremely improbable that when we come to understand the true nature of electrolysis we shall retain in any form the theory of molecular charges, for then we shall have obtained a secure basis on which to form a true theory of electric currents and so become independent of these provisional hypotheses."

[1] I, 375–86.

And as a matter of fact, Faraday's experiments had not shown at all that electrical charges on metallic conductors consist of specks of electricity, even though they had shown that the charges on ions in solutions have definite values which are always the same for univalent ions. It was entirely logical to assume, as Maxwell did, that an ion took into solution a definite quantity of electricity because of some property which it had of always charging up to the same amount from a charged plate. There was no reason for assuming the charge *on the electrode* to be made up of some exact number of electrical atoms.

On the other hand, Wilhelm Weber, in papers written in 1871,[1] built up his whole theory of electromagnetism on a basis which was practically identical with the modified Franklin theory and explained all the electrical phenomena exhibited by conductors, including thermoelectric and Peltier effects, on the assumption of two types of electrical constituents of atoms, one of which was very much more mobile than the other. Thus the hypothetical molecular current, which Ampere had imagined fifty years earlier to be continually flowing inside of molecules and thereby rendering these molecules little electromagnets, Weber definitely pictures to himself as the rotation of light, positive charges about heavy negative ones. His words are:

The relation of the two particles as regards their motions is determined by the ratio of their masses e and e', on the assumption that in e and e' are included the masses of the ponderable atoms which are attached to the electrical atoms. Let e be the positive electrical particle. Let the negative be exactly equal and opposite

---

[1] See *Werke*, IV, 281.

and therefore denoted by $-e$ (instead of e'). But let a ponderable atom be attracted to the latter so that its mass is thereby so greatly increased as to make the mass of the positive particle vanishingly small in comparison. The particle $-e$ may then be thought of as at rest and the particle $+e$ as in motion about the particle $-e$. The two unlike particles in the condition described constitute then an Amperian molecular current.

It is practically this identical point of view which has been elaborated and generalized by Lorenz and others within the past decade in the development of the modern electron theory, with this single difference, that we now have experimental proof that it is the negative particle whose mass or inertia is negligible in comparison with that of the positive instead of the reverse. Weber even went so far as to explain thermoelectric and Peltier effects by differences in the kinetic energies in different conductors of the electrical particles.[1] Nevertheless his explanations are here widely at variance with our modern conceptions of heat.

Again, in a paper read before the British Association at Belfast in 1874, G. Johnstone Stoney not only stated clearly the atomic theory of electricity, but actually went so far as to estimate the value of the elementary electrical charge, and he obtained a value which was about as reliable as any which had been found until within quite recent years. He got, as will be more fully explained in the next chapter, $.3 \times 10^{-10}$ absolute electrostatic units, and he got this result from the amount of electricity necessary to separate from a solution one gram of hydrogen, combined with kinetic theory estimates as to the number of atoms of hydrogen in two grams, i.e., in one

[1] *Op. cit.*, p. 294.

gram molecule of that element. This paper was entitled, "On the Physical Units of Nature," and though read in 1874 it was not published in full until 1881.[1] After showing that all physical measurements may be expressed in terms of three fundamental units, he asserts that it would be possible to replace our present purely arbitrary units (the centimeter, the gram, and the second) by three natural units, namely, the velocity of light, the coefficient of gravitation, and the elementary electrical charge. With respect to the last he says:

Finally nature presents us with a single definite quantity of electricity which is independent of the particular bodies acted on. To make this clear, I shall express Faraday's law in the following terms, which, as I shall show, will give it precision, viz.: *For each chemical bond which is ruptured within an electrolyte a certain quantity of electricity traverses the electrolyte which is the same in all cases.* This definite quantity of electricity I shall call E_1. If we make this our unit of electricity, we shall probably have made a very important step in our study of molecular phenomena.

Hence we have very good reason to suppose that in V_1, G_1, and E_2, we have three of a series of systematic units that in an eminent sense are the units of nature, and stand in an intimate relation with the work which goes on in her mighty laboratory.

Take one more illustration from prominent writers of this period. In his Faraday lecture delivered at the Royal Institution in 1881, Helmholtz spoke as follows:

Now the most startling result of Faraday's law is perhaps this, if we accept the hypothesis that the elementary substances are composed of atoms, we cannot avoid concluding that electricity also, positive as well as negative, is divided into definite elementary portions which behave like atoms of electricity.[2]

[1] *Phil. Mag.*, XI (1881; 5th series), 384.
[2] *Wissenschaftliche Abhandlungen*, III, 69.

This looks like a very direct and unequivocal statement of the atomic theory of electricity, and yet in the same lecture Helmholtz apparently thinks of metallic conduction as something quite different from electrolytic when he says:

All these facts show that electrolytic conduction is not at all limited to solutions of acids or salts. It will, however, be rather a difficult problem to find out how far the electrolytic conduction is extended, and I am not yet prepared to give a positive answer.

The context shows that he thought of extending the idea of electrolytic conduction to a great many insulators. But there is no indication that he thought of extending it to metallic conductors and imagining these electrical atoms as existing as discrete individual things on charged metals or as traveling along a wire carrying an electrical current. Nevertheless, the statement quoted above is one of the most unequivocal which can be found anywhere up to about 1899 as to the atomic nature of electricity.

The foregoing quotations are sufficient to show that the atomic theory of electricity, like the atomic theory of matter, is not at all new so far as the conception alone is concerned. In both cases there were individuals who held almost exactly the modern point of view. In both cases, too, the chief new developments have consisted in the appearance of new and exact *experimental* data which has silenced criticism and compelled the abandonment of other points of view which up to about 1900 flourished along with, and even more vigorously than, the atomic conception. Even in 1897 Lord Kelvin, with a full knowledge of all the new work which was appearing on X-rays and cathode rays, could seriously raise the

question whether electricity might not be a "continuous
homogeneous liquid." He does it in these words:

> Varley's fundamental discovery of the cathode rays, splendidly
> confirmed and extended by Crookes, seems to me to necessitate the
> conclusion that resinous electricity, not vitreous, is *The Electric
> Fluid*, if we are to have a one-fluid theory of electricity. Mathe-
> matical reasons prove that if resinous electricity is a continuous
> homogeneous liquid it must, in order to produce the phenomena
> of contact electricity, which you have seen this evening, be
> endowed with a cohesional quality. It is just conceivable, though
> it does not at present seem to me very probable, that this idea may
> deserve careful consideration. I leave it, however, for the present
> and prefer to consider an atomic theory of electricity foreseen as
> worthy of thought by Faraday and Clerk-Maxwell, very definitely
> proposed by Helmholtz in his last lecture to the Royal Institution,
> and largely accepted by present-day workers and teachers. Indeed
> Faraday's laws of electrolysis seem to necessitate something atomic
> in electricity, ...[1]

What was the new experimental work which already
in 1897 was working this change in viewpoint? Much
of it was at first little if at all more convincing than that
which had been available since Faraday's time. Nevertheless it set physicists to wondering whether stresses
and strains in the ether had not been a bit overworked,
and whether in spite of their undoubted existence electricity itself might not after all be something more
definite, more material, than the all-conquering Maxwell
theory had assumed it to be.

The result of the past fifteen years has been to bring
us back very close to where Franklin was in 1750, with
the single difference that our modern electron theory rests
upon a mass of very direct and very convincing evidence,
which it is the purpose of the next chapters to present.

---

[1] Kelvin, "Contact Electricity and Electrolysis," *Nature*, LVI
(1897), 84.

CHAPTER II

THE EXTENSION OF THE ELECTROLYTIC LAWS TO CONDUCTION IN GASES

I. THE ORIGIN OF THE WORD "ELECTRON"

The word "electron" was first suggested in 1891 by Dr. G. Johnstone Stoney as a name for the "natural unit of electricity," namely, that quantity of electricity which must pass through a solution in order to liberate at one of the electrodes one atom of hydrogen or one atom of any univalent substance. In a paper published in 1891 he says:

Attention must be given to Faraday's Law of Electrolysis, which is equivalent to the statement that in electrolysis a definite quantity of electricity, the same in all cases, passes for each chemical bond that is ruptured. The author called attention to this form of the law in a communication made to the British Association in 1874 and printed in the *Scientific Proceedings of the Royal Dublin Society* of February, 1881, and in the *Philosophical Magazine* for May, 1881, pp. 385 and 386 of the latter. It is there shown that the amount of this very remarkable quantity of electricity is about the twentiethet $\left(\text{that is } \frac{1}{10^{20}}\right)$ of the usual electromagnetic unit of electricity, i.e., the unit of the Ohm series. This is the same as 3 eleventhets $\left(\frac{3}{10^{11}}\right)$ of the much smaller C.G.S. electrostatic unit of quantity. A charge of this amount is associated in the chemical atom with each bond. There may accordingly be several such charges in one chemical atom, and there appear to be at least two in each atom. These charges, which it will be convenient to call "electrons," cannot be removed from the atom, but they become disguised when atoms chemically unite. If an

25

electron be lodged at the point P of the molecule which undergoes the motion described in the last chapter, the revolution of this charge will cause an electromagnetic undulation in the surrounding ether.[1]

It will be noticed from this quotation that the word "electron" was introduced to denote simply a definite elementary quantity of electricity without any reference to the mass or inertia which may be associated with it, and Professor Stoney implies that every atom must contain at least two electrons, one positive and one negative, because otherwise it would be impossible that the atom as a whole be electrically neutral. As a matter of fact the evidence is now considerable that the hydrogen atom does indeed contain just one positive and one negative electron.

It is unfortunate that modern writers have not been more careful to retain the original significance of the word introduced by Professor Stoney, for it is obvious that a word is needed which denotes merely the elementary unit of electricity and has no implication as to where that unit is found, to what it is attached, with what inertia it is associated, or whether it is positive or negative in sign; and it is also apparent that the word "electron" is the logical one to associate with this conception.[2]

[1] *Scientific Transactions of the Royal Dublin Society*, IV (1891; 11th series), 563.

[2] The most authoritative writers, Thomson, Rutherford, Campbell, Richardson, etc., have in fact retained the original significance of the word "electron" instead of using it to denote solely the free negative electron or corpuscle of J. J. Thomson, the mass of which is $\frac{1}{1845}$ of that of the hydrogen atom. All of these writers in books or articles written since 1913 have treated of positive as well as negative electrons, although the mass associated with the former is never less than that of the hydrogen atom.

J. J. Thomson's word "corpuscle" is a very appropriate one to denote the very minute inertia with which the negative electron is found associated in cathode rays.

II. THE DETERMINATION OF $\dfrac{e}{m}$ AND Ne FROM THE FACTS

OF ELECTROLYSIS

Faraday's experiments had of course not furnished the data for determining anything about how much electricity an electron represents in terms of the standard unit by which electrical charges are ordinarily measured in the laboratory. This is called the coulomb, and represents the quantity of electricity conveyed in one second by one ampere. Faraday had merely shown that a given current flowing in succession through solutions containing different univalent elements like hydrogen or silver or sodium or potassium would deposit weights of these substances which are exactly proportional to their respective atomic weights. This enabled him to assert that one and the same amount of electricity is associated in the process of electrolysis with an atom of each of these substances. He thought of this charge as carried by the atom, or in some cases by a group of atoms, and called the group with its charge an "ion," that is, a "goer," or "traveler." Just how the atoms come to be charged in a solution Faraday did not know, nor do we know now with any certainty. Further, we do not know how much of the solvent an ion associates with itself and drags with it through the solution. But we do know that when a substance like salt is dissolved in water many of the neutral NaCl molecules are split up by some action of the water into positively charged sodium (Na) ions and negatively charged chlorine (Cl) ions. The ions of opposite sign doubtless are all the time recombining, but others are probably continually forming, so that at each instant there are many uncombined ions. Again, we know that when a water solution of copper sulphate is formed many of the neutral $CuSO_4$ molecules are split up into positively charged Cu ions and negatively charged SO_4 ions. In this last case too we find that the same current which will deposit in a given time from a silver solution a weight of silver equal to its atomic weight will deposit from the copper-sulphate solution in the same time a weight of copper equal to exactly one-half its atomic weight. Hence we know that the copper ion carries in solution twice as much electricity as does the silver ion, that is, it carries a charge of two electrons.

But though we could get from Faraday's experiments no knowledge about the quantity of electricity, e, represented by one electron, we could get very exact information about the ratio of the ionic charge E to the mass of the atom with which it is associated in a given solution.

For, if the whole current which passes through a solution is carried by the ions—and if it were not we should not always find the deposits exactly proportional to atomic weights—then the ratio of the total quantity of electricity passing to the weight of the deposit produced must be the same as the ratio of the charge E on each ion to the mass m of that ion. But by international agreement one absolute unit of electricity has been defined in the electromagnetic system of units as the amount of electricity which will deposit from a silver solution 0.01118 grams of metallic silver. Hence if m

refers to the silver ion and E means the charge on the ion, we have

$$\text{for silver } \frac{E}{m} = \frac{1}{0.01118} = 89.44 \text{ electromagnetic units;}$$

or if m refers to the hydrogen ion, since the atomic weight of silver is $\dfrac{107.88}{1.008}$ times that of hydrogen,

$$\text{for hydrogen } \frac{E}{m} = \frac{1}{0.01118} \times \frac{107.88}{1.008} = 9{,}573,$$

which is about 10^4 electromagnetic units.

Thus in electrolysis $\dfrac{E}{m}$ varies from ion to ion, being for univalent ions, for which E is the same and equal to one electron e, inversely proportional to the atomic weight of the ion. For polivalent ions E may be 2, 3, 4, or 5 electrons, but since hydrogen is at least 7 times lighter than any other ion which is ever found in solution, and its charge is but one electron, we see that the largest value which $\dfrac{E}{m}$ ever has in electrolysis is its value for hydrogen, namely, about 10^4 electromagnetic units.

Although $\dfrac{E}{m}$ varies with the nature of the ion, there is a quantity which can be deduced from it which is a universal constant. This quantity is denoted by Ne, where e means as before an electron and N is the Avogadro constant or the number of molecules in 16 grams of oxygen, i.e., in one gram molecule. We can get this at once from the value of $\dfrac{E}{m}$ by letting m refer to the mass of that imaginary univalent atom which is the unit of our

atomic weight system, namely, an atom which is exactly
$1/16$ as heavy as oxygen or $1/107.88$ as heavy as silver.
For such an atom

$$\frac{E}{m} = \frac{e}{m} = \frac{107.88}{0.01118} = 9,650.$$

Multiplying both numerator and denominator by N and
remembering that for this gas one gram molecule means
1 gram, that is, $Nm = 1$, we have

$$Ne = 9650 \text{ absolute electromagnetic units,} \ldots \ldots (1)$$

and since the electromagnetic unit is equivalent to
3×10^{10} electrostatic units, we have

$$Ne = 28{,}950 \times 10^{10} \text{ absolute electrostatic units.}$$

Further, since a gram molecule of an ideal gas under
standard conditions, i.e., at $0°$ C. 76 cm. pressure,
occupies 22412 c.c., if n_1 represents the number of molecules of such a gas per cubic centimeter at $0°$ C., 76 cm.,
we have

$$n_1 e = \frac{28{,}950 \times 10^{10}}{22{,}412} = 1.292 \times 10^{10} \text{ electrostatic units.}$$

Or if n represent the number of molecules per cubic
centimeter at $15°$ C. 76 cm., we should have to multiply
the last number by the ratio of absolute temperatures,
i.e., by $273/288$ and should obtain then

$$ne = 1.225 \times 10^{10}. \ldots \ldots \ldots \ldots (2)$$

Thus, even though the facts of electrolysis give us no
information at all as to how much of a charge one electron
e represents, they do tell us very exactly that if we should
take e as many times as there are molecules in a gram

molecule we should get exactly 9,650 absolute electro-magnetic units of electricity. This is the amount of electricity conveyed by a current of 1 ampere in 10 seconds. Until quite recently we have been able to make nothing better than rough guesses as to the number of molecules in a gram molecule, but with the aid of these guesses, obtained from the Kinetic Theory, we have, of course, been enabled by (1) to make equally good guesses about e. These guesses, based for the most part on quite uncertain computations as to the average radius of a molecule of air, placed N anywhere between 2×10^2 and 20×10^{23}. It was in this way that G. Johnstone Stoney in 1874 estimated e at $.3 \times 10^{-10}$ E.S. units. In O. E. Meyer's *Kinetische Theorie der Gase* (p. 335; 1899), n, the number of molecules in a cubic centimeter is given as 6×10^{19}. This would correspond to $e = 2 \times 10^{-10}$. In all this e is the charge carried by a univalent ion in solution and N or n is a pure number, which is a characteristic gas constant, it is true, but the analysis has nothing whatever to do with gas conduction.

III.   THE NATURE OF GASEOUS CONDUCTION

The question whether gases conduct at all, and if so, whether their conduction is electrolytic or metallic or neither, was scarcely attacked until about 1895. Coulomb in 1785 had concluded that after allowing for the leakage of the supports of an electrically charged conductor, some leakage must be attributed to the air itself, and he explained this leakage by assuming that the air molecules became charged by contact and were then repelled—a wholly untenable conclusion, since, were it true, no conductor in air could hold a charge long even at low potentials, nor could a very highly charged conductor lose its charge very rapidly when charged above a certain potential and then when the potential fell below a certain critical value cease almost entirely to lose it. This is what actually occurs. Despite the erroneousness of this idea, it persisted in textbooks written as late as 1900.

Warburg in 1872 experimented anew on air leakage and was inclined to attribute it all to dust particles. The real explanation of gas conduction was not found until after the discovery of X-rays in 1895. The convincing experiments were made by J. J. Thomson, or at his instigation in the Cavendish Laboratory at Cambridge, England. The new work grew obviously and simply out of the fact that X-rays, and a year or two later radium rays, were found to discharge an electroscope, i.e., to produce conductivity in a gas. Theretofore no agencies had been known by which the electrical conductivity of a gas could be controlled at will. Thomson and his pupils found that the conductivity induced in gases by X-rays disappeared when the gas was sucked through glass wool.[1] It was also found to be reduced when the air was drawn through narrow metal tubes. Furthermore, it was removed entirely by passing the stream of conducting gas between plates which were maintained at a sufficiently large potential difference. The first two experiments showed that the conductivity was due to something which could be removed from the gas by filtration, or by diffusion to the walls of a metal tube; the last proved that this something was electrically charged.

[1] J. J. Thomson and E. Rutherford, *Phil. Mag.*, XLII (1896), 392.

When it was found, further, that the electric current obtained from air existing between two plates and traversed by X-rays, rose to a maximum as the P.D. between the plates increased, and then reached a value which was thereafter independent of this potential difference; and, further, that this conductivity of the air died out slowly through a period of several seconds when the X-ray no longer acted, it was evident that the qualitative proof was complete that gas conduction must be due to charged particles produced in the air at a definite rate by a constant source of X-rays, and that these charged particles, evidently of both plus and minus signs, disappear by recombination when the rays are removed. The maximum or *saturation* currents which could be obtained when a given source was ionizing the air between two plates whose potential difference could be varied was obviously due to the fact that when the electric field between the plates became strong enough to sweep all the ions to the plates as fast as they were formed, none of them being lost by diffusion or recombination, the current obtained could, of course, not be increased by further increase in the field strength. Thus gas conduction was definitely shown about 1896 to be electrolytic in nature.

IV.   COMPARISON OF THE GASEOUS ION AND THE
ELECTROLYTIC ION

But what sort of ions were these that were thus formed? We did not know the absolute value of the charge on a univalent ion in electrolysis, but we did know accurately ne. Could this be found for the ions taking part in gas conduction? That this question was answered affirmatively was due to the extraordinary insight and resourcefulness of J. J. Thomson and his pupils at the Cavendish Laboratory in Cambridge, both in working out new theoretical relations and in devising new methods for attacking the new problems of gaseous conduction. These workers found first a method of expressing the quantity ne in terms of two measurable constants, called (1) the mobility of gaseous ions and (2) the coefficient of diffusion of these ions. Secondly, they devised new methods of measuring these two constants—constants which had never before been determined. The theory of the relation between these constants and the quantity ne will be found in Appendix A. The result is

$$ne = \frac{v_0}{D}P, \qquad (3)$$

in which P is the pressure existing in the gas and v_0 and D are the mobility and the diffusion coefficients respectively of the ions at this pressure.

If then we can find a way of measuring the mobilities v_0 of atmospheric ions and also the diffusion coefficients D, we can find the quantity ne, in which n is a mere number, viz., the number of molecules of air per cubic centimeter at 15° C., 76 cm. pressure, and e is the average charge on an atmosphere ion. We shall then be in position to compare this with the product we found in (2) on p. 30, in which n had precisely the same significance as here, but e meant the average charge carried by a univalent ion in electrolysis.

The methods devised in the Cavendish Laboratory between 1897 and 1903 for measuring the mobilities and the diffusion coefficients of gaseous ions have been used in all later work upon these constants. The mobilities were first determined by Rutherford in 1897,[1] then more accurately by another method in 1898.[2] Zeleny devised a quite distinct method in 1900,[3] and Langevin still another method in 1903.[4] These observers all agree closely in finding the average mobility (velocity in unit field) of the negative ion in dry air about 1.83 cm. per second, while that of the positive ion was found but 1.35 cm. per second. In hydrogen these mobilities were about 7.8 cm. per second and 6.1 cm. per second, respectively, and in general the mobilities in different gases, though not in vapors, seem to be roughly in the inverse ratio of the square roots of the molecular weights.

The diffusion coefficients of ions were first measured in 1900 by Townsend, now professor of physics in Oxford, England,[5] by a method devised by him and since then used by other observers in such measurements. If we denote the diffusion coefficient of the positive ion by $D+$ and that of the negative by $D-$, Townsend's results in dry air may be stated thus:

$$D+ = 0.028$$
$$D- = 0.043.$$

These results are interesting in two respects. In the first place, they seem to show that for some reason the positive ion in air is more sluggish than the negative, since it travels but about 0.7 ($= 1.35/1.81$) as fast in a given electrical field and since it diffuses through air but about 0.7 ($= 28/43$) as rapidly. In the second place,

[1] *Phil. Mag.*, XLIV (1898), 422.

[2] *Proc. Camb. Phil. Soc.*, IX, 401.

[3] *Phil. Trans.*, A 195, p. 193.

[4] *Annale de Chimie et de Physique*, XXVIII, 289.

[5] *Phil. Trans.*, A 193, p. 129.

the results of Townsend show that an ion is very much more sluggish than is a molecule of air, for the coefficient of diffusion of oxygen through air is o. 178, which is four times the rate of diffusion of the negative ion through air and five times that of the positive ion. This sluggishness of ions as compared with molecules was at first universally considered to mean that the gaseous ion is not a single molecule with an attached electrical charge, but a cluster of perhaps from three to twenty molecules held together by such a charge. If this is the correct interpretation, then for some reason the positive ion in air is a larger cluster than is the negative ion.

It has been since shown by a number of observers that the ratio of the mobilities of the positive and negative ions is not at all the same in other gases as it is in air. In carbon dioxide the two mobilities have very nearly the same value, while in chlorine, water vapor, and the vapor of alcohol the positive ion apparently has a slightly larger mobility than the negative. There seems to be some evidence that the negative ion has the larger mobility in gases which are electro-positive, while the positive has the larger mobility in the gases which are strongly electro-negative. This dependence of the ratio of mobilities upon the electro-positive or electro-negative character of the gas has usually been considered strong evidence in favor of the cluster-ion theory.

Very recently, however, Loeb,[1] who has worked at the Ryerson Laboratory on mobilities in powerful electric fields, and Wellish,[2] who, at Yale, has measured mobilities

[1] Leonard B. Loeb, *Proc. Nat. Acad.*, II (1916), 345, and *Phys. Rev.*, 1917.

[2] Wellish, *Am. Jour. of Science*, XXXIX (1915), 583.

at very low pressures, have concluded that their results are not consistent with the cluster-ion theory, but must rather be interpreted in terms of the so-called Atom-ion Theory. This theory seeks to explain the relative sluggishness of ions, as compared with molecules, by the additional resistance which the gaseous medium offers to the motion of a molecule through it when that molecule is electrically charged. *According to this hypothesis, the ion would be simply an electrically charged molecule.*

Fortunately, the quantitative evidence for the electrolytic nature of gas conduction is in no way dependent upon the correctness of either one of the theories as to the nature of the ion. It depends simply upon the comparison of the values of ne obtained from electrolytic measurements, and those obtained from the substitution in equation 3 of the measured values of v_0 and D for gaseous ions.

As for these measurements, results obtained by Franck and Westphal,[1] who in 1908 repeated in Berlin both measurements on diffusion coefficients and mobility coefficients, agree within 4 or 5 per cent with the results published by Townsend in 1900. According to both of these observers, the value of ne for the negative ions produced in gases by X-rays, radium rays, and ultra-violet light came out, within the limits of experimental error, which were presumably 5 or 6 per cent, the same as the value found for univalent ions in solutions, namely, 1.23×10^{10} absolute electrostatic units. This result seems to show with considerable certainty that the negative ions in gases ionized by X-rays or similar

[1] *Verh. der deutsch. phys. Ges.*, XI (1909), 146 and 276.

agencies carry on the average the same charge as that borne by the univalent ion in electrolysis. When we consider the work on the positive ion, our confidence in the inevitableness of the conclusions reached by the methods under consideration is perhaps somewhat shaken. For Townsend found that the value of ne for the positive ion came out about 14 per cent higher than the value of this quantity for the univalent ion in electrolysis, a result which he does not seem at first to have regarded as inexplicable on the basis of experimental uncertainties in his method. In 1908, however,[1] he devised a second method of measuring the ratio of the mobility and the diffusion coefficient and obtained this time, as before, for the negative ion, $ne = 1.23 \times 10^{10}$, but for the positive ion twice that amount, namely, 2.46×10^{10}. From these last experiments he concluded that the positive ions in gases ionized by X-rays carried on the average twice the charge carried by the univalent ion in electrolysis. Franck and Westphal, however, found in their work that Townsend's original value for ne for the positive ions was about right, and hence concluded that only about 9 per cent of the positive ions could carry a charge of value $2e$. Work which will be described later indicates that neither Townsend's nor Franck and West-phal's conclusions are correct, and hence point to errors of some sort in both methods. But despite these difficulties with the work on positive ions, it is nevertheless fair to say that Townsend was the first to bring forward strong quantitative evidence that the mean charge carried by the negative ions in ionized gases is the same as the mean charge carried by univalent ions in solu-

[1] *Proc. Roy. Soc.*, LXXX (1908), 207.

tions, and that the mean charge carried by the positive ions in gases has not far from the same value.

But there is one other advance of fundamental importance which came with the study of the properties of gases ionized by X-rays. For up to this time the only type of ionization known was that observed in solution and here it is always some compound molecule like sodium chloride (NaCl) which splits up spontaneously into a positively charged sodium ion and a negatively charged chlorine ion. But the ionization produced in gases by X-rays was of a wholly different sort, for it was observable in pure gases like nitrogen or oxygen, or even in monatomic gases like argon and helium. Plainly then the neutral atom even of a monatomic substance must possess minute electrical charges as constituents. Here we had the first direct evidence (1) that an atom is a complex structure, and (2) that electrical charges enter into its make-up. *With this discovery, due directly to the use of the new agency, X-rays, the atom as an ultimate, indivisible thing was gone, and the era of the study of the constituents of the atom began.* And with astonishing rapidity during the past twenty years the properties of the subatomic world have been revealed.

Physicists began at once to seek diligently and to find at least partial answers to questions like these:

1. What are the masses of the constituents of the atoms torn asunder by X-rays and similar agencies?

2. What are the values of the charges carried by these constituents?

3. How many of these constituents are there?

4. How large are they, i.e., what volumes do they occupy?

5. What are their relations to the emission and absorption of light and heat waves, i.e., of electromagnetic radiation?

6. Do all atoms possess similar constituents? In other words, is there a primordial subatom out of which atoms are made?

The partial answer to the first of these questions came with the study of the electrical behavior of rarefied gases in so-called vacuum tubes. J. J. Thomson[1] and Wiechert[2] showed independently in 1897 that the value of $\frac{e}{m}$ for the negative ion in such exhausted tubes is about 1.8×10^7 electromagnetic units, or about 1,800 times the value of $\frac{e}{m}$ for the hydrogen ion in solutions. Since the approximate equality of ne in gases and solutions meant that e was at least of the same order in both, the only possible conclusion was that the negative ion which appears in discharges in exhausted tubes has a mass, i.e., an inertia only 1/1,800th of the mass of the lightest known atom, namely, the atom of hydrogen.

Furthermore, these and other experimenters have shown that $\frac{e}{m}$ for the negative carrier is always the same whatever be the nature of the residual gas in the discharge tube. This was an indication of an affirmative answer to the sixth question above—an indication which was strengthened by Zeeman's discovery in 1897 of the splitting by a magnetic field of a single spectral line into two or three lines; for this, when worked out quantita-

[1] *Phil. Mag.*, XLIV (1897), 298.

[2] *Verh. der phys.-ökon. Ges. zu Königsberg*, 1897.

tively, pointed to the existence *within* the atom of a negatively charged particle which had approximately the same value of $\frac{e}{m}$.

The study of $\frac{e}{m}$ for the *positive* ions in exhausted tubes, though first carried out quantitatively by Wien,[1] has been most elaborately and most successfully dealt with by J. J. Thomson.[2] The results of the work of all observers up to date seem to show quite conclusively that $\frac{e}{m}$ for a positive ion in gases is never larger than its value for the hydrogen ion in electrolysis, and that it varies with different sorts of residual gases just as it is found to do in electrolysis.

In a word, then, the act of ionization in gases appears to consist in the detachment from a neutral atom of one or more negatively charged particles, called by Thomson corpuscles. The residuum of the atom is of course positively charged, and it always carries practically the whole mass of the original atom. The detached corpuscle must soon attach itself, in a gas at ordinary pressure, to a neutral atom, since otherwise we could not account for the fact that the mobilities and the diffusion coefficients of negative ions are usually of the same order of magnitude as those of the positive ions. It is because of this tendency of the parts of the dissociated atom to form new attachments in gases at ordinary pressure that the inertias of these parts had to be worked out in the rarefied gases of exhausted tubes.

[1] W. Wien, *Wied. Ann.*, LXV (1898), 440.

[2] *Rays of Positive Electricity*, London: Longmans, 1913.

The foregoing conclusions as to the masses of the positive and negative constituents of atoms had all been reached before 1900, mostly by the workers in the Cavendish Laboratory, and subsequent investigation has not modified them in any essential particulars.

The history of the development of our present knowledge of the charges carried by the constituents will be detailed in the next chapters.

CHAPTER III

EARLY ATTEMPTS AT THE DIRECT DETER-MINATION OF e

Although the methods sketched in the preceding chapters had been sufficient to show that the mean charges carried by ions in gases are the same or nearly the same as the mean charges carried by univalent ions in solution, in neither case had we any way of determining what the absolute value of that mean charge is, nor, indeed, had we any proof even that all the ions of a given kind, e.g., silver or hydrogen, carry the same charge. Of course, the absolute value of e could be found from the measured value of ne if only n, the number of molecules in 1 c.c. of gas under standard conditions, were known. But we had only rough guesses as to this number. These guesses varied tenfold, and none of them were based upon considerations of recognized accuracy or even validity.

I. TOWNSEND'S WORK ON e

The first attempt at a direct determination of e was published by Townsend in a paper read before the Cambridge Philosophical Society on February 8, 1897.[1] Townsend's method was one of much novelty and of no little ingenuity. It is also of great interest because it contains all the essential elements of some of the subsequent determinations.

[1] *Proceedings*, IX (1897), 244.

It had been known, even to Laplace and Lavoisier a hundred years before, that the hydrogen gas evolved when a metal dissolves in an acid carries with it an electrical charge. This "natural method" of obtaining a charge on a gas was scarcely studied at all, however, until after the impulse to the study of the electrical properties of gases had been given by the discovery in 1896 that electrical properties can be artificially imparted to gases by X-rays. Townsend's paper appeared within a year of that time. Enright[1] had indeed found that the hydrogen given off when iron is dissolving in sulphuric acid carries with it a positive charge, but Oliver Lodge[2] had urged that it was not the gas itself which carries the charge but merely the spray, for the frictional electrification of spray was a well-known phenomenon. Indeed, it has always been assumed that the gas molecules which rise from the electrodes in electrolysis are themselves neutral. Townsend, however, first showed that some of these molecules are charged, although there are indeed a million million neutral ones for every one carrying a charge. He found that both the oxygen and the hydrogen which appear at the opposite electrodes when sulphuric acid is electrolyzed are positively charged, while when the electrolyte is caustic potash both the oxygen and the hydrogen given off are negative. Townsend's electrolyzing currents were from 12 to 14 amperes. He got in this way many more ions per cubic centimeter than he could produce with X-rays, the total charge per cubic centimeter being as large as 5×10^{-3} electrostatic units.

[1] *Phil. Mag.*, XXIX (1890; 5th series), 56.

[2] *Ibid.*, 292; *Nature*, XXXVI, 412.

When these charged gases were bubbled through water they formed a cloud. This cloud could be completely removed by bubbling through concentrated sulphuric acid or any drying agent, but when the gas came out again into the atmosphere of the room it again condensed moisture and formed a stable cloud. Townsend says that "the process of forming the cloud in positive or negative oxygen by bubbling through water, and removing it again by bubbling through sulphuric acid, can be gone through without losing more than 20 or 25 per cent of the original charge on the gas." This means simply that the ions condense the water about them when there is an abundance of moisture in the air, but when the cloud is carried into a perfectly dry atmosphere, such as that existing in a bubble surrounded on all sides by concentrated sulphuric acid, the droplets of water evaporate and leave the charge on a molecule of air as it was at first. The 20 or 25 per cent loss of charge represents the fraction of the droplets with their charges which actually got into contact with and remained in the liquids through which the gas was being bubbled.

In order to find the charge on each ion, Townsend took the following five steps:

1. He assumed that in saturated water vapor each ion condensed moisture about it, so that the number of ions was the same as the number of droplets.

2. He determined with the aid of a quadrant electrometer the total electrical charge per cubic centimeter carried by the gas.

3. He found the total weight of the cloud by passing it through drying tubes and determining the increase in weight of these tubes.

4. He found the average weight of the water droplets constituting the cloud by observing their rate of fall under gravity and computing their mean radius with the aid of a purely theoretical law known as Stokes's Law.

5. He divided the weight of the cloud by the average weight of the droplets of water to obtain the number of droplets which, if assumption 1 is correct, was the number of ions, and he then divided the total charge per cubic centimeter in the gas by the number of ions to find the average charge carried by each ion, that is, to find e.

A brief description of the way in which these experiments were carried out is contained in Appendix B.

One of the interesting side results of this work was the observation that clouds from negative oxygen fall faster than those from positive oxygen, thus indicating that the negative ions in oxygen act more readily than do the positive ions as nuclei for the condensation of water vapor. This observation was made at about the same time in another way by C. T. R. Wilson,[1] also in the Cavendish Laboratory, and it has played a rather important rôle in subsequent work. Wilson's discovery was that when air saturated with water vapor is ionized by X-rays from radioactive substances and then cooled by a sudden expansion, a smaller expansion is required to make a cloud form about the negative than about the positive ions. Thus when the expansion increased the volume in a ratio between 1.25 and 1.3, only negative ions acted as nuclei for cloudy condensation, while with expansions greater than 1.3 both negatives and positives were brought down.

[1] *Proc. Camb. Phil. Soc.*, IX (1897), 333.

Townsend first obtained by the foregoing method, when he worked with positive oxygen,

$$e = 2.8 \times 10^{-10} \text{ electrostatic units,}$$

and when he worked with negative oxygen,

$$e = 3.1 \times 10^{-10} \text{ electrostatic units.}$$

In later experiments[1] he obtained 2.4 and 2.9, respectively, in place of the numbers given above, but in view of the unavoidable errors, he concluded that the two charges might be considered equal and approximately 3×10^{-10} electrostatic units. Thus he arrived at about the same value for e as that which was then current because of the kinetic theory estimates of n, the number of molecules in a cubic centimeter of a gas.

The weak points in this first attempt at a direct determination of e consisted in: (1) the assumption that the number of ions is the same as the number of drops; (2) the assumption of Stokes's Law of Fall which had never been tested experimentally, and which from a theoretical standpoint might be expected to be in error when the droplets were small enough; (3) the assumption that the droplets were all alike and fell at a uniform rate wholly uninfluenced by evaporation or other causes of change; (4) the assumption of no convection currents in the gas when the rate of fall of the cloud was being measured.

II.   SIR JOSEPH THOMSON'S WORK ON e

This first attempt to measure e was carried out in Professor J. J. Thomson's laboratory. The second attempt was made by Professor Thomson himself[2] by a method

[1] *Proc. Camb. Phil. Soc.*, IX (1897), 345.

[2] *Phil. Mag.*, XLVI (1898), 528.

which resembled Townsend's very closely in all its essential particulars. Indeed, we may set down for Professor Thomson's experiment precisely the same five elements which are set down on p. 45 for Townsend's. The differences lay wholly in step 2, that is, in the way in which the electrical charge per cubic centimeter carried by the gas was determined, and in step 3, that is, in the way in which the total weight of the cloud was obtained. Thomson produced ions in the space A (Fig. 1) by an X-ray bulb which ran at a constant rate and measured first the current which under the influence of a very weak electromotive force E flows through A between the surface of the water and the aluminum plate which closes the top of the vessel. Then if n' is the whole number of ions of one sign per cubic centimeter, u the velocity of the positive and v that of the negative ion under unit electric force, i.e., if u and v are the mobilities of the positive and negative ions, respectively, then the current I per unit area is evidently given by

$$I = n'e(u+v) E \dots\dots\dots\dots\dots (4)$$

I and E were easily measured in any experiment; $u+v$ was already known from Rutherford's previous work, so that $n'e$, the charge of one sign per cubic centimeter of gas under the ionizing action of a constant source of X-rays, could be obtained at once from (4). This then simply replaces Townsend's method of obtaining the charge per cubic centimeter on the gas, and in principle the two methods are quite the same, the difference in experimental arrangements being due to the fact that Townsend's ions are of but one sign while Thomson's are of both signs.

Having thus obtained $n'e$ of equation (4), Thomson had only to find n' and then solve for e. To obtain n' he proceeded exactly as Townsend had done in letting the ions condense droplets of water about them and weighing the cloud thus formed. But in order to form the cloud, Thomson utilized C. T. R. Wilson's discovery

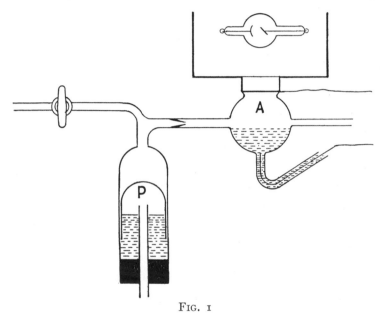

FIG. 1

just touched upon above, that a sudden expansion and consequent cooling of the air in A (Fig. 1) would cause the ions in A to act as nuclei for the formation of water droplets. To produce this expansion the piston P is suddenly pulled down so as to increase the volume of the space above it. A cloud is thus formed about the ions in A. Instead of measuring the weight of this cloud directly, as Townsend had done, Thomson computed it by a theoretical consideration of the amount of cooling produced by the expansion and the known difference between the densities of saturated water vapor at the temperature of the room and the temperature resulting from the expansion. This method of obtaining the weight of the cloud was less direct and less reliable than that used by Townsend, but it was the only one available with Thomson's method of obtaining an ionized gas and of measuring the charge per cubic centimeter on that gas. The average size of the droplets was obtained precisely as in Townsend's work by applying Stokes's Law to the observed rate of fall of the top of the cloud in chamber A.

The careful consideration of Thomson's experiment shows that it contains all the theoretical uncertainties involved in Townsend's work, while it adds considerably to the experimental uncertainties. The most serious of the theoretical uncertainties arise from (1) the assumption of Stokes's Law, and (2) the assumption that the number of ions is equal to the number of droplets. Both observers sought for some experimental justification for the second and most serious of these assumptions, but subsequent work by H. A. Wilson, by Quincke, and by myself has shown that clouds formed by C. T. R. Wilson's method consist in general of droplets some of which may carry one, some two, some ten, or almost any number of unit charges, and I have never been able, despite quite careful experimenting, to obtain conditions in which it was even approximately true that each droplet carried but a single unit charge. Quincke has recently published results from which he arrives at the same conclusion.[1]

[1] *Verh. der deutsch. phys. Ges.*, XVI (1914), 422.

Again, when we compare the *experimental* uncertainties in Townsend's and Thomson's work, it is at once obvious that the assumption that the clouds are not evaporating while the rate of fall is being determined is even more serious in Thomson's experiment than in Townsend's, for the reason that in the former case the clouds are formed by a sudden expansion and a consequent fall in temperature, and it is certain that during the process of the return of the temperature to initial conditions the droplets must be evaporating. Furthermore, this sudden expansion makes the likelihood of the existence of convection currents, which would falsify the computations of the radius of the drop from the observed rate of fall, more serious in Thomson's work than in Townsend's. The results which Thomson attained in different experiments gave values ranging from 5.5×10^{-10} to 8.4×10^{-10}. He published as his final value 6.5×10^{-10}. In 1903, however,[1] he published some new work on *e* in which he had repeated the determination, using the radiation from radium in place of that from X-rays as his ionizing agent and obtained the result $e = 3.4 \times 10^{-10}$. He explained the difference by the assumption that in his preceding work the more active negative ions had monopolized the aqueous vapor available and that the positive ions had not been brought down with the cloud as he had before assumed was the case. He now used more sudden expansions than he had used before, and concluded that the assumption made in the earlier experiments that the number of ions was equal to the number of particles, although shown to be incorrect for the former case, was correct for these

[1] *Phil. Mag.*, V (1903; 6th series), 354.

second experiments. As a matter of fact, if he had obtained only half the ions in the first experiments and all of them in the second, his second result should have come out approximately one-half as great as the first, which it actually did. Although Thomson's experiment was an interesting and important modification of Townsend's, it can scarcely be said to have added greatly to the accuracy of our knowledge of e.

The next step in advance in the attempt at the determination of e was made in 1903 by H. A. Wilson,[1] also in the Cavendish Laboratory.

III.   H. A. WILSON'S METHOD

Wilson's modification of Thomson's work consisted in placing inside the chamber A two horizontal brass plates $3\frac{1}{2}$ cm. in diameter and from 4 to 10 mm. apart and connecting to these plates the terminals of a 2,000-volt battery. He then formed a negative cloud by a sudden expansion of amount between 1.25 and 1.3, and observed first the rate of fall of the top surface of this cloud between the plates when no electrical field was on; then he repeated the expansion and observed the rate of fall of the cloud when the electrical field as well as gravity was driving the droplets downward. If mg represents the force of gravity acting on the droplets in the top surface of the cloud and $mg+Fe$ the force of gravity plus the electrical force arising from the action of the field F on the charge e, and if v_1 is the velocity of fall under the action of gravity alone, and v_2 the velocity when both gravity and the electrical field are acting, then, if the ratio between the force acting and

[1] *Op. cit.*, p. 429.

the velocity produced is the same when the particle is charged as when it is uncharged, we have

$$\frac{mg}{mg+Fe}=\frac{v_{1}}{v_{2}} \quad \dots \dots \dots \dots \dots \dots \dots (5)$$

Combining this with the Stokes's Law equation which runs

$$v_{1}=\frac{2}{9}\frac{ga^{2}\sigma}{\eta} \quad \dots \dots \dots \dots \dots \dots (6)$$

in which a is the radius, σ the density, v_{1} the velocity of the drop under gravity g, and η is the viscosity of the air, and then eliminating m by means of

$$m=\tfrac{4}{3}\pi a^{3}\sigma \quad \dots \dots \dots \dots \dots \dots \dots (7)$$

Wilson obtained after substituting for η and σ the appropriate values (not accurately known, it is true, for saturated air at the temperature existing immediately after the expansion),

$$e=3.1\times 10^{-9}\frac{g}{F}(v_{2}-v_{1})v_{1}^{\frac{1}{2}} \quad \dots \dots \dots \dots \dots (8)$$

Wilson's method constitutes a real advance in that it eliminates the necessity of making the very awkward assumption that the number of droplets is equal to the number of negative ions, for since he observes only the rate of fall of the *top* of the cloud, and since the more heavily charged droplets will be driven down more rapidly by the field than the less heavily charged ones, his actual measurements would always be made upon *the least heavily charged droplets*. All of the other difficulties and assumptions contained in either Townsend's or Thomson's experiments inhere also in Wilson's, and in addition one fresh and rather serious assumption is introduced, namely, that the clouds formed in successive expansions are identical as to size of droplets. For we wrote down the first equation of Wilson's method as though the v_1 and v_2 were measurements made upon the same droplet, when as a matter of fact the measurements are actually made on wholly different droplets. I have myself found the duplication of cloud conditions in successive expansions a very uncertain matter. Furthermore, Wilson's method assumes uniformity in the field between the plates, an assumption which might be quite wide of the truth.

Although the elimination of the assumption of equality of the number of droplets and the number of ions makes Wilson's determination of e more reliable as to method than its predecessors, the accuracy actually attained was not great, as can best be seen from his own final summary of results. He made eleven different determinations which varied from $e = 2 \times 10^{-10}$ to $e = 4.4 \times 10^{-10}$. His eleven results are:

TABLE I

e	e
2.3×10^{-10}	3.8×10^{-10}
2.6 "	3.0 "
4.4 "	3.5 "
2.7 "	2.0 "
3.4 "	2.3 "
3.8 "	

Mean $\quad 3.1 \times 10^{-10}$

In 1906, being dissatisfied with the variability of these results, the author repeated Wilson's experiment without obtaining any greater consistency than that which the latter had found. Indeed, the instability, distortion, and indefiniteness of the top surface of the cloud were somewhat disappointing, and the results were not considered worth publishing. Nevertheless, it was concluded from these observations that the accuracy might be improved by using radium instead of X-rays for the ionizing agent, by employing stronger electrical fields, and thus increasing the difference between v_1 and v_2, which in Wilson's experiment had been quite small, and by observing the fall of the cloud through smaller distances and shorter times in order to reduce the error due to the evaporation of the cloud during the time of observation. Accordingly, a 4,000-volt storage battery was built and in the summer of 1908 Mr. Begeman and the author, using radium as the ionizing agent, again repeated the experiment and published some results which were somewhat more consistent than those reported by Wilson.[1] We gave as the mean of ten observations which varied from 3.66 to 4.37 the value $e = 4.06 \times 10^{-10}$. We stated at the time that although we had not eliminated altogether the error due to evaporation, we thought that we had rendered it relatively harmless, and that our final result, although considerably larger than either Wilson's or Thomson's (3.1 and 3.4, respectively), must be considered an approach at least toward the correct value.

IV. THE BALANCED-DROP METHOD

Feeling, however, that the amount of evaporation of the cloud was still a quite unknown quantity, I next endeavored to devise a way of eliminating it entirely. The plan now was to use an electrical field which was strong enough, not merely to increase or decrease slightly the speed of fall under gravity of the top surface of the

[1] *Phys. Rev.*, XXVI (1908), 198.

cloud, as had been done in all the preceding experiments, but also sufficiently strong to hold the top surface of the cloud stationary, so that the rate of its evaporation could be accurately observed and allowed for in the computations.

This attempt, while not successful in the form in which it had been planned, led to a modification of the cloud method which seemed at the time, and which has actually proved since, to be of far-reaching importance. *It made it for the first time possible to make all the measurements on individual droplets*, and thus not merely to eliminate ultimately all of the questionable assumptions and experimental uncertainties involved in the cloud method of determining e, but, more important still, it made it possible to examine the properties of individual isolated electrons and to determine whether different ions actually carry one and the same charge. That is to say, it now became possible to determine whether electricity in gases and solutions is actually built up out of electrical atoms, each of which has exactly the same value, or whether the electron which had first made its appearance in Faraday's experiments on solutions and then in Townsend's and Thomson's experiments on gases is after all only a *statistical mean* of charges which are themselves greatly divergent. This latter view had been strongly urged up to and even after the appearance of the work which is now under consideration. It will be given further discussion presently.

The first determination which was made upon the charges carried by individual droplets was carried out in the spring of 1909. A report of it was placed upon the program of the British Association meeting at Winnipeg in August, 1909, as an additional paper, was printed in abstract in the *Physical Review* for December, 1909, and in full in the *Philosophical Magazine* for February, 1910, under the title "A New Modification of the Cloud Method of Determining the Elementary Electrical Charge and the Most Probable Value of That Charge."[1] The following extracts from that paper show clearly what was accomplished in this first determination of the charges carried by individual droplets.

THE BALANCING OF INDIVIDUAL CHARGED DROPS BY AN ELECTROSTATIC FIELD

My original plan for eliminating the evaporation error was to obtain, if possible, an electric field strong enough exactly to balance the force of gravity upon the cloud and then by means of a sliding contact to vary the strength of this field so as to hold the cloud balanced throughout its entire life. In this way it was thought that the whole evaporation-history of the cloud might be recorded, and that suitable allowances might then be made in the observations on the rate of fall to eliminate entirely the error due to evaporation. It was not found possible to balance the cloud, as had been originally planned, but it was found possible to do something much better: namely, to hold individual charged drops suspended by the field for periods varying from 30 to 60 seconds. I have never actually timed drops which lasted more than 45 seconds, although I have several times observed drops which in my judgment lasted considerably longer than this. The drops which it was found possible to balance by an electrical field always carried multiple charges, and the difficulty experienced in balancing such drops was less than had been anticipated.

The procedure is simply to form a cloud and throw on the field immediately thereafter. The drops which have charges of the same sign as that of the upper plate or too weak charges of the opposite sign rapidly fall, while those which are charged with too many multiples of the sign opposite to that of the upper plate are

[1] *Phil. Mag.*, XIX (1910), 209.

jerked up against gravity to this plate. The result is that after a lapse of 7 or 8 seconds the field of view has become quite clear save for a relatively small number of drops which have just the right ratio of charge to mass to be held suspended by the electric field. These appear as perfectly distinct bright points. I have on several occasions obtained but one single such "star" in the whole field and held it there for nearly a minute. For the most part, however, the observations recorded below were made with a considerable number of such points in view. Thin, flocculent clouds, the production of which seemed to be facilitated by keeping the water-jackets J_1 and J_2 (Fig. 2) a degree or two above the temperature of the room, were found to be particularly favorable to observations of this kind.

Furthermore, it was found possible so to vary the mass of a drop by varying the ionization, that drops carrying in some cases two, in some three, in some four, in some five, and in some six, multiples could be held suspended by nearly the same field. The means of gradually varying the field which had been planned were therefore found to be unnecessary. If a given field would not hold any drops suspended it was varied by steps of 100 or 200 volts until drops were held stationary, or nearly stationary. When the P.D. was thrown off it was often possible to see different drops move down under gravity with greatly different speeds, thus showing that these drops had different masses and correspondingly different charges.

The life-history of these drops is as follows: If they are a little too heavy to be held quite stationary by the field they begin to move slowly down under gravity. Since, however, they slowly evaporate, their downward motion presently ceases, and they become stationary for a considerable period of time. Then the field gets the better of gravity and they move slowly upward. Toward the end of their life in the space between the plates, this upward motion becomes quite rapidly accelerated and they are drawn with considerable speed to the upper plate. This, taken in connection with the fact that their whole life between plates only 4 or 5 mm. apart is from 35 to 60 seconds, will make it obvious that during a very considerable fraction of this time their motion must be exceedingly slow. I have often held drops through a period of from 10 to 15 seconds, during which it was impossible to see that they were moving at all. Shortly after an expansion I have seen drops which at first seemed stationary, but which then began to move slowly down in the direction of gravity, then become stationary again, then finally began to move slowly up. This is probably due to the fact that large multiply charged drops are not in equilibrium with smaller singly charged drops near them, and hence, instead of evaporating, actually grow for a time at the expense of their small neighbors. Be this as it may, however, it is by utilizing the experimental fact that there is a considerable period during which the drops are essentially stationary that it becomes possible to make measurements upon the rate of fall in which the error due to evaporation is wholly negligible in comparison with the other errors of the experiment. Furthermore, in making measurements of this kind the observer is just as likely to time a drop which has not quite reached its stationary point as one which has just passed through that point, so that the mean of a considerable number of observations would, even from a theoretical standpoint, be quite free from an error due to evaporation.

THE METHOD OF OBSERVATION

The observations on the rate of fall were made with a short-focus telescope T (see Fig. 2) placed about 2 feet away from the plates. In the eyepiece of this telescope were placed three equally spaced cross-hairs, the distance between those at the extremes corresponding to about one-third of the distance between the plates. A small section of the space between the plates was illuminated by a narrow beam from an arc light, the heat of the arc being absorbed by three water cells in series. The air between the plates was ionized by 200 mg. of radium, of activity 20,000, placed from 3 to 10 cm. away from the plates. A second or so after expansion the radium was removed, or screened off with a lead screen, and the field thrown on by hand by means of a double-throw switch. If drops were not found to be held suspended by the field, the P.D. was changed or the expansion varied until they were so held. The cross-hairs were set near the lower plate, and as soon as a stationary drop was found somewhere above the upper cross-hair, it was watched for a few seconds to make sure that it was not moving, and then the field was thrown off and the plates short-circuited by means of the double-throw switch, so as to make sure that they retained no charge. The drop was then timed by means of an accurate stop watch as it passed across the three cross-hairs, one of the two hands of the watch being stopped at the instant of

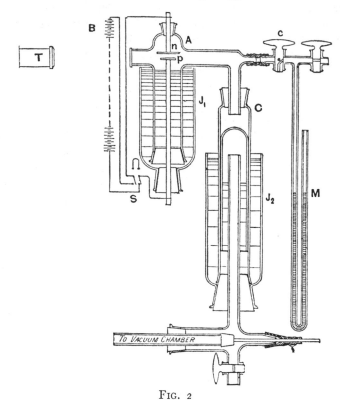

FIG. 2

passage across the middle cross-hair, the other at the instant of passage across the lower one. It will be seen that this method of observation furnishes a double check upon evaporation; for if the drop is stationary at first, it is not evaporating sufficiently to influence the reading of the rate of fall, and if it begins to evaporate appreciably before the reading is completed, the time required to pass through the second space should be greater than that required to pass through the first space.   It will be seen from the observations which follow that this was not, in general, the case.

It is an exceedingly interesting and instructive experiment to watch one of these drops start and stop, or even reverse its direction of motion, as the field is thrown off and on.   I have often caught a drop which was just too light to remain stationary and moved it back and forth in this way four or five times between the same two cross-hairs, watching it first fall under gravity when the field was thrown off and then rise against gravity when the field was thrown on.   The accuracy and certainty with which the instants of passage of the drops across the cross-hairs can be determined are precisely the same as that obtainable in timing the passage of a star across the cross-hairs of a transit instrument.

Furthermore, since the observations upon the quantities occurring in equation (4) [see (8) p. 53 of this volume] are all made upon the same drop, all uncertainties as to whether conditions can be exactly duplicated in the formation of successive clouds obviously disappear.   There is no theoretical uncertainty whatever left in the method unless it be an uncertainty as to whether or not Stokes's Law applies to the rate of fall of these drops under gravity.   The experimental uncertainties are reduced to the uncertainty in a time determination of from 3 to 5 seconds, when the object being timed is a single moving bright point.   This means that when the time interval is say 5 seconds, as it is in some of the observations given below, the error which a practiced observer will make with an accurate stop watch in any particular observation will never exceed 2 parts in 50.   The error in the mean of a considerable number of concordant observations will obviously be very much less than this.

Since in this form of observation the v_2 of equation (5) [(8) of this volume] is zero, and since F is negative in sign, equation (5) reduces to the simple form:

$$e = 3.422 \times 10^{-9} \times \frac{X}{g} (v_1)^{\frac{3}{2}} \dots \dots \dots \dots \dots (6)[1]$$

[1] I had changed the constant in Wilson's equation from 3.1 to 3.422 because of careful measurements on the temperature existing in the cloud chamber about 10 seconds after expansion and because of new measurements on the viscosity of the saturated air.

It will perhaps be of some interest to introduce two tables from this paper to show the exact nature of these

TABLE II

SERIES 1 (BALANCED POSITIVE WATER DROPS)

SERIES 2 (BALANCED POSITIVE WATER DROPS)

Distance between plates .545 cm.
Measured distance of fall .155 cm.

Distance between plates .545 cm.
Measured distance of fall .155 cm.

Volts	Time 1 Space	Time 2 Spaces
2,285	2.4 sec.	4.8 sec.
2,285	2.4	4.8
2,275	2.4	4.8
2,325	2.4	4.8
2,325	2.6	4.8
2,325	2.2	4.8
2,365	2.4	4.8
2,312	2.4	4.8

Mean time for .155 cm.=4.8 sec.

$$e_3 = 3.422 \times 10^{-9} \times \frac{980.3}{14.14} \times \left(\frac{.155}{4.8}\right)^{\frac{3}{2}}$$
$$= 13.77 \times 10^{-10}$$

Therefore $e = 13.85 \times 10^{-10} \div 3$
$$= 4.59 \times 10^{-10}.$$

Volts	Time 1 Space	Time 2 Spaces
2,365	1.8 sec.	4.0 sec.
2,365	1.8	4.0
2,365	2.2	3.8
2,365	1.8	4.0
2,395	2.0	4.0
2,395	2.0	4.0
2,395	2.0	3.8
2,365	1.8	4.0
2,365	1.8	4.0
2,365	1.8	4.0
2,374	1.90	3.96

Mean time for .155 cm.=3.91 sec.

$$e_4 = 3.422 \times 10^{-9} \times \frac{980.3}{14.52} \times \left(\frac{.155}{3.91}\right)^{\frac{3}{2}}$$
$$= 18.25 \times 10^{-10}$$

Therefore $e = 18.25 \div 4$
$$= 4.56 \times 10^{10}.$$

TABLE III

Series	Charge	Value of e	Weight Assigned
1	$3e$	4.59	7
2	$4e$	4.56	7
3	$2e$	4.64	6
4	$5e$	4.83	4
5	$2e$	4.87	1
6	$6e$	4.69	3

Simple mean $e = 4.70 \times 10^{-10}$
Weighted mean $e = 4.65 \times 10^{-10}$

earliest measurements on the charges carried by individual particles.

In connection with these experiments I chanced to observe a phenomenon which interested me very much at the time and suggested quite new possibilities. While working with these "balanced drops" I noticed on several occasions on which I had failed to screen off the rays from the radium that now and then one of them would suddenly change its charge and begin to move up or down in the field, evidently because it had captured in the one case a positive, in the other a negative, ion. This opened up the possibility of measuring with certainty, not merely the charges on individual droplets as I had been doing, but the charge carried by a single atmospheric ion. *For by taking two speed measurements on the same drop, one before and one after it had caught an ion, I could obviously eliminate entirely the properties of the drop and of the medium and deal with a quantity which was proportional merely to the charge on the captured ion itself.*

Accordingly, in the fall of 1909 there was started the series of experiments described in the succeeding chapter.

The problem had already been so nearly solved by the work with the water droplets that there seemed no possibility of failure. It was only necessary to get a charged droplet entirely free from evaporation into the space between the plates of a horizontal air condenser and then, by alternately throwing on and off an electrical field, to keep this droplet pacing its beat up and down between the plates until it could catch an atmospheric ion in just the way I had already seen the water droplets do. The change in the speed in the field would then be exactly proportional to the charge on the ion captured.

CHAPTER IV

GENERAL PROOF OF THE ATOMIC NATURE OF ELECTRICITY

Although the "balanced-droplet method" just described had eliminated the chief sources of uncertainty which inhered in preceding work on e and had made it possible to assert with much confidence that the unit charge was a real physical entity and not merely a "statistical mean," it was yet very far from an exact method of studying the properties of gaseous ions. The sources of error or uncertainty which still inhered in it arose from (1) the lack of stagnancy in the air through which the drop moved; (2) the lack of perfect uniformity of the electrical field used; (3) the gradual evaporation of the drops, rendering it impossible to hold a given drop under observation for more than a minute or to time a drop as it fell under gravity alone through a period of more than five or six seconds; and (4) the assumption of the validity of Stokes's Law.

The method which was devised to replace it was not only entirely free from all of these limitations, but it constituted an entirely new way of studying ionization and one which at once yielded important results in a considerable number of directions. This chapter deals with some of these by-products of the determination of e which are of even more fundamental interest and importance than the mere discovery of the exact size of the electron.

I.   ISOLATION OF INDIVIDUAL IONS AND MEASUREMENT OF THEIR RELATIVE CHARGES

In order to compare the charges on different ions, the procedure adopted was to blow with an ordinary commercial atomizer an oil spray into the chamber C (Fig. 3).

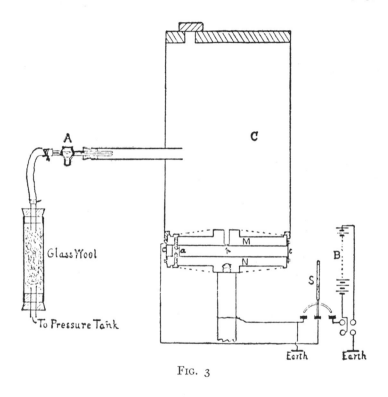

FIG. 3

The air with which this spray was blown was first rendered dust-free by passage through a tube containing glass wool.   The minute droplets of oil constituting the spray, most of them having a radius of the order of a one-thousandth of a millimeter, slowly fell in the chamber C, and occasionally one of them would find its way through the minute pinhole p in the middle of the circular brass plate M, 22 cm. in diameter, which formed one of the plates of the air condenser. The other plate, N, was held 16 mm. beneath it by three ebonite posts a. By means of the switch S these plates could be charged, the one positively and the other negatively, by making them the terminals of a 10,000-volt storage battery B, while throwing the switch the other way (to the left) short-circuited them and reduced the field between them to zero. The oil droplets which entered at p were illuminated by a powerful beam of light which passed through diametrically opposite windows in the encircling ebonite strip c. As viewed through a third window in c on the side toward the reader, it appeared as a bright star on a black background. These droplets which entered p were found in general to have been strongly charged by the frictional process involved in blowing the spray, so that when the field was thrown on in the proper direction they would be pulled up toward M. Just before the drop under observation could strike M the plates would be short-circuited and the drop allowed to fall under gravity until it was close to N, when the direction of motion would be again reversed by throwing on the field. In this way the drop would be kept traveling back and forth between the plates. The first time the experiment was tried an ion was caught within a few minutes, and the fact of its capture was signaled to the observer by the change in the speed with which it moved up when the field was on. The significance of the experiment can best be appreciated by examination of the complete record of one of the early experiments when the timing was done merely with a stop watch.

The column headed t_g gives the successive times which the droplet required to fall between two fixed cross-hairs in the observing telescope whose distance apart corresponded in this case to an actual distance of fall of .5222 cm. It will be seen that these numbers are all the same within the limits of error of a stop-watch measurement. The column marked t_F gives the successive times

TABLE IV

t_g	t_F
13.6	12.5
13.8	12.4
13.4	21.8
13.4	34.8
13.6	84.5
13.6	85.5
13.7	34.6
13.5	34.8
13.5	16.0
13.8	34.8
13.7	34.6
13.8	21.9
13.6	
13.5	
13.4	
13.8	
13.4	

Mean 13.595

which the droplet required to rise under the influence of the electrical field produced by applying in this case 5,051 volts of potential difference to the plates M and N. It will be seen that after the second trip up, the time changed from 12.4 to 21.8, indicating, since in this case the drop was positive, that a negative ion had been caught from the air. The next time recorded under t_F, namely, 34.8, indicates that another negative ion had been caught. The next time, 84.5, indicates the capture of still another negative ion. This charge was held for two trips, when the speed changed back again to 34.6, showing that a positive ion had now been caught which carried precisely the same charge as the negative ion which before caused the inverse change in time, i.e., that from 34.8 to 84.5.

In order to obtain some of the most important consequences of this and other similar experiments we need make no assumption further than this, that the velocity with which the drop moves is proportional to the force acting upon it and is independent of the electrical charge which it carries. Fortunately this assumption can be put to very delicate experimental test, as will presently be shown, but introducing it for the time being as a mere assumption, as Townsend, Thomson, and Wilson had done before, we get

$$\frac{v_1}{v_2} = \frac{mg}{Fe_n - mg} \text{ or } e_n = \frac{mg}{Fv_1}(v_1 + v_2) \dots \dots (9)$$

The negative sign is used in the denominator because v_2 will for convenience be taken as positive when the drop is going up in the direction of F, while v_1 will be taken as positive when it is going down in the direction of g. e_n denotes the charge on the drop, and must not be confused with the charge on an ion. If now by the capture of an ion the drop changes its charge from e_n to e_{n^1}, then the value of the captured charge e_i is

$$e_i = e_{n^1} - e_n = \frac{mg}{Fv_1}(v_2' - v_2) \dots \dots (10)$$

and since $\frac{mg}{Fv_1}$ is a constant for this drop, any charge which it may capture will always be proportional to

$(v_2'-v_2)$, that is, to the change produced in the velocity in the field F by the captured ion.   The successive values of v_2 and of $(v_2'-v_2)$ are shown in Table V.

TABLE V

v_2	$(v_1'-v_2)$
$\dfrac{.5222}{12.45}=.04196$	
	$.01806 \div 2 = .00903$
$\dfrac{.5222}{21.5}=.02390$	
	$.00885 \div 1 = .00885$
$\dfrac{.5222}{34.7}=.01505$	
	$.00891 \div 1 = .00891$
$\dfrac{.5222}{85.0}=.006144$	
	$.00891 \div 1 = .00891$
$\dfrac{.5222}{34.7}=.01505$	
	$.01759 \div 2 = .00880$
$\dfrac{.5222}{16.0}=.03264$	
	$.01759 \div 2 = .00880$
$\dfrac{.5222}{34.7}=.01505$	
	$.00891 \div 1 = .00891$
$\dfrac{.5222}{21.85}=.02390$	

It will be seen from the last column that within the limits of error of a stop-watch measurement, all the charges captured have exactly the same value save in three cases.   In all of these three the captured charges were just twice as large as those appearing in the other changes.   Relationships of exactly this sort have been found to hold absolutely without exception, no matter in what gas the drops have been suspended or what sort of droplets were used upon which to catch the ions.   In many cases a given drop has been held under observation for five or six hours at a time and has been seen to catch not eight or ten ions, as in the above experiment, but hundreds of them. Indeed, I have observed, all told, the capture of many thousands of ions in this way, and in no case have I ever found one the charge of which, when tested as above, did not have either exactly the value of the smallest charge ever captured or else a very small multiple of that value. *Here, then, is direct, unimpeachable proof that the electron is not a "statistical mean," but that rather the electrical charges found on ions all have either exactly the same value or else small exact multiples of that value.*

II. PROOF THAT ALL STATIC CHARGES BOTH ON CONDUCTORS AND INSULATORS ARE BUILT UP OF ELECTRONS

The foregoing experiment leads, however, to results of much more fundamental importance than that mentioned in the preceding section. The charge which the droplet had when it first came under observation had been acquired, not by the capture of ions from the air, but by the ordinary frictional process involved in blowing the spray. If then ordinary static charges are built up of electrons, this charge should be found to be an exact multiple of the ionic charge which had been found from the most reliable measurement shown in Table V to be proportional to the velocity .00891. This initial charge e_n on the drop is seen from equations (9) and (10) to bear the same relation to (v_1+v_2) which the ionic charge $e_n'-e_n$ bears to $(v_2'-v_2)$. Now, $v_1 = .5222/13.595 = .03842$, hence $v_1+v_2 = .03842 + .04196 = .08038$. Dividing this by 9 we obtain .008931, which is within about one-fifth of 1 per cent of the value found in the last column of Table V as the smallest charge carried by an ion. *Our experiment has then given us for the first time a means of comparing a frictional charge with the ionic charge, and the frictional charge has in this instance been found to contain exactly 9 electrons.* A more exact means of making this comparison will be given presently, but suffice it to say here that experiments like the foregoing have now been tried on thousands of drops in different media, some of the drops being made of non-conductors like oil, some of semi-conductors like glycerin, some of excellent metallic conductors like mercury. In every case, without a single exception, the initial charge placed upon the drop by the frictional process, and all of the dozen or more charges which have resulted from the capture by the drop of a larger or smaller number of ions, have been found to be exact multiples of the smallest charge caught from the air. Some of these drops have started with no charge at all, and one, two, three, four, five, and six elementary charges or electrons have been picked up. Others have started with seven or eight units, others with twenty, others with fifty, others with a hundred, others with a hundred and fifty elementary units, and have picked up in each case a dozen or two of elementary charges on either side of the starting-point, so that in all drops containing every possible number of electrons between one and one hundred and fifty have been observed and the number of electrons which each drop carried has been accurately counted by the method described. When the number is less than fifty there is not a whit more uncertainty about this count than there is in counting one's own fingers and toes. It is not found possible to determine with certainty the number of electrons in a charge containing more than one hundred or two hundred of them, for the simple reason that the method of measurement used fails to detect the difference between 200 and 201, that is, we cannot measure $v_2' - v_2$ with an accuracy greater than one-half of 1 per cent.   But it is quite inconceivable that large charges such as are dealt with in commercial applications of electricity can be built up in an essentially different way from that in which the small charges whose electrons we are able to count are found to be.   Furthermore, since it has been definitely proved that an electrical current is nothing but the motion of an electrical charge over or through a conductor, it is evident that the experiments under consideration furnish not only the most direct and convincing of evidence that all electrical charges are built up out of these very units which we have been dealing with as individuals in these experiments, but that all electrical currents consist merely in the transport of these electrons through the conducting bodies.

In order to show the beauty and precision with which these multiple relationships stand out in all experiments of this kind, a table corresponding to much more precise measurements than those given heretofore is here introduced (Table VI).   The time of fall and rise shown in the first and second columns were taken with a Hipp chronoscope reading to one-thousandths of a second. The third column gives the reciprocals of these times. These are used in place of the velocities v_2 in the field, since distance of fall and rise is always the same.   The fourth column gives the successive changes in speed due

to the capture of ions.   These also are expressed merely
as time reciprocals.   For reasons which will be explained
in the next section, each one of these changes may correspond to the capture of not merely one but of several distinct ions.   The numbers in the fifth column represent

TABLE VI

t_g Sec.	t_F Sec.	$\frac{1}{t_F}$	$\left(\frac{1}{t'_F}-\frac{1}{t_F}\right)$	n'	$\frac{1}{n'}\left(\frac{1}{t'_F}-\frac{1}{t_F}\right)$	$\left(\frac{1}{t_g}+\frac{1}{t_F}\right)$	n	$\frac{1}{n}\left(\frac{1}{t_g}+\frac{1}{t_F}\right)$
11.848	80.708	.01236				.09655	18	.005366
11.890	22.366		.03234	6	.005390			
11.908	22.390	.04470				.12887	24	.005371
11.904	22.368		.03751	7	.005358			
11.882	140.565	.007192	.005348	1	.005348	.09138	17	.005375
11.906	79.600	.01254				.09673	18	.005374
11.838	34.748		.01616	3	.005387			
11.816	34.762	.02870				.11289	21	.005376
11.776	34.846							
11.840	29.286	.03414				.11833	22	.005379
11.904	29.236		.026872	5	.005375			
11.870	137.308	.007268	.021572	4	.005393	.09146	17	.005380
11.952	34.638	.02884				.11303	21	.005382
11.860			.01623	3	.005410			
11.846	22.104	.04507				.12926	24	.005386
11.912	22.268		.04307	8	.005384			
11.910	500.1	.002000				.08619	16	.005387
11.918	19.704	.05079	.04879	9	.005421			
11.870	19.668		.03874	7	.005401	.13498	25	.005399
11.888	77.630	.01285				.09704	18	.005390
11.894	77.806		.01079	2	.005395	.10783	20	.005392
11.878	42.302	.02364						
11.880			Means		.005386			.005384

Duration of exp.	=45 min.	Pressure	=75.62 cm.
Plate distance	=16 mm.	Oil density	=.9199
Fall distance	=10.21 mm.	Air viscosity	=1,824×10⁻⁷
Initial volts	=5,088.8	Radius (a)	=.000276 cm.
Final volts	=5,081.2	$\frac{l}{a}$	=.034
Temperature	=22.82° C.	Speed of fall	=.08584 cm./sec.

$$e_1=4.991\times10^{-10}$$

simply the small integer by which it is found that the
numbers in the fourth column must be divided in order
to obtain the numbers in the sixth column.   These will
be seen to be exactly alike within the limits of error of the
experiment.   The mean value at the bottom of the sixth
column represents, then, the smallest charge ever caught

from the air, that is, it is the elementary *ionic* charge. The seventh column gives the successive values of v_1+v_2 expressed as reciprocal times. These numbers, then, represent the successive values of the *total* charge carried by the droplet. The eighth column gives the integers by which the numbers in the seventh column must be divided to obtain the numbers in the last column. These also will be seen to be invariable. The mean at the bottom of the last column represents, then, *the electrical unit out of which the frictional charge on the droplet was built up, and it is seen to be identical with the ionic charge represented by the number at the bottom of the sixth column.*

It may be of interest to introduce one further table (Table VII) arranged in a slightly different way to show

TABLE VII

n	$4.917 \times n$	Observed Charge	n	$4.917 \times n$	Observed Charge
1............	4.917	....	10.........	49.17	49.41
2............	9.834	....	11.........	54.09	53.91
3............	14.75	....	12.........	59.00	59.12
4............	19.66	19.66	13.........	63.92	63.68
5............	24.59	24.60	14.........	68.84	68.65
6............	29.50	29.62	15.........	73.75	....
7............	34.42	34.47	16.........	78.67	78.34
8............	39.34	39.38	17.........	83.59	83.22
9............	44.25	44.42	18.........	88.51	....

how infallibly the atomic structure of electricity follows from experiments like those under consideration.

In this table 4.917 is merely a number obtained precisely as above from the change in speed due to the capture of ions and one which is proportional in this experiment to the ionic charge. The column headed $4.917 \times n$ contains simply the whole series of exact mul-

tiples of this number from 1 to 18.   The column headed
"Observed Charge" gives the successive observed values
of $(v_1 + v_2)$.   It will be seen that during the time of observation, about four hours, this drop carried all possible
multiples of the elementary charge from 4 to 18, save only
15. *No more exact or more consistent multiple relationship
is found in the data which chemists have amassed on the
combining powers of the elements and on which the atomic
theory of matter rests than is found in the foregoing numbers.*

Such tables as these—and scores of them could be
given—place beyond all question the view that an
electrical charge wherever it is found, whether on an
insulator or a conductor, whether in electrolytes or in
metals, has a definite granular structure, that it consists
of an exact number of specks of electricity (electrons) all
exactly alike, which in static phenomena are scattered over the surface of the charged body and in current
phenomena are drifting along the conductor.   Instead
of giving up, as Maxwell thought we should some day do,
the "provisional hypothesis of molecular charges," we
find ourselves obliged to make all our interpretations of
electrical phenomena, *metallic as well as electrolytic,* in
terms of it.

III.   MECHANISM OF CHANGE OF CHARGE OF A DROP

All of the changes of charge shown in Table IV were
spontaneous changes, and it has been assumed that all
of these changes were produced by the capture of ions
from the air.   When a negative drop suddenly increases
its speed in the field, that is, takes on a larger charge of
its own kind than it has been carrying, there seems to be
no other conceivable way in which the change can be

produced. But when the charge suddenly *decreases* there is no a priori reason for thinking that the change may not be due as well to the direct loss of a portion of the charge as to the neutralization of this same amount of electricity by the capture of a charge of opposite sign. That, however, the changes do actually occur, when no X-rays or radioactive rays are passing between the plates, only by the capture of ions from the air, was rendered probable by the fact that drops not too heavily charged showed the same tendency on the whole to increase as to decrease in charge. This should not have been the case if there were two causes tending to decrease the charge, namely, direct loss and the capture of opposite ions, as against one tending to increase it, namely, capture of like ions. The matter was very convincingly settled, however, by making observations when the gas pressures were as low as 2 or 3 mm. of mercury. Since the number of ions present in a gas is in general directly proportional to the pressure, spontaneous changes in charge should almost never occur at these low pressures; in fact, it was found that drops could be held for hours at a time without changing. The frequency with which the changes occur decreases regularly with the pressure, as it should if the changes are due to the capture of ions. For the number of ions formed by a given ionizing agent must vary directly as the pressure.

Again, the changes do not, in general, occur when the electrical field is on, for then the ions are driven instantly to the plates as soon as formed, at a speed of, say, 10,000 cm. per second, and so do not have any opportunity to accumulate in the space between them. When the field is off, however, they do so accumulate, until, in ordinary air, they reach the number of, say, 20,000 per cubic centimeter. These ions, being endowed with the kinetic energy of agitation characteristic of the temperature, wander rapidly through the gas and become a part of the drop as soon as they impinge upon it. It was thus that all the changes recorded in Table IV took place.

It is possible, however, so to control the changes as to place electrons of just such sign as one wishes, and of just such number as one wishes, within limits, upon a given drop. If, for example, it is desired to place a positive electron upon a given drop the latter is held with the aid of the field fairly close to the negative plate, say the upper plate; then an ionizing agent—X-rays or radium—is arranged to produce uniform ionization in the gas between the plates. Since now all the positive ions move up while the negatives move down, the drop is in a shower of positive ions, and if the ionization is intense enough the drop is sure to be hit. In this way a positive charge of almost any desired strength may be placed upon the drop.

Similarly, in order to throw a negative ion or ions upon the drop it is held by the field close to the lower, i.e., to the positive, plate in a shower of negative ions produced by the X-rays. It was in this way that most of the changes shown in Table VI were brought about. This accounts for the fact that they correspond in some instances to the capture of as many as six electrons.

When X-rays are allowed to fall directly upon the drop itself the change in charge may occur, not merely because of the capture of ions, but also because the rays eject beta particles, i.e., negative electrons, from the molecules of the drop. That changes in charge were actually produced in this way in our experiments was proved conclusively in 1910 by the fact that when the pressure was reduced to a very low value and X-rays were allowed to pass through the air containing the drop, the latter would change readily in the direction of increasing positive or decreasing negative charge, but it could almost never be made to change in the opposite direction. This is because at these low pressures the rays can find very few gas molecules to ionize, while they detach negative electrons from the drop as easily as at atmospheric pressure. *This experiment proved directly that the charge carried by an ion in gases is the same as the charge on the beta or cathode-ray particle.*

When it was desired to avoid the direct loss of negative electrons by the drop, we arranged lead screens so that the drop itself would not be illuminated by the rays, although the gas underneath it was ionized by them.[1]

IV. DIRECT OBSERVATION OF THE KINETIC ENERGY OF AGITATION OF A MOLECULE

I have already remarked that when a drop carries but a small number of electrons it appears to catch ions of its own sign as rapidly as those of opposite signs—a result which seems strange at first, since the ions of opposite sign must be attracted, while those of like sign must be repelled. Whence, then, does the ion obtain the energy which enables it to push itself up against this electrostatic repulsion and attach itself to a drop already strongly charged with its own kind of electricity? It cannot obtain it from the field, since the phenomenon of capture occurs when the field is not on. It cannot

[1] See *Phil. Mag.*, XXI (1911), 757.

obtain it from any explosive process which frees the ion from the molecule at the instant of ionization, since in this case, too, ions would be caught as well, or nearly as well, when the field is on as when it is off. Here, then, is an absolutely direct proof that the ion must be endowed with a kinetic energy of agitation which is sufficient to push it up to the surface of the drop against the electrostatic repulsion of the charge on the drop.

This energy may easily be computed as follows: Let us take a drop, such as was used in one of these experiments, of radius .000197 cm. The potential at the surface of a charged sphere can be shown to be the charge divided by the radius. The value of the elementary electrical charge obtained from the best observations of this type, is 4.774×10^{-10} absolute electrostatic units. Hence the energy required to drive an ion carrying the elementary charge e up to the surface of a charged sphere of radius r, carrying 16 elementary charges, is

$$\frac{16e^2}{r} = \frac{16 \times (4.774 \times 10^{-10})^2}{.000197} = 1.95 \times 10^{-14} \text{ ergs.}$$

Now, the kinetic energy of agitation of a molecule as deduced from the value of e herewith obtained, and the kinetic theory equation, $p = \frac{1}{3}nm\overline{c^2}$, is 5.75×10^{-14} ergs. According to the Maxwell-Boltzmann Law of the partition of energy, which certainly holds in gases, this should also be the kinetic energy of agitation of an ion. It will be seen that the value of this energy is approximately three times that required to push a single ion up to the surface of the drop in question. Hence the electrostatic forces due to 16 electrons on the drop are too weak to exert much influence upon the motion of an approaching ion. But if it were possible to load up a drop with negative electricity until the potential energy of its charge were about three times as great as that computed above for this drop, then the phenomenon here observed of the catching of new negative ions by such a negatively charged drop should not take place, save in the exceptional case in which an ion might acquire an energy of agitation considerably larger than the mean value. Now, as a matter of fact, it was regularly observed that the heavily charged drops had a very much smaller tendency to pick up new negative ions than the more lightly charged drops, and, in one instance, we watched for four hours another negatively charged drop of radius .000658 cm., which carried charges varying from 126 to 150 elementary units, and which therefore had a potential energy of charge (computed as above on the assumption of uniform distribution) varying from 4.6×10^{-14} to 5.47×10^{-14}. In all that time this drop picked up but one single negative ion when the field was off, and that despite the fact that the ionization was several times more intense than in the case of the drop of Table I. Positive ions too were being caught at almost every trip down under gravity. (The strong negative charge on the drop was maintained by forcing on negative ions by the field as explained above.)

V. POSITIVE AND NEGATIVE ELECTRONS EXACTLY EQUAL

The idea has at various times been put forth in connection with attempts to explain chemical and cohesive forces from the standpoint of electrostatic attractions that the positive and negative charges in a so-called neutral atom may not after all be exactly equal, in other

words, that there is really no such thing as an entirely
neutral atom or molecule. As a matter of fact, it is
difficult to find decisive tests of this hypothesis. The
present experiments, however, make possible the following sort of test. I loaded a given drop first with negative
electrons and took ten or twelve observations of rise and
fall, then with the aid of X-rays, by the method indicated
in the last section, I reversed the sign of the charge on
the drop and took a corresponding number of observations of rise and fall, and so continued observing first the
value of the negative electron and then that of the positive.   Table VIII shows a set of such observations taken
in air with a view to subjecting this point to as rigorous a
test as possible.   Similar, though not quite so elaborate,
observations have been made in hydrogen with the same
result. The table shows in the first column the sign of
the charge; in the second the successive values of the
time of fall under gravity; in the third the successive
times of rise in the field $F;$ in the fourth the number of
electrons carried by the drop for each value of $t_F;$ and in
the fifth the number, characteristic of this drop, which
is proportional to the charge of one electron.   This number is obtained precisely as in the two preceding tables
by finding the greatest common divisor of the successive
values of (v_1+v_2) and then multiplying this by an
arbitrary constant which has nothing to do with the
present experiment and hence need not concern us here
(see chap. v).

It will be seen that though the times of fall and of
rise, even when the same number of electrons is carried
by the drop, change a trifle because of a very slight
evaporation and also because of the fall in the potential

TABLE VIII

Sign of Drop	t_g Sec.	t_F Sec.	n	e
—	63.118			
	63.050			
	63.186	41.728⎱	8	
	63.332	41.590⎰		
	62.328			$e_1 = 6.713$
	62.728	25.740⎱		
	62.926	25.798⎰	11	
	62.900	25.510		
	63.214	25.806		
	Mean = 62.976			
+	63.538	22.694⎱	12	
	63.244	22.830⎰		
	63.114	25.870		
	63.242	25.876	11	
	63.362	25.484		
	63.136	10.830		$e_1 = 6.692$
	63.226	10.682		
	63.764	10.756	22	
	63.280	10.778		
	63.530	10.672		
	63.268	10.646		
	Mean = 63.325			
+	63.642			
	63.020	71.664⎱	6	
	62.820	71.248⎰		
	63.514	52.668		
	63.312	52.800	7	$e_1 = 6.702$
	63.776	52.496		
	63.300	52.860		
	63.156	71.708	6	
	63.126			
	Mean = 63.407			

TABLE VIII—*Continued*

Sign of Drop	t_g Sec.	t_F Sec.	n	e
—	63.228 63.294 63.184	42.006 41.920 42.108	8	$e_1 = 6.686$
	63.260 63.478 63.074 63.306	53.210 52.922 53.034 53.438	7	
	63.414 63.450 63.446 63.556	12.888 12.812 12.748 12.824	19	
	Mean = 63.335			

Duration of experiment 1 hr. 40 min. Mean $e+ = 6.697$
Initial volts = 1723.5   Mean $e- = 6.700$
Final volts = 1702.1
Pressure   = 53.48 cm.

of the battery, yet the mean value of the positive electron, namely, 6.697, agrees with the mean value of the negative electron, namely, 6.700, or to within less than 1 part in 2,000. Since this is about the limit of the experimental error (the probable error by least squares is 1 part in 1,500), *we may with certainty conclude that there are no differences of more than this amount between the values of the positive and negative electrons.* This is the best evidence I am aware of for the exact neutrality of the ordinary molecules of gases. Such neutrality, if it is actually exact, would seem to preclude the possibility of explaining gravitation as a result of electrostatic forces of any kind. The electromagnetic effect of moving charges might, however, still be called upon for this purpose.

VI. RESISTANCE OF MEDIUM TO MOTION OF DROP THROUGH IT THE SAME WHEN DROP IS CHARGED AS WHEN UNCHARGED

A second and equally important conclusion can be drawn from Table VIII. It will be seen from the column headed *"n"* that during the whole of the time corresponding to the observations in the third group from the top the drop carried either 6 or 7 electrons, while, during the last half of the time corresponding to the observations in the second group from the top, it carried three times as many, namely, 22 electrons. Yet the mean times of fall under gravity in the two groups agree to within about one part in one thousand. The time of fall corresponding to the heavier charge happens in this case to be the smaller of the two. We may conclude, therefore, that *in these experiments the resistance which the medium offers to the motion of a body through it is not sensibly increased when the body becomes electrically charged. This demonstrates experimentally the exact validity for this work of the assumption made on p. 68 that the velocity of the drop is strictly proportional to the force acting upon it, whether it is charged or uncharged.*

The result is at first somewhat surprising since, according to Sutherland's theory of the small ion, the small mobility or diffusivity of charged molecules, as compared with uncharged, is due to the additional resistance which the medium offers to the motion through it of a charged molecule. This additional resistance is due to the fact that the charge on a molecule drags into collision with it more molecules than would otherwise hit it. But with oil drops of the sizes here used

$(a = 50 \times 10^{-6})$ the total number of molecular collisions against the surface of the drop is so huge that even though the small number of charges on it might produce a few more collisions, their number would be negligible in comparison with the total number. At any rate the experiment demonstrates conclusively that the charges on our oil drops do not influence the resistance of the medium to the motion of the drop. This conclusion might also have been drawn from the data contained in Table VI. The evidence for its absolute correctness has been made more convincing still by a comparison of drops which carried but 1 charge and those which carried as many as 68 unit charges. Further, I have observed the rate of fall under gravity of droplets which were completely discharged, and in every case that I have ever tried I have found this rate precisely the same, within the limits of error of the time measurements, as when it carried 8 or 10 unit charges.

VII. DROPS ACT LIKE RIGID SPHERES

It was of very great importance for the work, an account of which will be given in the next chapter to determine whether the drops ever suffer—either because of their motion through a resisting medium, or because of the electrical field in which they are placed—any appreciable distortion from the spherical form which a freely suspended liquid drop must assume. The complete experimental answer to this query is contained in the agreement of the means at the bottom of the last and the third from the last columns in Table VI and in similar agreements shown in many other tables, which may be found in the original articles.[1] Since $\dfrac{1}{t_g}$ is in this experiment large compared to $\dfrac{1}{t_F}$, the value of the greatest common divisor at the bottom of the last column of Table VI is determined almost wholly by the rate of fall of the particle under gravity when there is no field at all between the plates, while the velocity at the bottom of the third from the last column is a difference between two velocities in a strong electrical field. If, therefore, the drop were distorted by the electrical field, so that it exposed a larger surface to the resistance of the medium than when it had the spherical form, the velocity due to a given force, that is, the velocity given at the bottom of the third from the last column, would be less than that found at the bottom of the last column, which corresponds to motions when the drop certainly was spherical.

Furthermore, if the drops were distorted by their motion through the medium, then this distortion would be greater for high speeds than for low, and consequently the numbers in the third from the last column would be consistently larger for high speeds than for low. No such variation of these numbers with speed is apparent either in Table VI or in other similar tables.

We have then in the exactness and invariableness of the multiple relations shown by successive differences in speed and the successive sums of the speeds in the third from the last and the last columns of Table VI complete experimental proof that in this work the droplets act under all circumstances like undeformed spheres. It is of interest that Professor Hadamard,[2] of the University of

---

[1] *Phys. Rev.*, Series 1, XXXII (1911), 349; Series 2, II (1913), 109.
[2] *Comptes rendus* (1911), 1735.

Paris, and Professor Lunn,[1] of the University of Chicago, have both shown from theoretical considerations that this would be the case with oil drops as minute as those with which these experiments deal, so that the conclusion may now be considered as very firmly established, both by the experimentalist and the theorist.

[1] *Phys. Rev.*, XXXV (1912), 227.

CHAPTER V

THE EXACT EVALUATION OF e

I. DISCOVERY OF THE FAILURE OF STOKES'S LAW

Although complete evidence for the atomic nature of electricity is found in the fact that all of the charges which can be placed upon a body as measured by the sum of speeds $v_1 + v_2$, and all the changes of charge which this body can undergo as measured by the differences of speed $(v_2' - v_2)$ are invariably found to be exact multiples of a particular speed, yet there is something still to be desired if we must express this greatest common divisor of all the observed series of speeds merely as a velocity which is a characteristic constant of each particular drop but which varies from drop to drop. We ought rather to be able to reduce this greatest common divisor to electrical terms by finding the proportionality factor between speed and charge, and, that done, we should, of course, expect to find that the charge came out a universal constant independent of the size or kind of drop experimented upon. The attempt to do this by the method which I had used in the case of the water drops (p. 53), namely, by the assumption of Stokes's Law, heretofore taken for granted by all observers, led to the interesting discovery that this law is not valid.[1]   Accord-

[1] Cunningham (*Proc. Roy. Soc.*, LXXXIII [1910], 357) and the author came independently to the conclusion as to the invalidity of Stokes's Law, he from theoretical considerations developed at about the same time, I from my experimental work.

ing to this law the rate of fall of a spherical drop under gravity, namely, v_1, is given by

$$v_1 = \frac{2ga^2}{9\eta}(\sigma - \rho) \quad \dots\dots\dots\dots\dots (11)$$

in which η is the viscosity of the medium, a the radius and σ the density of the drop, and ρ the density of the medium. This last quantity was neglected in (6), p. 53, because, with the rough measurements there possible, it was useless to take it into account, but with our oil drops in dry air all the other factors could be found with great precision.

When we assume the foregoing equation of Stokes and combine it with equation (5) on p. 53, an equation whose exact validity was proved experimentally in the last chapter, we obtain, after substitution of the purely geometrical relation $m = 4/3 \, a^3 \, (\sigma - \rho)$, the following expression for the charge e_n carried by a drop loaded with n electrons which we will assume to have been counted by the method described:

$$e_n = \frac{4}{3\pi}\left(\frac{9\eta}{2}\right)^{\frac{3}{2}}\left(\frac{1}{g(\sigma - \rho)}\right)^{\frac{1}{2}}\frac{(v_1 + v_2)v_1^{\frac{1}{2}}}{F} \quad \dots\dots\dots (12)$$

According to this equation the elementary charge e_1 should be obtained by substituting in this the greatest common divisor of all the observed series of values of $(v_1 + v_2)$ or of $(v_2' - v_2)$. Thus, if we call this $(v_1 + v_2)_0$, we have

$$e_1 = \frac{4}{3\pi}\left(\frac{9\eta}{2}\right)^{\frac{3}{2}}\left(\frac{1}{g(\sigma - \rho)}\right)^{\frac{1}{2}}\frac{(v_1 + v_2)_0 v_1^{\frac{1}{2}}}{F} \quad \dots\dots\dots (13)$$

But when this equation was tested out upon different drops, although it yielded perfectly concordant results so long as the different drops all fell with about the same speed, when drops of different speeds, and, therefore, of different sizes, were used, the values of e_1 obtained were consistently larger the smaller the velocity under gravity. For example, e_1 for one drop for which $v_1 = .01085$ cm. per second came out 5.49×10^{-10}, while for another of almost the same speed, namely, $v_1 = .01176$, it came out 5.482; but for two drops whose speeds were five times as large, namely, $.0536$ and $.0553$, e_1 came out 5.143 and 5.145, respectively. This could mean nothing save that Stokes's Law did not hold for drops of the order of magnitude here used, something like $a = .0002$ cm. (see Section IV below), and it was surmised that the reason for its failure lay in the fact that the drops were so small that they could no longer be thought of as moving through the air as they would through a continuous homogeneous medium, which was the situation contemplated in the deduction of Stokes's Law. This law ought to begin to fail as soon as the inhomogeneities in the medium—i.e., the distances between the molecules—began to be at all comparable with the dimensions of the drop. Furthermore, it is easy to see that as soon as the holes in the medium begin to be comparable with the size of the drop, the latter must begin to increase its speed, for it may then be thought of as beginning to reach the stage in which it can fall freely through the holes in the medium. This would mean that the observed speed of fall would be more and more in excess of that given by Stokes's Law the smaller the drop became. But the apparent value of the electronic charge, namely, e_1, is seen from equation (13) to vary directly with the speed $(v_1 + v_2)_0$ imparted by a given force. Hence e_1 should come out larger and larger the smaller the radius of the drop, that is, the smaller its velocity under gravity. Now, this was exactly the behavior shown consistently by all the oil drops studied. Hence it looked as though we had discovered, not merely the failure of Stokes's Law, but also the line of approach by means of which it might be corrected.

In order to be certain of our ground, however, we were obliged to initiate a whole series of new and some-what elaborate experiments.

These consisted, first, in finding very exactly what is the coefficient of viscosity of air under conditions in which it may be treated as a homogeneous medium, and, second, in finding the limits within which Stokes's Law may be considered valid.

II.   THE COEFFICIENT OF VISCOSITY OF AIR

The experiments on the coefficient of viscosity of air were carried out in the Ryerson Laboratory by Dr. Lachen Gilchrist, now of Toronto University, and Dr. I. M. Rapp, now of the University of Oklahoma. Dr. Gilchrist used a method[1] which was in many respects new and which may fairly be said to be freer from theo-retical uncertainties than any method which has ever been used. He estimated that his results should not be in error by more than .1 or .2 of 1 per cent. Dr. Rapp used a form of the familiar capillary-tube method, but under conditions which seemed to adapt it better to an absolute evaluation of η for air than capillary-tube arrangements have ordinarily been.

[1] *Phys. Rev.*, I, N.S. (1913), 124.

These two men, as the result of measurements which were in progress for more than two years, obtained final means which were in very close agreement with one another as well as with the most careful of preceding determinations. It will be seen from Table IX that

TABLE IX

η_{23} for Air	
.00018227	Rapp, Capillary-tube method, 1913 (*Phys. Rev.*, II, 363).
.00018257	Gilchrist, Constant deflection method, 1913 (*Phys. Rev.*, I, 124).
.00018229	Hogg, Damping of oscillating cylinders, 1905 (*Proc. Am. Acad.*, XL, 611).
.00018258	Tomlinson, Damping of Swinging Pendulum, 1886 (*Phil. Trans.*, CLXXVII, 767).
.00018232	Grindley and Gibson, Flow through pipe, 1908 (*Proc. Roy. Soc.*, LXXX, 114).
Mean.... .00018240	

every one of the five different methods which have been used for the absolute determination of η for air leads to a value that differs by less than one part in one thousand from the following mean value, $\eta_{23} = .00018240$. It was concluded, therefore, that we could depend upon the value of η for the viscosity of air under the conditions of our experiment to at least one part in one thousand. Very recently Dr. E. Harrington[1] has improved still further the apparatus designed by Dr. Gilchrist and the author and has made with it in the Ryerson Laboratory a determination of η which is, I think, altogether unique in its reliability and precision. I give to it alone greater

[1] *Phys. Rev.*, December, 1916.

weight than to all the other work of the past fifty years in this field taken together. The final value is

$$\eta_{23} = .00018226$$

and the error can scarcely be more than one part in two thousand.

III. LIMITS OF VALIDITY OF STOKES'S LAW

In the theoretical derivation of Stokes's Law the following five assumptions are made: (1) that the inhomogeneities in the medium are small in comparison with the size of the sphere; (2) that the sphere falls as it would in a medium of unlimited extent; (3) that the sphere is smooth and rigid; (4) that there is no slipping of the medium over the surface of the sphere; (5) that the velocity with which the sphere is moving is so small that the resistance to the motion is all due to the viscosity of the medium and not at all due to the inertia of such portion of the media as is being pushed forward by the motion of the sphere through it.

If these conditions were all realized then Stokes's Law ought to hold. Nevertheless, there existed up to the year 1910 no experimental work which showed that actual experimental results may be accurately predicted by means of the unmodified law, and Dr. H. D. Arnold accordingly undertook in the Ryerson Laboratory to test how accurately the rates of fall of minute spheres through water and alcohol might be predicted by means of it.

His success in these experiments was largely due to the ingenuity which he displayed in producing accurately spherical droplets of rose-metal. This metal melts at about 82° C. and is quite fluid at the temperature of boiling water. Dr. Arnold placed some of this metal in a glass tube drawn to form a capillary at one end and suspended the whole of the capillary tube in a glass tube some 70 cm. long and 3 cm. in diameter. He then filled the large tube with water and applied heat in such a way that the upper end was kept at about 100° C., while the lower end was at about 60°. He then forced the molten metal, by means of compressed air, out through the capillary into the hot water. It settled in the form of spray, the drops being sufficiently cooled by the time they reached the bottom to retain their spherical shape. This method depends for its success on the relatively slow motion of the spheres and on the small temperature gradient of the water through which they fall. The slow and uniform cooling tends to produce homogeneity of structure, while the low velocities allow the retention of very accurately spherical shape. In this way Dr. Arnold obtained spheres of radii from .002 cm. to .1 cm., which, when examined under the microscope, were found perfectly spherical and practically free from surface irregularities. He found that the slowest of these drops fell in liquids with a speed which could be computed from Stokes's Law with an accuracy of a few tenths of 1 per cent, and he determined experimentally the limits of speed through which Stokes's Law was valid.

Of the five assumptions underlying Stokes's Law, the first, third, and fourth were altogether satisfied in Dr. Arnold's experiment. The second assumption he found sufficiently realized in the case of the very smallest drops which he used, but not in the larger ones. The question, however, of the effect of the walls of the vessel upon the motion of drops through the liquid contained in the vessel had been previously studied with great ability by Ladenburg,[1] who, in working with an exceedingly viscous oil, namely Venice turpentine, obtained a formula by which the effects of the wall on the motion might be eliminated. If the medium is contained in a cylinder of circular cross-section of radius R and of length L, then, according to Ladenburg, the simple Stokes formula should be modified to read

$$V = \frac{2}{9} \frac{ga^2(\sigma - \rho)}{\eta\left(1 + 2.4\frac{a}{R}\right)\left(1 + 3.1\frac{a}{L}\right)}.$$

Arnold found that this formula held accurately in all of his experiments in which the walls had any influence on the motion. Thus he worked under conditions under which all of the first four assumptions underlying Stokes's Law were taken care of. This made it possible for him to show that the law held rigorously when the fifth assumption was realized, and also to find by experiment the limits within which this last assumption might be considered as valid. Stokes had already found from theoretical considerations[2] that the law would not hold unless the radius of the sphere were small in comparison with $\frac{\eta}{v\rho}$, in which ρ is the density of the medium, η its viscosity, and v the velocity of the sphere. This radius is called the critical radius. But it was not known how near it was possible to approach to the critical radius. Arnold's experiments showed that the inertia of the medium has no appreciable effect upon the rate of

[1] *Ann. der Phys.*, XXII (1907), 287; XXIII (1908), 447.
[2] *Math. and Phys. Papers*, III, 59.

motion of a sphere so long as the radius of that sphere is less than .6 of the critical radius.

Application of this result to the motion of our oil drops established the fact that even the very fastest drops which we ever observed fell so slowly that not even a minute error could arise because of the inertia of the medium. This meant that the fifth condition necessary to the application of Stokes's Law was fulfilled. Furthermore, our drops were so small that the second condition was also fulfilled, as was shown by the work of both Ladenburg and Arnold. The third condition was proved in the last chapter to be satisfied in our experiments. Since, therefore, Arnold's work had shown very accurately that Stokes's Law does hold when all of the five conditions are fulfilled, the problem of finding a formula for replacing Stokes's Law in the case of our oil-drop experiments resolved itself into finding in just what way the failure of assumptions 1 and 4 affected the motion of these drops.

IV. CORRECTION OF STOKES'S LAW FOR INHOMOGE-NEITIES IN THE MEDIUM

The first procedure was to find how badly Stokes's Law failed in the case of our drops. This was done by plotting the apparent value of the electron e_1 against the observed speed under gravity. This gave the curve shown in Fig. 4, which shows that though for very small speeds e_1 varies rapidly with the change in speed, for speeds larger than that corresponding to the abscissa marked 1,000 there is but a slight dependence of e_1 on speed. This abscissa corresponds to a speed of .1 cm. per second. We may then conclude that for drops which are large enough to fall at a rate of 1 cm. in ten seconds or faster, Stokes's Law needs but a small correction, because of the inhomogeneity of the air.

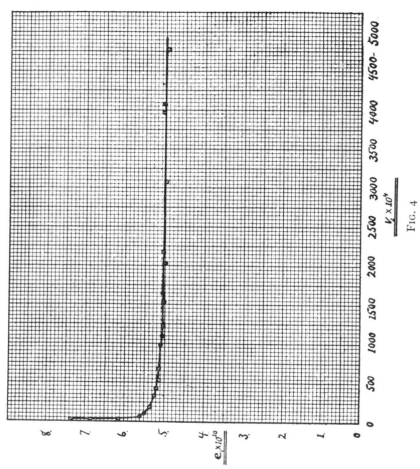

Fig. 4

To find an exact expression for this correction we may proceed as follows: The average distance which a gas molecule goes between two collisions with its neighbors, a quantity well known and measured with some approach to precision in physics and called "the mean free path" of a gas molecule, is obviously a measure of the size of the holes in a gaseous medium. When Stokes's Law begins to fail as the size of the drops diminish, it must be because the medium ceases to be homogeneous, as looked at from the standpoint of the drop, and this means simply that the radius of the drop has begun to be comparable with the mean size of the holes—a quantity which we have decided to take as measured by the mean free path l. The increase in the speed of fall over that given by Stokes's Law, when this point is reached, must then be some function of $\dfrac{l}{a}$. In other words, the correct expression for the speed v_1 of a drop falling through a gas, instead of being

$$v_1 = \frac{2}{9}\frac{ga^2}{\eta}(\sigma - \rho) ,$$

as Arnold showed that it was when the holes were negligibly small—as the latter are when the drop falls through a liquid—should be of the form

$$v_1 = \frac{2}{9}\frac{ga^2}{\eta}(\sigma - \rho)\left(1 + f\frac{l}{a}\right) \ldots \ldots \ldots \ldots (14)$$

If we were in complete ignorance of the form of the function f we could still express it in terms of a series of undetermined constants A, B, C, etc., thus

$$f = A\frac{l}{a} + B\left(\frac{l}{a}\right)^2 + C\left(\frac{l}{a}\right)^3 , \text{ etc.,}$$

and so long as the departures from Stokes's Law were small as Fig. 4 showed them to be for most of our drops, we could neglect the second-order terms in $\dfrac{l}{a}$ and have therefore

$$v_1 = \frac{2}{9}\frac{ga^2}{\eta}(\sigma - \rho)\left(1 + A\frac{l}{a}\right) \dots\dots\dots\dots (15)$$

Using this corrected form of Stokes's Law to combine with (9) (p. 68), we should obviously get the charge e_n in just the form in which it is given in (13), save that wherever a velocity appears in (13) we should now have to insert in place of this velocity $\dfrac{v}{1 + A\dfrac{l}{a}}$. And since the velocity of the drop appears in the 3/2 power in (13), if we denote now by e the absolute value of the electron and by e_1, as heretofore, the apparent value obtained from the assumption of Stokes's Law, that is, from the use of (13), we obtain at once

$$e = \frac{e_1}{\left(1 + A\dfrac{l}{a}\right)^{\frac{3}{2}}} \dots\dots\dots\dots (16)$$

In this equation e_1 can always be obtained from (13), while l is a known constant, but e, A, and a are all unknown. If a can be found our observations permit at once of the determination of both e and A, as will be shown in detail under Section VI (see p. 103).

However, the possibility of determining e if we know a can be seen in a general way without detailed analysis. For the determination of the radius of the drop is equivalent to finding its weight, since its density is known. That we can find the charge on the drop as soon as we can determine its weight is clear from the simple consideration that the velocity under gravity is proportional to its weight, while the velocity in a given electrical field is proportional to the charge which it carries. Since we measure these two velocities directly, we can obtain either the weight, if we know the charge, or the charge, if we know the weight. (See equation 9, p. 67.)

V.   WEIGHING THE DROPLET

The way which was first used for finding the weight of the drop was simply to solve Stokes's uncorrected equation (11) (p. 89) for a in the case of each drop. Since the curve of Fig. 4 shows that the departures from Stokes's Law are small except for the extremely slow drops, and since a appears in the second power in (11), it is clear that, if we leave out of consideration the very slowest drops, (11) must give us very nearly the correct values of a. We can then find the approximate value of A by the method of the next section, and after it is found we can solve (15) for the correct value of a. This is a method of successive approximations which theoretically yields a and A with any desired degree of precision. As a matter of fact the whole correction term, $A\dfrac{l}{a}$ is a small one, so that it is never necessary to make more than two approximations to obtain a with much more precision than is needed for the exact evaluation of e.

As soon as e was fairly accurately known it became possible, as indicated above, to make a direct weighing of extraordinarily minute bodies with great certainty and with a very high degree of precision. For we have already shown experimentally that the equation

$$\frac{v_1}{v_2} = \frac{mg}{Fe_n - mg} \quad \cdots\cdots\cdots\cdots\cdots (17)$$

is a correct one and it involves no assumption whatever
as to the shape, or size, or material of the particle. If
we solve this equation for the weight mg of the particle
we get

$$mg = Fe_n\frac{v_1}{v_1+v_2}\dots\dots\dots\dots(18)$$

In this equation e_n is known with the same precision as e,
for we have learned how to count n. It will presently be
shown that e is probably now known with an accuracy
of one part in a thousand, hence mg can now be determined with the same accuracy for any body which can
be charged up with a counted number n of electrons and
then pulled up against gravity by a known electrical
field, or, if preferred, simply balanced against gravity
after the manner used in the water-drop experiment and
also in part of the oil-drop work.[1] *This device is simply
an electrical balance in place of a mechanical one, and it
will weigh accurately and easily to one ten-billionth of a
milligram.*

Fifty years ago it was considered the triumph of
the instrument-maker's art that a balance had been
made so sensitive that one could weigh a piece of
paper, then write his name with a hard pencil on the
paper and determine the difference between the new
weight and the old—that is, the weight of the name.
This meant determining a weight as small as one-tenth
or possibly one-hundredth of a milligram (a milligram is
about 1/30,000 of an ounce). Some five years ago
Ramsay and Spencer, in London, by constructing a
balance entirely out of very fine quartz fibers and placing
it in a vacuum, succeeded in weighing objects as small

[1] See *Phil. Mag.*, XIX (1860), 216; XXI (1862), 757.

as one-millionth of a milligram, that is, they pushed the
limit of the weighable down about ten thousand times.
The work which we are now considering pushed it down
at least ten thousand times farther and made it possible
to weigh accurately bodies so small as not to be visible
at all to the naked eye. For it is only necessary to
float such a body in the air, render it visible by reflected
light in an ultra-microscope arrangement of the sort we
were using, charge it electrically by the capture of ions,
count the number of electrons in its charge by the method
described, and then vary the potential applied to the
plates or the charge on the body until its weight is just
balanced by the upward pull of the field. The weight
of the body is then exactly equal to the product of the
known charge by the strength of the electric field. We
made all of our weighings of our drops and the determination of their radii in this way as soon as we had
located e with a sufficient degree of precision to warrant
it.[1]   Indeed, even before e is very accurately known it
is possible to use such a balance for a fairly accurate
evaluation of the radius of a spherical drop. For when
we replace m in (18) by $4/3ma^3(\sigma-\rho)$ and solve for a
we obtain

$$a=\sqrt[3]{\frac{3Fe_n}{4\pi g(\sigma-\rho)}\frac{v_1}{v_1+v_2}}\ \ldots\ldots\ldots\ldots(19)$$

The substitution in this equation of an approximately
correct value of e yields a with an error but one-third as
great as that contained in the assumed value of e, for a
is seen from this equation to vary as the cube root of e.
This is the method which, in view of the accurate evalua-

[1] *Phys. Rev.*, II (1913), 117. This paper was read before the
Deutsche physikalische Gesellschaft in Berlin in June, 1912.

tion of e, it is now desirable to use for the determination of the weight or dimensions of any minute body, for the method is quite independent of the nature of the body or of the medium in which it is immersed. Indeed, it constitutes as direct and certain a weighing of the body as though it were weighed on a mechanical balance.

VI. THE EVALUATION OF e AND A

With e_1 and $\dfrac{l}{a}$ known, we can easily determine e and A from the equation

$$e = \frac{e_1}{\left(1 + A\dfrac{l}{a}\right)^{\frac{3}{2}}}$$

for if we write this equation in the form

$$e^{\frac{2}{3}}\left(1 + A\frac{l}{a}\right) = e_1^{\frac{2}{3}} \quad \ldots\ldots\ldots\ldots\ldots (20)$$

and then plot the observed values of e_1 as ordinates and the corresponding values of $\dfrac{l}{a}$ as abscissae we should get a straight line, provided our corrected form of Stokes's Law (15) (p. 99) is adequate for the correct representation of the phenomena of fall of the droplets within the range of values of $\dfrac{l}{a}$ in which the experiments lie. If no such linear relation is found, then an equation of the form of (15) is not adequate for the description of the phenomena within this range. As a matter of fact, a linear relation was found to exist for a much wider range of values of $\dfrac{l}{a}$ than was anticipated would be the case. The

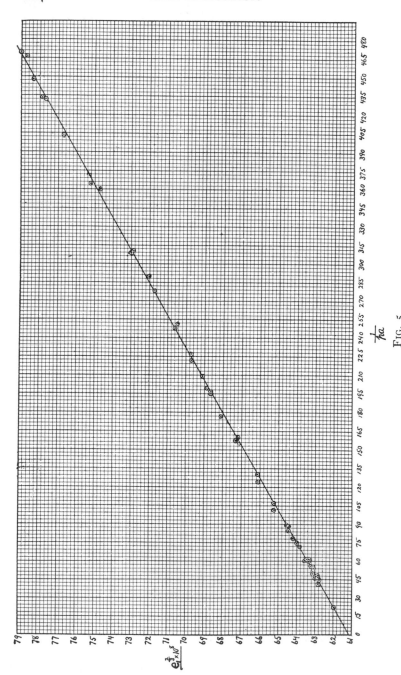

FIG. 5

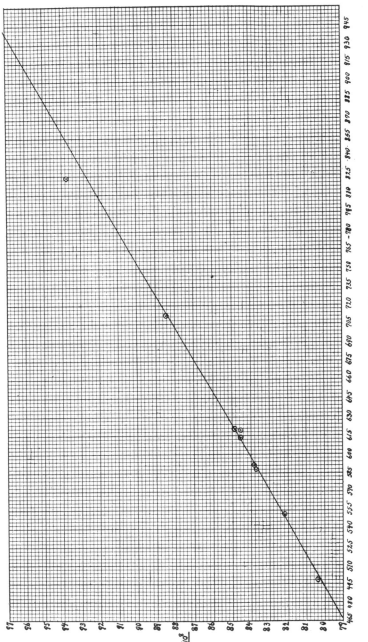

Fig. 6

intercept of this line on the axis of ordinates, that is, the value of e_1 when $\dfrac{l}{a} = 0$ is seen from (20) to be $e^{\frac{2}{3}}$, and we have but to raise this to the 3/2 power to obtain the absolute value of e. Again, A is seen from (20) to be merely the slope of this line divided by the intercept on the $e_1^{\frac{2}{3}}$ axis.

In order to carry this work out experimentally it is necessary to vary $\dfrac{l}{a}$ and find the corresponding values of e_1. This can be done in two ways. First, we may hold the pressure constant and choose smaller and smaller drops with which to work, or we may work with drops of much the same size but vary the pressure of the gas in which our drops are suspended, for the mean free path l is evidently inversely proportional to the pressure.

Both procedures were adopted, and it was found that a given value of e_1 always corresponded to a given value of $\dfrac{l}{a}$, no matter whether l was kept constant and a reduced to, say, one-tenth of its first value, or a kept about the same and l multiplied tenfold. The result of one somewhat elaborate series of observations which was first presented before the Deutsche physikalische Gesellschaft in June, 1912, and again before the British Association at Dundee in September, 1912,[1] is shown in Figs. 5 and 6. The numerical data from which these curves are plotted are given fairly fully in Table IX. It will be seen that this series of observations embraces a study of 58 drops. These drops represent all of those studied for 60 consecutive days, no single one being

[1] *Phys. Rev.*, II (1913), 136.

TABLE IX

No.	Tem. °C.	P.D. (Volts)	t_g (Sec.)	v_1 cm./sec.	$(v_1+v_2)_0$	n	$a \times 10^5$ cm.	p (cm. Hg)	$\frac{1}{pa}$	$\frac{l}{a}$	$e_1 \times 10^{10}$	$e_1^{\frac{2}{3}} \times 10^8$	$e^{\frac{2}{3}} \times 10^8$
1	23.00	5,168	4.363	.2357	.003293	77–102	58.56	75.80	22.52	.01615	4.877	61.90	61.14
2	22.80	5,120	8.492	.1202	.004070	27–36	32.64	75.00	40.85	.02933	4.881	62.82	61.26
3	23.46	5,100	9.905	.1032	.004996	22–27	30.29	73.71	44.88	.03212	4.971	62.75	61.04
4	22.85	5,163	10.758	.09489	.005211	18–36	28.94	75.20	45.92	.03288	5.001	63.00	61.24
5	23.08	5,072	10.663	.09575	.005176	20–30	29.14	73.25	46.85	.03353	4.982	62.82	61.13
6	22.82	5,085	11.880	.08584	.005497	17–24	27.54	75.62	48.11	.03437	4.991	62.93	61.09
7	23.79	5,090	11.950	.08368	.005480	19–22	27.57	75.10	48.44	.03466	4.981	62.82	61.07
8	23.50	5,158	12.540	.08141	.005623	16–19	26.90	75.30	49.52	.03544	5.016	63.12	61.23
9	22.87	5,139	13.562	.07375	.005962	19–23	25.71	75.00	51.73	.03702	5.016	63.13	61.15
10	23.25	5,015	15.380	.06641	.006174	13–22	24.31	76.27	54.09	.03871	5.010	63.08	61.02
11	23.01	5,066	15.193	.06720	.006087	11–14	24.36	73.90	55.52	.03973	5.015	63.12	61.00
12	23.00	5,080	15.985	.06375	.006416	12–16	23.70	75.14	56.15	.04018	5.028	63.24	61.10
13	23.00	5,024	15.695	.05463	.006873	9–15	21.91	76.06	59.94	.04290	5.043	63.35	61.06
14	23.09	5,077	18.730	.05451	.006988	8–16	21.85	75.28	60.78	.04348	5.064	63.53	61.21
15	23.85	5,078	18.959	.05274	.006966	8–18	21.78	75.24	61.03	.04368	5.040	63.33	61.07
16	23.70	5,103	18.738	.05449	.007005	9–18	21.87	74.68	61.33	.04390	5.065	63.54	61.21
17	23.06	5,060	18.415	.05545	.006890	9–18	22.06	73.47	61.69	.04411	5.054	63.43	61.00
18	22.83	5,093	26.130	.03907	.008339	5–13	18.45	75.54	71.74	.05134	5.098	63.82	61.08
19	22.95	5,033	28.568	.03570	.008651	5–9	17.63	75.87	74.77	.05350	5.120	64.00	61.12
20	23.00	5,094	9.480	.10772	.005958	23–32	30.54	41.77	78.40	.05612	5.145	64.22	61.23
21	23.08	5,018	35.253	.02893	.006660	4–11	15.80	74.32	85.08	.06089	5.166	64.36	61.11
22	23.22	5,005	40.542	.02515	.010332	3–9	14.75	76.42	88.70	.06350	5.168	64.40	61.01
23	22.76	5,098	39.900	.02554	.010510	3–6	14.85	75.40	89.35	.06395	5.190	64.59	61.18
24	23.16	5,050	12.466	.08189	.005896	15–28	26.44	37.19	101.8	.07283	5.269	65.24	61.35
25	22.08	5,066	15.157	.06737	.006399	12–17	24.01	38.95	107.2	.07660	5.278	65.28	61.20
26	23.08	4,572	7.875	.12980	.004324	33–40	33.07	24.33	124.4	.08892	5.379	66.06	61.31
27	23.18	4,570	9.408	.1085	.004730	23–29	30.23	25.37	130.4	.09330	5.381	66.16	61.18
28	23.00	5,145	84.270	.1211	.01595	1–4	4.69	75.83	130.3	.09322	5.379	66.14	61.16
29	22.99	5,073	23.223	.04393	.008488	6–12	19.06	33.47	156.8	.1117	5.529	67.36	61.37

Mean = 61.120

Mean = 61.138

TABLE IX—Continued

Mean = 61.138

No.	Tem. °C.	P.D. (Volts)	t_g (Sec.)	v_1 cm./sec.	$(v_1+v_2)_0$	n	$a \times 10^5$ cm.	p (cm. Hg)	$\frac{1}{pa}$	$\frac{l}{a}$	$e_1 \times 10^{10}$	$e_1^{\frac{2}{3}} \times 10^8$	$e^{\frac{2}{3}} \times 10^8$
30	23.19	5,090	26.830	.03801	.009111	5–10	17.77	35.18	160.2	.1147	5.597	67.18	61.06
31	22.89	5,098	38.479	.02649	.011180	3–5	14.71	36.51	176.5	.1263	5.621	68.12	61.38
32	23.06	5,070	14.060	.07246	.006762	12–17	24.29	21.12	195.0	.1394	5.692	68.67	61.22
33	23.07	4,582	18.229	.05001	.006981	10–13	21.33	23.86	196.6	.1405	5.687	68.64	61.13
34	23.06	5,061	38.010	.02682	.011205	3–8	14.72	34.01	199.8	.1429	5.714	68.84	61.20
35	23.00	4,246	9.265	.11032	.004653	27–34	29.84	16.00	209.5	.1499	5.739	69.07	61.07
36	22.91	4,236	9.879	.10340	.004863	24–28	28.74	15.67	222.0	.1589	5.820	69.71	61.23
37	23.06	4,236	12.040	.08496	.005302	18–24	26.27	15.75	227.5	.1625	5.821	69.72	61.03
38	22.94	2,556	10.657	.09581	.003109	32–43	27.49	14.70	247.5	.1771	5.935	70.61	61.16
39	23.00	5,054	19.950	.05115	.008370	8–15	20.12	19.73	251.8	.1802	5.910	70.41	61.09
40	23.09	5,058	21.130	.04830	.008865	7–9	18.38	18.54	278.3	.1993	6.076	71.72	60.97
41	23.05	5,062	24.008	.04254	.009496	6–8	18.16	19.01	289.6	.2073	6.110	72.03	60.95
42	22.94	4,238	18.347	.05564	.007110	9–17	20.60	15.72	308.8	.2210	6.224	73.04	61.24
43	23.18	3,909	13.909	.07340	.004729	16–28	23.70	13.55	311.0	.2227	6.214	72.83	60.95
44	23.04	4,231	29.114	.03503	.009273	5–9	16.16	17.17	360.6	.2579	6.466	74.77	61.00
45	22.97	3,317	29.776	.03425	.007430	5–12	15.90	17.27	364.2	.2606	6.537	75.30	61.39
46	22.81	3,401	25.909	.03937	.007311	6–19	16.00	14.68	403.3	.2886	6.719	76.71	61.30
47	22.83	2,550	12.891	.07921	.003935	18–42	23.80	9.70	432.8	.3097	6.841	77.66	61.13
48	22.80	2,559	32.326	.03150	.006286	7–14	15.01	15.35	433.8	.3104	6.866	77.85	61.28
49	23.02	3,370	14.983	.06815	.011353	8–9	22.00	10.10	448.8	.3221	6.936	78.36	61.22
50	23.45	2,535	11.659	.08757	.003783	25–30	24.88	8.60	466.7	.3340	6.978	78.67	60.85
51	23.48	2,539	10.924	.09346	.003615	27–34	25.69	8.26	470.7	.3368	7.024	79.02	61.04
52	22.98	2,451	50.400	.02021	.010775	2–6	11.83	16.95	498.5	.3568	7.210	80.40	61.36
53	23.16	2,451	33.379	.03055	.006023	5–10	14.39	12.61	551.3	.3945	7.470	82.19	61.13
54	23.46	2,533	19.227	.05347	.005314	11–17	18.87	9.03	587.8	.4112	7.661	83.73	61.18
55	22.90	2,546	24.254	.04206	.006041	9–18	16.72	10.11	591.5	.4233	7.672	83.82	61.22
56	23.21	1,700	5.058	.20256	.001861	117–136	36.53	4.46	614.2	.4396	7.777	84.57	61.11
57	23.12	2,321	15.473	.06599	.004360	18–24	20.85	7.74	619.7	.4435	7.774	84.54	60.87
58	23.03	3,388.5	24.33	.04196	.008183	6–10	16.62	9.070	620.2	.4439	7.810	84.83	61.14

Mean of all numbers in last column = 61.138
Mean of first 23 numbers = 61.120

omitted. They represent a thirty-fold variation in $\dfrac{l}{a}$ (from .016, drop No. 1, to .444, drop No. 58), a seventeen-fold variation in the pressure p (from 4.46 cm., drop No. 56, to 76.27 cm., drop No. 10), a twelvefold variation in a (from 4.69×10^{-5} cm., drop No. 28, to 58.56×10^{-5} cm., drop No. 1), and a variation in the

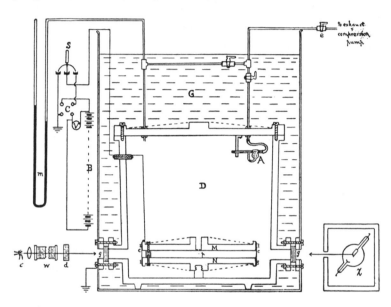

FIG. 7

number of free electrons carried by the drop from 1 on drop No. 28 to 136 on drop No. 56.

The experimental arrangements are shown in Fig. 7. The brass vessel D was built for work at all pressures up to 15 atmospheres, but since the present observations have to do only with pressures from 76 cm. down, these were measured with a very carefully made mercury manometer m, which at atmospheric pressure gave precisely the same reading as a standard barometer. Complete stagnancy of the air between the condenser plates M and N was attained, first, by absorbing all of the heat rays from the arc A by means of a water cell w, 80 cm. long, and a cupric chloride cell d, and, secondly, by immersing the whole vessel D in a constant temperature bath G of gas-engine oil (40 liters), which permitted, in general, fluctuations of not more than .02° C. during an observation. This constant-temperature bath was found essential if such consistency of measurement as is shown here was to be obtained. A long search for causes of slight irregularity revealed nothing so important as this, and after the bath was installed all of the irregularities vanished. The atomizer A was blown by means of a puff of carefully dried and dust-free air introduced through cock e. The air about the drop p was ionized when desired, or electrons discharged directly from the drop, by means of Röntgen rays from X, which readily passed through the glass window g. To the three windows g (two only are shown) in the brass vessel D correspond, of course, three windows in the ebonite strip c, which encircles the condenser plates M and N. Through the third of these windows, set at an angle of about 28° from the line Xpa and in the same horizontal plane, the oil drop is observed through a short-focus telescope having a scale in the eyepiece to make possible the exact measurement of the speeds of the droplet-star.

In plotting the actual observations I have used the reciprocal of the pressure $\frac{1}{p}$ in place of l, for the reason that l is a theoretical quantity which is necessarily proportional to $\frac{1}{p}$, while p is the quantity actually measured.

This amounts to writing the correction-term to Stokes's Law in the form $\left(1+\dfrac{b}{pa}\right)$ instead of in the form $1+A\dfrac{l}{a}$ and considering b the undetermined constant which is to be evaluated, as was A before, by dividing the slope of our line by its y-intercept.

Nevertheless, in view of the greater ease of visualization of $\dfrac{l}{a}$ all the values of this quantity corresponding to successive values of $\dfrac{1}{pa}$ are given in Table IX. Fig. 5 shows the graph obtained by plotting the values of e_1 against $\dfrac{1}{pa}$ for the first 51 drops of Table IX, and Fig. 6 shows the extension of this graph to twice as large values of $\dfrac{1}{pa}$ and e_1. It will be seen that there is not the slightest indication of a departure from a linear relation between e_1 and $\dfrac{1}{pa}$ up to the value $\dfrac{1}{pa}=620.2$, which corresponds to a value of $\dfrac{l}{a}$ of .4439 (see drop No. 58, Table IX). Furthermore, the scale used in the plotting is such that a point which is one division above or below the line in Fig. 5 represents in the mean an error of 2 in 700. *It will be seen from Figs. 5 and 6 that there is but one drop in the 58 whose departure from the line amounts to as much as 0.5 per cent. It is to be remarked, too, that this is not a selected group of drops, but represents all of the drops experimented upon during 60 consecutive days,* during which time the apparatus was taken down several times and set up anew. It is certain, then, that an equation of the form (15) holds very accurately up to

$\frac{l}{a} = .4$. The last drop of Fig. 6 seems to indicate the beginning of a departure from this linear relationship. Since such departure has no bearing upon the evaluation of e, discussion of it will not be entered into here, although it is a matter of great interest for the molecular theory.

Attention may also be called to the completeness of the answers furnished by Figs. 5 and 6 to the question raised in chap. iv as to a possible dependence of the drag which the medium exerts on the drop upon the amount of the latter's charge; also, as to a possible variation of the density of the drop with its radius. Thus drops Nos. 27 and 28 have practically identical values of $\frac{1}{pa}$, but while No. 28 carries, during part of the time, but 1 unit of charge (see Table IX), drop No. 27 carries 29 times as much and it has about 7 times as large a diameter. Now, if the small drop were denser than the large one, or if the drag of the medium upon the heavily charged drop were greater than its drag upon the one lightly charged, then for both these reasons drop No. 27 would move more slowly relatively to drop No. 28 than would otherwise be the case, and hence e_1 for drop No. 27 would fall below e_1 for drop No. 28. Instead of this the two e_1 fall so nearly together that it is impossible to represent them on the present scale by two separate dots. Drops Nos. 52 and 56 furnish an even more striking confirmation of the same conclusion, for both drops have about the same value for $\frac{l}{a}$ and both are exactly on the line, though drop No. 56 carries at one time 68 times as heavy a charge as drop No. 52 and has three times as large a radius. In general, the fact that

Figs. 5 and 6 show no tendency whatever on the part of either the very small or the very large drops to fall above or below the line is experimental proof of the joint correctness of the assumptions of constancy of drop-density and independence of drag of the medium on the charge on the drop.

The values of $e_{.}^{\frac{2}{3}}$ and b obtained graphically from the *y*-intercept and the slope in Fig. 5 are $e^{\frac{2}{3}} = 61.13 \times 10^{-8}$ and $b = .000625$, p being measured, for the purposes of Fig. 5 and of this computation in centimeters of Hg at 23° C. and a being measured in centimeters. The value of A in equations 15 and 16 (p. 99) corresponding to this value of b is .874.

Instead, however, of taking the result of this graphical evaluation of e, it is more accurate to reduce each of the observations on e_1 to e by means of the foregoing value of b and the equation

$$e^{\frac{2}{3}}\left(1 + \frac{b}{pa}\right) = e_1^{\frac{2}{3}}$$

The results of this reduction are contained in the last column of Table IX. These results illustrate very clearly the sort of consistency obtained in these observations. *The largest departure from the mean value found anywhere in the table amounts to 0.5 per cent and "the probable error" of the final mean value computed in the usual way is 16 in 61,000.*

Instead, however, of using this final mean value as the most reliable evaluation of e, it was thought preferable to make a considerable number of observations at atmospheric pressure on drops small enough to make t_g determinable with great accuracy and yet large enough so that the whole correction term to Stokes's Law amounted to but a small percentage, since in this case, even though there might be a considerable error in the correction-term constant b, such error would influence the final value of e by an inappreciable amount. The first 23 drops of Table IX represent such observations. It will be seen that they show slightly greater consistency than do the remaining drops in the table and that the correction-term reductions for these drops all lie between 1.3 per cent (drop No. 1) and 5.6 per cent (drop No. 23), so that even though b were in error by as much as 3 per cent (its error is actually not more than 1.5 per cent), e would be influenced by that fact to the extent of but 0.1 per cent. The mean value of $e^{\frac{2}{3}}$ obtained from the first 23 drops is 61.12×10^{-8}, a number which differs by 1 part in 3,400 from the mean obtained from all the drops.

When correction is made for the fact that the numbers in Table IX were obtained on the basis of the assumption $\eta = .0001825$, instead of $\eta = .0001824$ (see Section II), which was the value of η_{23} chosen in 1913 when this work was first published, the final mean value of e obtained from the first 23 drops is 61.085×10^{-8}. This corresponds to

$$e = 4.774 \times 10^{-10} \text{ electrostatic units.}$$

I have already indicated that as soon as e is known it becomes possible to find with the same precision which has been attained in its determination the exact number of molecules in a given weight of any substance, the absolute weight of any atom or molecule, the average kinetic energy of agitation of an atom or molecule at any temperature, and a considerable number of other important molecular and radioactive constants. In addition, it has recently been found that practically all of the important radiation constants like the wave-lengths of X-rays, Planck's *h*, the Stefan-Boltzmann constant σ, the Wien constant c_2, etc., depend for their most reliable evaluation upon the value of *e*. In a word, *e* is increasingly coming to be regarded, *not only as the most fundamental of physical or chemical constants, but also the one of most supreme importance for the solution of the numerical problems of modern physics.* It seemed worth while, therefore, to drive the method herewith developed for its determination to the limit of its possible precision. Accordingly, I built two years ago a new condenser having surfaces which were polished optically and made flat to within two wave-lengths of sodium light. These were 22 cm. in diameter and were separated by 3 pieces of echelon plates, 14.9174 mm. thick, and all having optically perfect plane-parallel surfaces. The dimensions of the condenser, therefore, no longer introduced an uncertainty of more than about 1 part in 10,000. The volts were determined after each reading in terms of a Weston standard cell and are uncertain by no more than 1 part in 3,000. The times were obtained from an exceptionally fine printing chronograph built by William Gaertner & Co. It is controlled by a standard astronomical clock and prints directly the time to hundredths of a second. All the other elements of the problem were looked to with a care which was the outgrowth of five years of experience with measurements of this kind. The present form of the apparatus is shown in diagram in Fig. 8, and in Fig. 9 is shown a photograph taken before the enclosing oil tank had been added. This work

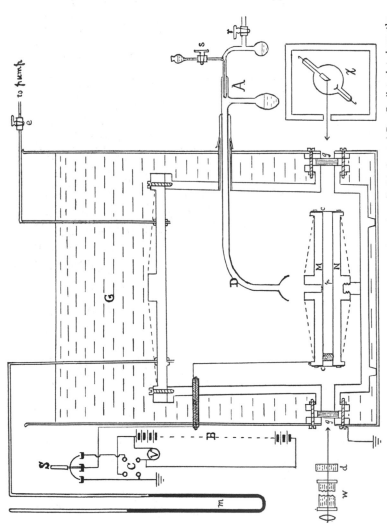

FIG. 8.—A, atomizer through which the oil spray is blown into the cylindrical vessel D. G, oil tank to keep the temperature constant. M and N, circular brass plates, electrical field produced by throwing on 10,000-volt battery B. Light from arc lamp a after heat rays are removed by passage through w and d, enters chamber through glass window g and illuminates droplet p between plates M and N through the pinhole in M. Additional ions are produced about p by X-rays from the bulb X.

FIG. 9

was concluded in August, 1916, and occupied the better part of two years of time. The final table of results and the corresponding graph are given in Table X and in Fig. 10. The final value of $e^{\frac{2}{3}}$ computed on the basis $\eta_{23} = .0001824$ is seen to be now 61.126×10^{-8} instead of 61.085, or $.07$ per cent higher than the value found in 1913. But Dr. Harrington's new value of η_{23}, namely, $.00018226$, is more reliable than the old value and is lower than it by $.07$ per cent. Since η appears in the first power in $e^{\frac{2}{3}}$, it will be seen that the new value[1] of e, determined with new apparatus and with a completely new determination of all the factors involved, comes out to the fourth place exactly the same as the value published in 1913, namely,

$$e = 4.774 \times 10^{-10} \text{ absolute electrostatic units.}$$

The corresponding values of b and A are now $.000617$ and $.863$, respectively.

Since the value of the Faraday constant has now been fixed virtually by international agreement[2] at 9,650 absolute electromagnetic units, and since this is the number N of molecules in a gram molecule times the elementary electrical charge, we have

$$N \times 4.774 \times 10^{-10} = 9,650 \times 2.9990 \times 10^{-10},$$
$$N = 6.062 \times 10^{23}$$

Although the probable error in this number computed by the method of least squares from Table X is but one part in 4,000, it would be erroneous to infer that e and N are now known with that degree of precision, for there are

---

[1] For full details see Millikan, *Phil. Mag.*, June, 1917.
[2] At. wt. of Ag. $= 107.88$; electrochem. eq't. of Ag. $= 0.01188$.

four constant factors entering into all of the results in Table X and introducing uncertainties as follows: The coefficient of viscosity η which appears in the $3/2$ power introduces into e and N a maximum possible uncertainty of less than 0.1 per cent, say 0.07 per cent. The cross-hair distance which is uniformly duplicatable to one part in two thousand appears in the $3/2$ power and introduces an uncertainty of no more than 0.07 per cent. All the other factors, such as the volts and the distance between the condenser plates, introduce errors which are negligible in comparison. The uncertainty in e and N is then that due to two factors, each of which introduces a maximum possible uncertainty of about 0.07 per cent. Following the usual procedure, we may estimate the uncertainty in e and N as the square root of the sum of the squares of these two uncertainties, that is, as about one part in 1000. We have then:

$$e = 4.774 \pm .005 \times 10^{-10}$$
$$N = 6.062 \pm .006 \times 10^{23}$$

Perhaps these numbers have little significance to the general reader who is familiar with no electrical units save those in which his monthly light bills are rendered. If these latter seem excessive, it may be cheering to reflect that the number of electrons contained in the quantity of electricity which courses every second through a common sixteen-candle-power electric-lamp filament, and for which we pay $1/100,000$ of 1 cent, is so large that if all the two and one-half million inhabitants of Chicago were to begin to count out these electrons and were to keep on counting them out each at the rate of two a second, and if no one of them were ever to stop to eat, sleep, or die,

TABLE X

No.	Tem. ° C.	P.D. (Volts)	t_g (Sec.)	$v_{1,1}$ cm./Sec.)	n	a×10⁵ cm.	p (cm. Hg)	$\frac{1}{pa}$	$\frac{l}{a}$	$e^{\frac{2}{3}}\times 10^8$	$e^{\frac{2}{3}}\times 10^8$
1	23.07	6,650	16.50	.06194	7–13	23.40	74.49	57.45	.04111	63.21	61.03
2	23.00	6,100	16.76	.06099	8–11	23.22	75.00	57.5	.04115	63.204	61.03
3	23.05	5,368	19.73	.05180	7–15	21.34	74.49	63.0	.04509	63.54	61.16
4	23.08	4,132	37.82	.02703	4–6	15.33	75.37	86.7	.06205	64.27	60.97
5	23.06	4,661	40.09	.02521	3–6	14.84	75.00	90.6	.06484	64.63	61.21
6	23.12	4,111	51.53	.01983	3–4	13.05	75.77	101.3	.06502	65.02	61.19
7	23.08	5,299	51.48	.01985	2–5	13.05	74.98	102.4	.07329	65.07	61.20
8	23.01	6,661	56.06	.01823	1–3	12.50	75.40	106.3	.07608	65.13	61.11
9	23.00	6,082	59.14	.01728	1–4	12.17	75.04	109.7	.07850	65.19	61.05
10	23.10	4,077	57.46	.01779	3–8	12.34	75.67	107.3	.07680	65.21	61.16
11	23.13	4,663	16.58	.06165	10–12	22.72	29.26	150.6	.1078	66.70	61.01
12	23.11	4,661	29.18	.03502	5–7	17.08	36.61	160.1	.1146	67.12	61.07
13	22.98	4,687	18.81	.05432	8–10	21.26	30.27	155.6	.1114	67.14	61.26
14	23.12	4,651	47.65	.02145	2–7	13.20	36.80	206.4	.1477	68.90	61.11
15	23.10	4,648	32.72	.03129	4–6	15.92	31.35	200.7	.1437	68.97	61.39
16	23.15	3,393	18.34	.05572	12–16	21.11	20.58	227.8	.1630	60.88	61.27
17	23.12	4,669	46.82	.02294	2–4	13.12	29.10	262.4	.1878	70.85	60.94
18	23.12	4,691	26.62	.03819	5–7	17.32	20.54	281.4	.2014	71.60	60.98
19	23.14	3,339	14.10	.07249	15–19	23.00	13.24	321.4	.2297	73.34	61.22
20	23.14	4,682	39.24	.02605	10–13	14.00	20.72	345.4	.2472	74.27	61.20
21	23.14	3,350	18.30	.05585	3–5	20.47	13.62	359.1	.2570	74.54	60.97
22	23.00	3,370	43.88	.02329	3–6	13.17	20.47	371.5	.2659	75.00	60.97
23	23.13	3,381	46.90	.02179	3–6	12.69	20.74	380.6	.2724	75.62	61.24
24	23.09	3,345	19.65	.05201	9–12	19.65	13.12	388.5	.2781	75.92	61.24
25	23.15	3,344	26.76	.03819	6–9	16.57	13.80	438.3	.3137	77.74	61.18

Mean = 61.126.

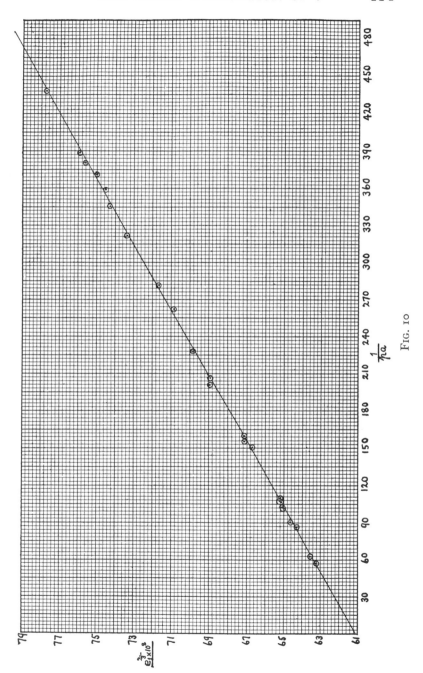

FIG. 10

it would take them just twenty thousand years to finish the task.

Let us now review, with Figs. 5 and 10 before us, the essential elements in the measurement of e. We discover, first, that electricity is atomic, and we measure the electron in terms of a characteristic speed for each droplet. To reduce these speed units to electrical terms, and thus obtain an absolute value of e, it is necessary to know how in a given medium and in a given field the speed due to a given charge on a drop is related to the size of the drop. This we know accurately from Stokes's theory and Arnold's experiments when the holes in the medium, that is, when the values of $\frac{l}{a}$ are negligibly small, but when $\frac{l}{a}$ is large we know nothing about it. *Consequently there is but one possible way to evaluate e, namely, to find experimentally how the apparent value of e, namely, e_1 varies with $\frac{l}{a}$ or $\frac{1}{pa}$, and from the graph of this relation to find what value e_1 approaches as $\frac{l}{a}$ or $\frac{1}{pa}$ approaches zero.* So as to get a linear relation we find by analysis that we must plot $e_1^{\frac{2}{3}}$ instead of e_1 against $\frac{l}{a}$ or $\frac{1}{pa}$. We then get e from the intercept of an experimentally determined straight line on the y-axis of our diagram. This whole procedure amounts simply to reducing our drop-velocities to what they would be if the pressure were so large or $\frac{1}{pa}$ so small that the holes in the medium were all closed up. *For this case and for this case alone we know both from Stokes's and Arnold's work exactly the law of motion of the droplet.*

CHAPTER VI

THE MECHANISM OF IONIZATION OF GASES BY X-RAYS AND RADIUM RAYS

I. EARLY EVIDENCE

Up to the year 1908 the only experiments which threw any light whatever upon the question as to what the act of ionization of a gas consists in were those performed by Townsend[1] in 1900. He had concluded from the theory given on p. 34 and from his measurements on the diffusion coefficients and the mobilities of gaseous ions that both positive and negative ions in gases carry unit charges. This conclusion was drawn from the fact that the value of ne in the equation $ne = \dfrac{v_0 P}{D}$ came out about 1.23×10^{10} electrostatic units, as it does in the electrolysis of hydrogen.

In 1908, however, Townsend[2] devised a method of measuring directly the ratio $\dfrac{v_0}{D}$ and revised his original conclusions. His method consisted essentially in driving ions by means of an electric field from the region between two plates A and B (Fig. 11), where they had been produced by the direct action of X-rays, through the gauez in B, and observing what fraction of these ions was driven by a field established between the plates B and C to the central disk D and what fraction drifted by virtue of diffusion to the guard-ring C.

[1] *Phil. Trans.*, CXCIII (1900), 129.
[2] *Proc. Roy. Soc.*, LXXX (1908), 207.

By this method Townsend found that ne for the negative ions was accurately 1.23×10^{10}, but for the positive ions it was 2.41×10^{10}. From these results the conclusion was drawn that in X-ray ionization *all* of the positive ions are bivalent, i.e., presumably, that the act of ionization by X-rays consists in the detachment from a neutral molecule of two elementary electrical charges.

Townsend accounted for the fact that his early experiments had not shown this high value of ne for the positive ions by the assumption that by the time the

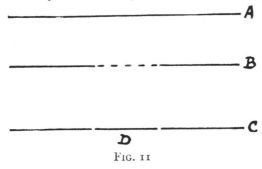

Fig. 11

doubly charged positive ions in these experiments had reached the tubes in which D was measured, most of them had become singly charged through drawing to themselves the singly charged negative ions with which they were mixed. This hypothesis found some justification in the fact that in the early experiments the mean value of ne for the positive ions had indeed come out some 15 or 20 per cent higher than 1.23×10^{10}—a discrepancy which had at first been regarded as attributable to experimental errors, and which in fact might well be attributed to such errors in view of the discordance between the observations on different gases.

Franck and Westphal,[1] however, in 1909 redetermined ne by a slight modification of Townsend's original method, measuring both v_0 and D independently, and not only found, when the positive and negative ions are separated by means of an electric field so as to render impossible such recombination as Townsend suggested, that D was of exactly the same value as when they were not so separated, but also that ne for the positive ions produced by X-rays was but 1.4×10^{10} instead of 2.41×10^{10}. Since this was in fair agreement with Townsend's original mean, the authors concluded that only a small fraction— about 9 per cent—of the positive ions formed by X-rays are doubles, or other multiples, and the rest singles. In their experiments on the ionization produced by a-rays, β-rays, and γ-rays, they found no evidence for the existence of doubly charged ions.

In summarizing, then, the work of these observers it could only be said that, although both Townsend and Franck and Westphal drew the conclusion that doubly charged ions exist in gases ionized by X-rays, there were such contradictions and uncertainties in their work as to leave the question unsettled. In gases ionized by other agencies than X-rays no one had yet found any evidence for the existence of ions carrying more than a single charge.

II. OIL-DROP EXPERIMENTS ON VALENCY IN GASEOUS IONIZATION

The oil-drop method is capable of furnishing a direct and unmistakable answer to the question as to whether the act of ionization of a gas by X-rays or other agencies

[1] *Verh. deutsch. phys. Ges.*, March 5, 1909.

consists in the detachment of one, of several, or of many electrons from a single neutral molecule. For it makes it possible to catch the residue of such a molecule practically at the instant at which it is ionized and to count directly the number of charges carried by that residue. The initial evidence obtained from this method seemed to favor the view that the act of ionization may consist in the detachment of quite a number of electrons from a single molecule, for it was not infrequently observed that a balanced oil drop would remain for several seconds unchanged in charge while X-rays were passing between the plates, and would then suddenly assume a speed which corresponded to a change of quite a number of electrons in its charge.

It was of course recognized from the first, however, that it is very difficult to distinguish between the practically simultaneous advent upon a drop of two or three separate ions and the advent of a doubly or trebly charged ion, but a consideration of the frequency with which ions were being caught in the experiments under consideration, a change occurring only once in, say, 10 seconds, seemed at first to render it improbable that the few double, or treble, or quadruple catches observed when the field was on could represent the simultaneous advent of separate ions. It was obvious, however, that the question could be conclusively settled by working with smaller and smaller drops. For the proportion of double or treble to single catches made in a field of strength between 1,000 and 6,000 volts per centimeter should be independent of the size of the drops if the doubles are due to the advent of doubly charged ions, while this proportion should decrease with the square of the radius of the drop if the doubles are due to the simultaneous capture of separate ions.

Accordingly, Mr. Harvey Fletcher and the author,[1] suspended, by the method detailed in the preceding chapter, a very small positively charged drop in the upper part of the field between M and N (Fig. 12), adjusting either the charge upon the drop or the field strength until the drop was nearly balanced. We then produced beneath the drop a sheet of X-ray ionization. With the arrangement shown in the figure, in which M

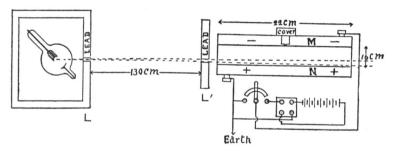

FIG. 12

and N are the plates of the condenser previously described, and L and L' are thick lead screens, the positive ions are thrown practically at the instant of formation to the upper plate. When one of them strikes the drop it increases the positive charge upon it, and the amount of the charge added by the ion to the drop can be computed from the observed change in the speed of the drop.

For the sake of convenience in the measurement of successive speeds a scale containing 70 equal divisions was placed in the eyepiece of the observing cathetometer telescope, which in these experiments produced a

[1] *Phil. Mag.*, XXIII (1911), 753.

magnification of about 15 diameters.   The method of procedure was, in general, first, to get the drop nearly
balanced by shaking off its initial charge by holding a
little radium near the observing chamber, then, with a
switch, to throw on the X-rays until a sudden start in
the drop revealed the fact that an ion had been caught,
then to throw off the rays and take the time required
for it to move over 10 divisions, then to throw on the
rays until another sudden quickening in speed indicated
the capture of another ion, then to measure this speed
and to proceed in this way without throwing off the field
at all until the drop got too close to the upper plate, when
the rays were thrown off and the drop allowed to fall
under gravity to the desired distance from the upper
plate.   In order to remove the excess of positive charge
which the drop now had because of its recent captures,
some radium was brought near the chamber and the
field thrown off for a small fraction of a second.   As
explained in preceding chapters, ions are caught by the
drop many times more rapidly when the field is off than
when it is on.   Hence it was in general an easy matter
to bring the positively charged drop back to its balanced
condition, or indeed to any one of the small number of
working speeds which it was capable of having, and then
to repeat the series of catches described above.   In this
way we kept the same drop under observation for hours
at a time, and in one instance we recorded 100 successive
captures of ions by a given drop, and determined in each
case whether the ion captured carried a single or a
multiple charge.

     The process of making this determination is exceed-
ingly simple and very reliable.   For, since electricity is

atomic in structure, there are only, for example, three possible speeds which a drop can have when it carries 1, 2, or 3 elementary charges, and it is a perfectly simple matter to adjust conditions so that these speeds are of such different values that each one can be recognized unfailingly even without a stop-watch measurement. Indeed, the fact that electricity is atomic is in no way more beautifully shown than by the way in which, as reflected in Table XI, these relatively few possible working speeds recur. After all the possible speeds have been located it is only necessary to see whether one of them is ever skipped in the capture of a new ion in order to know whether or not that ion was a double. Table XI represents the results of experiments made with very hard X-rays produced by means of a powerful 12-inch Scheidel coil, a mercury-jet interrupter, and a Scheidel tube whose equivalent spark-length was about 5 inches. No attempt was made in these experiments to make precise determinations of speed, since a high degree of accuracy of measurement was not necessary for the purpose for which the investigation was undertaken. Table XI is a good illustration of the character of the observations. The time of the fall under gravity recorded in the column headed "t_g" varies slightly, both because of observational errors and because of Brownian movements. Under the column headed "t_F" are recorded the various observed values of the times of rise through 10 divisions of the scale in the eyepiece. A star (*) after an observation in this column signifies that the drop was moving with gravity instead of against it. The procedure was in general to start with the drop either altogether neutral (so that it fell when the field was on with the same speed as when the field was off), or having one single positive charge, and then to throw on positive

TABLE XI

Plate Distance 1.6 cm. Distance of Fall .0975 cm. Volts 1,015.
Temperature 23° C. Radius of Drop 000063 cm.

t_g	t_F	No. of Charges on Drop	No. of Charges on Ion Caught	t_g	t_F	No. of Charges on Drop	No. of Charges on Ion Caught
19.0	100.0	1 P		20.0	10.0*	1 N	
	16.0	2 P	1 P		20.0*	0	1 P
	8.0	3 P	1 P		100.0	1 P	1 P
					20.0*	0	1 N
20.0	16.0	2 P			100.0	1 P	1 P
	8.0	3 P	1 P		16.0	2 P	1 P
					8.0	3 P	1 P
	100.0	1 P					
	17.0	2 P	1 P		104.0	1 P	
	8.2	3 P	1 P		15.0	2 P	1 P
	6.0	4 P	1 P		9.0	3 P	1 P
					6.0	4 P	1 P
	7.0*	2 N					
	9.8*	1 N	1 P		6.5*	2 N	
	7.0*	2 N	1 N		10.0*	1 N	1 P
					20.0*	0	1 P
21.0	20.0*	0			100.0	1 P	1 P
	95.0	1 P	1 P		15.5	2 P	1 P
	16.5	2 P	1 P		8.0	3 P	1 P
	8.0	3 P	1 P		6.0	4 P	
	6.0	4 P	1 P				
					100.0	1 P	1 P
	100.0	1 P			16.5	2 P	
	16.0	2 P	1 P				
	8.4	3 P	1 P		20.0*	0	1 P
					100.0	1 P	1 P
20.0	106.0	1 P			16.6	2 P	1 P
	16.0	2 P	1 P		8.8	3 P	1 P
	8.4	3 P	1 P		5.7	4 P	
	10.0*	1 N			100.0	1 P	
	20.0*	0	1 P		20.0*	0	1 N
	100.0	1 P	1 P		10.0*	1 N	1 N
	16.0	2 P	1 P		20.0*	0	1 P
	100.0	1 P	1 P			44 catches, all singles	
	16.0	2 P	1 P				
	8.0	3 P					

charges until its speed came to the 6.0 second value, then to make it neutral again with the aid of radium, and to begin over again.

It will be seen from Table XI that in 4 cases out of 44 we caught negatives, although it would appear from the arrangement shown in Fig. 12 that we could catch only positives. These negatives are doubtless due to secondary rays which radiate in all directions from the air molecules when these are subjected to the primary X-ray radiation.

Toward the end of Table XI is an interesting series of catches. At the beginning of this series, the drop was charged with 2 negatives which produced a speed in the direction of gravity of 6.5 seconds. It caught in succession 6 single positives before the field was thrown off. The corresponding times were 6.5*, 10*, 20*, 100, 15.5, 8.0, 6.0. The mean time during which the X-rays had to be on in order to produce a "catch" was in these experiments about six seconds, though in some instances it was as much as a minute. The majority of the times recorded in column t_F were actually measured with a stop watch as recorded, but since there could be no possibility of mistaking the 100-second speed, it was observed only four or five times. It will be seen from Table XI that out of 44 catches of ions produced by every hard X-ray there is not a single double. As a result of observing from 500 to 1,000 catches in the manner illustrated in Table XI, we came to the conclusion that, although we had entered upon the investigation with the expectation of proving the existence of valency in gaseous ionization, *we had instead obtained direct, unmistakable evidence that the act of ionization of air* *molecules by both primary and secondary X-rays of widely varying degrees of hardness, as well as by β- and γ-rays, uniformly consists, under all the conditions which we were able to investigate, in the detachment from a neutral molecule of one single elementary electrical charge.*

III.   RECENT EVIDENCE AS TO NATURE OF IONIZATION PRODUCED BY ETHER WAVES

Although Townsend and Franck and Westphal dissented from the foregoing conclusion, all the evidence which has appeared since has tended to confirm it.   Thus Salles,[1] using a new method due to Langevin of measuring directly the ratio $\left(\dfrac{v_0}{D}\right)$ of the mobility to the diffusion coefficient, concluded that when the ionization is produced by γ-rays there are no ions bearing multiple charges. Again, the very remarkable photographs (see plate opposite p. 187) taken by C. T. R. Wilson in the Cavendish Laboratory of the tracks made by the passage of X-rays through gases show no indication of a larger number of negatively than of positively charged droplets. Such an excess is to be expected if the act of ionization ever consists in these experiments in the detachment of two or more negative electrons from a neutral molecule. Further, if the initial act of ionization by X-rays ever consists in the ejection of two or more corpuscles from a single atom, there should appear in these Wilson photographs a rosette consisting of a group of zigzag lines starting from a common point.   A glance at the plate opposite p. 189 shows that this is not the case, each zigzag line having its own individual starting-point.

[1] *Le Radium,* X (1913), 113, 119.

There are two other types of experiments which throw light on this question.

When in the droplet experiments the X-rays are allowed to fall directly upon the droplet, we have seen that they detach negative electrons from it, and if the gas is at so low a pressure that there is very little chance of the capture of ions by the droplet, practically all of its changes in charge have this cause. Changes produced under these conditions appear, so far as I have yet been able to discover, to be uniformly unit changes, though I have not yet made a systematic or exhaustive study of this point. Also, when the changes are produced by the incidence on the droplet of ultra-violet light, so far as experiments carried out in the Ryerson Laboratory go, they usually, though not always, have appeared to correspond to the loss of one single electron. The same seems to have been true in the experiments reported by A. Joffé,[1] who has given this subject careful study. Meyer and Gerlach, however,[2] seem very often to observe changes corresponding to the simultaneous loss of several electrons.

It is to be noted, however, that their drops are generally quite heavily charged, carrying from 10 to 30 electrons. Under such conditions the loss of a single electron makes but a minute change in speed, and is therefore likely not only to be unnoticed, but to be almost impossible to detect *until the change has become more pronounced through the loss of several electrons. This question, then, can be studied reliably only when the field is powerful enough to hold the droplet balanced with only one*

---

[1] *Sitzungsber. d. k. Bayerischen Akad. d. Wiss.* (1913), p. 19.

[2] *Ann. d. Phys.*, XLV, 177; XLVII, 227.

or two free electrons upon it. I do not consider, therefore, that the experiments of Meyer and Gerlach contain any evidence that the act of ionization by ultra-violet light detaches more than one electron from a single atom. Nor indeed do they claim that it does, while the evidence accumulated in the Ryerson Laboratory, though not yet complete, points strongly the other way.

Table XII contains one series of observations taken with my apparatus by Mr. P. I. Pierson. The first column gives the volts applied to the plates of the condenser shown in Fig. 7, p. 109. These were made variable so that the drop might always be pulled up with a slow speed even though its positive charge were continually increasing. The second and third columns give the times required to move 1 cm. under gravity and under the field respectively. The fourth column gives the time intervals required for the drop to experience a change in charge under the influence of a constant source of ultra-violet light—a quartz mercury lamp. The fifth column gives the total charge carried by the drop computed from equation (12), p. 89. The sixth column shows the change in charge computed from equation (10), p. 68. This is seen to be as nearly a constant as could be expected in view of Brownian movements and the inexact measurements of volts and times. The mean value of e_1 is seen to be 5.1×10^{-10} which yields with the aid of equation (16), p. 99, after the value of A found for oil drops has been inserted, $e = 4.77 \times 10^{-10}$, which is in better agreement with the result obtained with oil drops than we had any right to expect. In these experiments the light was weak so that the changes come only after an average interval of 29 seconds and it will be seen that *they are all unit changes.* When the light was more intense we sometimes appeared to get double and in one case treble

TABLE XII

MERCURY DROPLET OF RADIUS $a = 8 \times 10^{-5}$ CM. DISCHARGING ELECTRONS UNDER THE INFLUENCE OF ULTRA-VIOLET LIGHT

Volts	Drop No. 1 t_g Sec. Per Cm.	t_F Sec. per Cm.	Time Interval between Discharges in Seconds	$e_n \times 10^{10}$	Change in e	Change in n
2,260.....	11.0	− 1200		49.4		
3,070.....	11.0	+ 32.8		50.5		
			11		4.4	1
1,960.....	11.0	− 194.		54.4		
			12.8			
1,960.....	....	+ 190		60.8	6.4	1
			23			
1,820.....	11.2	+ 220		65.0	4.2	1
			40			
1,690.....	....	+ 230		69.8	4.8	1
			15.2			
1,550.....	....	+ 332		75.1	5.3	1
	Drop No. 2					
3,040.....	10.4	+ 98		43.5		
			5.6			
2,540.....	....	+ 200		49.4	5.9	1
			18.6			
2,230.....	....	+ 300		55.2	5.8	1
			35.0			
2,230.....	....	+ 76		60.7	5.5	1
			42			
1,930.....	....	+ 200		65.0	4.3	1
			54			
1,810.....	....	+ 176		69.6	4.6	1
			70			
1,650.....	....	+ 250		75.2	5.6	1
			45			
1,520.....	....	+ 500		79.4	4.2	1
			9.8			
1,520.....	....	119		85.1	5.5	1
		Mean..	29	Mean..	5.1	

changes, but since these uniformly appear with less and less frequency both as the charge diminishes and as the interval between the changes is made larger, the inference is inevitable that when multiple changes appear frequently, as they do in Meyer and Gerlach's work, it is because some of the changes in speed escape the notice of the observer.

So long, then, as we are considering the ionization of neutral atoms through the absorption of an ether wave of any kind, the evidence at present available indicates that the act always consists in the detachment from the atom of one single negative electron, the energy with which this electron is ejected from the atom depending, as we shall see in chap. x, in a very definite and simple way upon the frequency of the ether wave which ejects it.

IV. IONIZATION BY β-RAYS

When the ionization is due to the passage of β-rays through matter, the evidence of the oil-drop experiments as well as that of C. T. R. Wilson's experiments (see chap. IX) on the photographing of the tracks of the β-rays is that here, too, the act consists in the detachment of one single electron from a single atom. This experimental result is easy to understand in the case of the β-rays, when it is remembered that Wilson's photographs prove directly the fact, long known from other types of evidence, that a β-ray, in general, ionizes but a very minute fraction of the number of atoms through which it shoots before its energy is expended. If, then, its chance, in shooting through an atom, of coming near enough to one of the electronic constituents of that atom to knock it out is only one in one thousand, or one in one million, then its chance of getting near enough to two electronic constituents of the same atom to knock them both out is likely to be negligibly small. The argument here rests, however, on the assumption that the corpuscles within the atom are independent of one another, which is not necessarily the case, so that the matter must be decided after all solely by experiment.

The difference between the act of ionization when produced by a β-ray and when produced by an ether wave seems, then, to consist wholly in the difference in the energy with which the two agencies hurl the electron from its mother atom. Wilson's photographs show that β-rays do not eject electrons from atoms with appreciable speeds, while ether waves may eject them with tremendous energy. Some of Wilson's photographs showing the effect of passing X-rays through air are shown in the most interesting plate opposite p. 189. The original X-rays have ejected electrons with great speeds from a certain few of the atoms of the gas, and it is the tracks of these electrons as they shoot through the atoms of the gas, ionizing here and there as they go, which constitute the wiggly lines shown in the photograph. Most of the ionization, then, which is produced by X-rays is a secondary effect due to the negative electrons, i.e., the β-rays which the X-rays eject. If these β-rays could in turn eject electrons with ionizing speeds, each of the dots in one of these β-ray tracks would be the starting-point of a new wiggly line like the original one. But such is not the case. We may think, then, of the β-rays as simply shaking loose electronic dust from some of the atoms through which they pass while we think of the X-rays as taking hold in some way of the negative electrons within an atom and hurling them out with enormous energy.

V.   IONIZATION BY α-RAYS

But what happens to the electronic constituents of an atom when an α-particle, that is, a helium atom, shoots through it? Some of Bragg's experiments and Wilson's photographs show that the α-particles shoot in straight lines through from 3 to 7 cm. of air before they are brought to rest. We must conclude, then, that an atom has so loose a structure that another atom, *if endowed with enough speed*, can shoot straight through it without doing anything more than, in some instances, to shake off from that atom an electron or two. The tracks shown in Figs. 14 and 15, p. 187, are Wilson's photographs of the tracks of the α-particles of radium. They ionize so many of the atoms through which they pass that the individual droplets of water which form about the ions produced along the path of the ray, and which are the objects really photographed, are not distinguishable as individuals. The sharp changes in the direction of the ray toward the end of the path are convincing evidence that the α-particle actually goes through the atoms instead of pushing them aside as does a bullet. For if one solar system, for example, endowed with a stupendous speed, were to shoot straight through another similar system, but without an actual impact of their central bodies, the deflection from its straight path which the first system experienced might be negligibly small *if its speed were high enough*, and that for the simple reason that the two systems would not be in one another's vicinity long enough to produce a deflecting effect. In technical terms the time integral of the force would be negligibly small. The slower the speed, however, the longer this time, and hence

the greater the deflection. Thus it is only when the
α-particle shown in Fig. 15 has lost most of its velocity—
i.e., it is only toward the end of its path—that the nuclei
of the atoms through which it passes are able to deflect
it from its straight path. If it pushed the molecules
aside as a bullet does, instead of going through them,
the resistance to its motion would be greatest when the
speed is highest. Now, the facts are just the opposite of
this. The α-particle ionizes several times more violently
toward the end of its path than toward the beginning,
and it therefore loses energy more rapidly when it is going
slowly than when it is going rapidly. Further, it is
deflected more readily then, as the photograph shows.
All of this is just as it should be if the α-particle shoots
straight through the molecules in its path instead of
pushing them aside.

These photographs of Wilson's are then the most
convincing evidence that we have that the atom is a sort
of miniature stellar system with constituents which are
unquestionably just as minute with respect to the total
volume occupied by the atom as are the sun and planets
and other constituents of the solar system with respect
to the whole volume inclosed within the confines of this
system. When two molecules of a gas are going as
slowly as they are in the ordinary motion of thermal
agitation, say a mile a second, when their centers come
to within a certain distance—about o. 2 $\mu\mu$ (millionths of
a millimeter)—they repel one another and so the two
systems do not inter-penetrate. This is the case of an
ordinary molecular collision. But endow one of these
molecules with a large enough energy and it will shoot
right through the other, sometimes doubtless without so

much as knocking out a single electron. This is the case of an α-particle shooting through air.

But the question to which we are here seeking an answer is, does the α-particle ever knock more than one electron from a single atom or molecule through which it passes, so as to leave that atom doubly or trebly charged? The oil-drop method used at low pressures has just given a very definite negative answer to this question. *In no gas or vapor which we can find, and many, including mercury compounds, have been tried, does an α-ray ever knock more than one electron from a single atom.*

J. J. Thomson has, however, brought forward evidence[1] that the positive residues of atoms which shoot through discharge tubes in a direction opposite to that of the cathode rays do sometimes detach several electrons from certain kinds of atoms. Indeed, he thinks that he has evidence that the ionization of a mercury atom consists either in the detachment of 1 negative electron or else in the detachment of 8. This evidence, too, seems to me quite convincing, and indeed a slow-moving positive ray may well do more damage to an atom through which it passes than a high-speed α-ray.

VI.   SUMMARY

The results of the studies reviewed in this chapter may be summarized thus:

1. The act of ionization by β-rays seems to consist in the shaking off without any appreciable energy of one single electron from an occasional molecule through

[1] *Rays of Positive Electricity*, 1913, p. 46.

which the β-ray passes.   The faster the β-ray the less frequently does it ionize.

2. The act of ionization by ether waves, i.e., by X-rays or light, seems to consist in the hurling out with an energy which may be very large, but which depends upon the frequency of the incident ether wave, of one single electron from an occasional molecule over which this wave passes.

3. The act of ionization by rapidly moving α-particles consists in the shaking loose of one single electron from the atom through which it passes[1], but a slow-moving positive ray appears in some cases to be able to detach several electrons from a single atom.

[1] See Gottschalk and Kelly, *Phys. Rev.*, 1917.

CHAPTER VII

BROWNIAN MOVEMENTS IN GASES

I. HISTORICAL SUMMARY

In 1827 the English botanist, Robert Brown, first made mention of the fact that minute particles of dead matter in suspension in liquids can be seen in a high-power microscope to be endowed with irregular wiggling motions which strongly suggest "life."[1] Although this phenomenon was studied by numerous observers and became known as the phenomenon of the Brownian movements, it remained wholly unexplained for just fifty years. The first man to suggest that these motions were due to the continual bombardment to which these particles are subjected because of the motion of thermal agitation of the molecules of the surrounding medium was the Belgian Carbonelle, whose work was first published by his collaborator, Thirion, in 1880,[2] although three years earlier Delsaulx[3] had given expression to views of this sort but had credited Carbonelle with priority in adopting them. In 1881 Bodoszewski[4] studied the Brownian movements of smoke particles and other suspensions *in air* and saw in them "an approximate image of the movements of the gas molecules as postulated by the kinetic theory of gases." Others, notably Gouy,[5]

[1] *Phil. Mag.*, IV (1828), 161.

[2] *Revue des questions scientifiques*, Louvain, VII (1880), 5.

[3] *Ibid.*, II (1877), 319.

[4] *Dinglers polyt. Jour.*, CCXXXIX (1881), 325.

[5] *Jour. de Phys.*, VII (1888), 561; *Comptes rendus*, CIX (1889), 102.

urged during the next twenty years the same interpretation, but it was not until 1905 that a way was found to subject the hypothesis to a quantitative test. Such a test became possible through the brilliant theoretical work of Einstein[1] of Bern, Switzerland, who, starting merely with the assumption that the mean kinetic energy of agitation of a particle suspended in a fluid medium must be the same as the mean kinetic energy of agitation of a gas molecule at the same temperature, developed by unimpeachable analysis an expression for the mean distance through which such a particle should drift in a given time through a given medium because of this motion of agitation. This distance could be directly observed and compared with the theoretical value. Thus, suppose one of the wiggling particles is observed in a microscope and its position noted on a scale in the eyepiece at a particular instant, then noted again at the end of τ (for example, 10) seconds, and the displacement Δx in that time along one particular axis recorded. Suppose a large number of such displacements Δx in intervals all of length τ are observed, each one of them squared, and the mean of these squares taken and denoted by $\overline{\Delta x^2}$: Einstein showed that the theoretical value of $\overline{\Delta x^2}$ should be

$$\overline{\Delta x^2} = \frac{RT}{NK}\tau \dots\dots\dots\dots\dots (21)$$

in which R is the universal gas constant per gram molecule, namely, $831.5 \times 10^5 \frac{ergs}{degrees}$, T the temperature on the absolute scale, N the number of molecules in one gram molecule, and K a resistance factor depending

[1] *Ann. d. Phys.* (4), XVII (1905), 549; XIX (1906), 371; XXII (1907), 569.

upon the viscosity of the medium and the size of the drop, and representing the ratio between the force applied to the particle in any way and the velocity produced by that force. If Stokes's Law, namely, $F = 6\pi\eta av$, held for the motion of the particle through the medium, then $K = \dfrac{F}{v}$ would have the value $6\pi\eta a$, so that Einstein's formula would become

$$\overline{\Delta x^2} = \frac{RT}{N\,3\pi\eta a}\tau \dots\dots\dots\dots\dots (22)$$

This was the form which Einstein originally gave to his equation, a very simple derivation of which has been given by Langevin.[1] The essential elements of this derivation will be found in Appendix C.

The first careful test of this equation was made on suspensions in liquids by Perrin,[2] who used it for finding N the number of molecules in a gram molecule. He obtained the mean value $N = 68.2 \times 10^{22}$, which, in view of the uncertainties in the measurement of both K and $\overline{\Delta x^2}$, may be considered as proving the correctness of Einstein's equation within the limits of error of Perrin's measurements, which differ among themselves by as much as 30 per cent.

II. QUANTITATIVE MEASUREMENTS IN GASES

Up to 1909 there had been no quantitative work whatever on Brownian movements in gases. Bodoszewski had described them fully and interpreted them correctly

---

[1] *Comptes rendus*, CXLVI (1908), 530.

[2] *Ibid.*, p. 967; CXLVII (1908), 475, 530, 594; CLII (1911), 1380, 1569; see also Perrin, *Brownian Movements and Molecular Reality*, Engl. tr. by Soddy, 1912.

in 1881. In 1906 Smoluchowski[1] had computed how large the mean displacements in air for particles of radius $a = 10^{-4}$ ought to be, and in 1907 Ehrenhaft[2] had recorded displacements of the computed order with particles the sizes of which he made, however, no attempt to measure, so that he knew nothing at all about the resistance factor K. There was then nothing essentially quantitative about this work.

In March, 1908, De Broglie, in Paris,[3] made the following significant advance. He drew the metallic dust arising from the condensation of the vapors coming from an electric arc or spark between metal electrodes (a phenomenon discovered by Hemsalech and De Watteville[4]) into a glass box and looked down into it through a microscope upon the particles rendered visible by a beam of light passing horizontally through the box and illuminating thus the Brownian particles in the focal plane of the objective. His addition consisted in placing two parallel metal plates in vertical planes, one on either side of the particles, and in noting that upon applying a potential difference to these plates some of the particles moved under the influence of the field toward one plate, some remained at rest, while others moved toward the other plate, thus showing that a part of these particles were positively electrically charged and a part negatively. In this paper he promised a study of the charges on these particles. In May, 1909, in fulfilling this promise[5] he

[1] *Ann. der Phys.*, IV (1906), 21, 756.

[2] *Wiener Berichte*, CXVI (1907), II, 1175.

[3] *Comptes rendus*, CXLVI (1908), 624, 1010.

[4] *Ibid.*, CXLIV (1907), 1338.

[5] *Ibid.*, CXLVIII (1909), 1316.

made the first quantitative study of Brownian movements in gases. The particles used were minute droplets of water condensed upon tobacco smoke. The average rate at which these droplets moved in Broglie's horizontal electric field was determined. The equation for this motion was

$$Fe = Kv \dots \dots \dots \dots \dots (23)$$

The mean $\overline{\Delta x^2}$ was next measured for a great many particles and introduced into Einstein's equation:

$$\overline{\Delta x^2} = \frac{2RT}{NK}\tau.$$

From these two equations K was eliminated and e obtained in terms of N. Introducing Perrin's value of N, De Broglie obtained from one series of measurements $e = 4.5 \times 10^{-10}$; from another series on larger particles he got a mean value several times larger—a result which he interpreted as indicating multiple charges on the larger particles. Although these results represent merely mean values for many drops which are not necessarily all alike, either in radius or charge, yet they may be considered as the first experimental evidence that Einstein's equation holds approximately, in gases, and they are the more significant because nothing has to be assumed about the size of the particles, if they are all alike in charge and radius, or about the validity of Stokes's Law in gases, the K-factor being eliminated.

The development of the oil-drop method made it possible to subject the Brownian-movement theory to a more accurate and convincing experimental test than had heretofore been attainable, and that for the following reasons:

1. It made it possible to hold, with the aid of the vertical electrical field, one particular particle under observation for hours at a time and to measure as many displacements as desired on it alone instead of assuming the identity of a great number of particles, as had been done in the case of suspensions in liquids and in De Broglie's experiments in gases.

2. Liquids are very much less suited than are gases to convincing tests of any kinetic hypothesis, for the reason that prior to Brownian-movement work we had no satisfactory kinetic theory of liquids at all.

3. The absolute amounts of the displacements of a given particle in air are 8 times greater and in hydrogen 15 times greater than in water.

4. By reducing the pressure to low values the displacements can easily be made from 50 to 200 times greater in gases than in liquids.

5. The measurements can be made independently of the most troublesome and uncertain factor involved in Brownian-movement work in liquids, namely, the factor K, which contains the radius of the particle and the law governing its motion through the liquid.

Accordingly, there was begun in the Ryerson Laboratory, in 1910, a series of very careful experiments in Brownian movements in gases. Svedberg,[1] in reviewing this subject in 1913, considers this "the only exact investigation of quantitative Brownian movements in gases." A brief summary of the method and results was published by the author.[2] A full account was

[1] *Jahrbuch der Radioaktivität und Elektronik*, X (1913), 513.

[2] *Science*, February 17, 1911.

published by Mr. Harvey Fletcher in May, 1911,[1] and further work on the variation of Brownian movements with pressure was presented by the author the year following.[2]   The essential contribution of this work as regards method consisted in the two following particulars:

1. By combining the characteristic and fully tested equation of the oil-drop method, namely,

$$e = \frac{mg}{Fv_1}(v_1+v_2)_0 = \frac{K}{F}(v_1+v_2)_0 \ldots \ldots \ldots (24)$$

with the Einstein Brownian-movement equation, namely,

$$\overline{\Delta x^2} = \frac{2RT}{NK}\tau \ldots \ldots \ldots \ldots (25)$$

it was possible to obtain the product Ne without any reference to the size of the particle or the resistance of the medium to its motion.   This quantity could then be compared with the same product obtained with great precision from electrolysis.   The experimental procedure consists in balancing a given droplet and measuring, as in any Brownian-movement work, the quantity $\overline{\Delta x^2}$, then unbalancing it and measuring F, v_1 and $(v_1+v_2)_0$; the combination of (24) and (25) then gives

$$\overline{\Delta x^2} = \frac{2RT}{F}\frac{(v_1+v_2)_0}{Ne} \ldots \ldots \ldots \ldots (26)$$

Since it is awkward to square each displacement Δx before averaging, it is preferable to modify by substituting from the Maxwell distribution law, which holds

[1] *Phys. Zeitschr.*, XII (1911), 202–8; see also *Phys. Rev.*, XXXIII (1911), 81.

[2] *Phys. Rev.*, I, N.S. (1913), 218.

for Brownian displacements as well as for molecular velocities, the relation

$$\overline{\Delta x} = \sqrt{\frac{2}{\pi}\overline{\Delta x^2}} \;.$$

We obtain thus

$$\overline{\Delta x} = \sqrt{\frac{4}{\pi}\frac{RT(v_1+v_2)_0}{F(Ne)}\tau} \ldots \ldots \ldots \ldots (27)$$

or

$$Ne = \frac{4}{\pi}\frac{RT(v_1+v_2)_0\tau}{F(\overline{\Delta x})^2} \; \ldots \ldots \ldots \ldots (28)$$

The possibility of thus eliminating the size of the particle and with it the resistance of the medium to its motion can be seen at once from the simple consideration that *so long as we are dealing with one and the same particle* the ratio K between the force acting and the velocity produced by it must be the same, whether the acting force is due to gravity or an electrical field, as in the oil-drop experiments, or to molecular impacts as in Brownian-movement work. De Broglie might have made such an elimination and calculation of Ne in his work, had his Brownian displacements and mobilities in electric fields been made on one and the same particle, but when the two sets of measurements are made on different particles, such elimination would involve the very uncertain assumption of identity of the particles in both charge and size. Although De Broglie did actually make this assumption, he did not treat his data in the manner indicated, and the first publication of this method of measuring Ne as well as the first actual determination was made in the papers mentioned above.

Some time later E. Weiss reported similar work to the Vienna Academy.[1]

2. Although it is possible to make the test of Ne in just the method described and although it was so made in the case of one or two drops, Mr. Fletcher worked out a more convenient method, which involves expressing the displacements Δx in terms of the fluctuations in the time required by the particle to fall a given distance and thus dispenses with the necessity of balancing the drop at all. I shall present another derivation which is very simple and yet of unquestionable validity.

In equation (28) let τ be the time required by the particle, if there were no Brownian movements, to fall between a series of equally spaced cross-hairs whose distance apart is d. In view of such movements the particle will have moved up or down a distance Δx in the time τ. Let us suppose this distance to be up. Then the actual time of fall will be $\tau + \Delta t$, in which Δt is now the time it takes the particle to fall the distance Δx. If now Δt is small in comparison with τ, that is, if Δx is small in comparison with d (say $1/10$ or less), then we shall introduce a negligible error (of the order $1/100$ at the most) if we assume that $\Delta x = v_1 \Delta t$ in which v_1 is the mean velocity under gravity. Replacing then in (28) $\overline{(\Delta x)}^2$ by $v_1^2 \overline{(\Delta t)}^2$, in which $\overline{(\Delta t)}^2$ is the square of the average difference between an observed time of fall and the mean time of fall t_g, that is, the square of the average

[1] It was read before the Academy on July 6: *Wiener Berichte*, CXX (1911), II, 1021, but appeared first in print in the August 1st number of the *Phys. Zeitschr.* (1911), p. 63. Fletcher's article is found in brief in an earlier number of the same volume of the *Phys. Zeitschr.*, p. 203, and was printed in full in the July number of *Le Radium*, VIII (1911), 279.

fluctuation in the time of fall through the distance d, we obtain after replacing the ideal time τ by the mean time $t_g^{\scriptscriptstyle 1}$

$$Ne = \frac{4}{\pi}\frac{RT(v_1+v_2)_0 t_g}{Fv_1^2(\overline{\Delta t})^2} \quad \dots\dots\dots\dots (29)$$

In any actual work $\overline{\Delta t}$ will be kept considerably less than $1/10$ the mean time t_g if the irregularities due to the observer's errors are not to mask the irregularities due to the Brownian movements, so that (29) is sufficient for practically all working conditions.[1]

The work of Mr. Fletcher and of the author was done by both of the methods represented in equations (28) and (29). The 9 drops reported upon in Mr. Fletcher's paper in 1911[2] yielded the results shown below in which n is the number of displacements used in each case in determining $\overline{\Delta x}$ or $\overline{\Delta t}$.

TABLE XIII

$\sqrt{Ne} \times 10^7$	n
1.68	125
1.67	136
1.645	321
1.695	202
1.73	171
1.65	200
1.66	84
1.785	411
1.65	85

When weights are assigned proportional to the number of observations taken, as shown in the last column

---

[1] No error is introduced here if, as assumed, $\overline{\Delta t}$ is small in comparison with t_g. However, for more rigorous equations see Fletcher, *Phys. Rev.*, IV (1914), 442; also Smoluchowski, *Phys. Zeitschr.*, XVI (1915), 321.

[2] *Le Radium*, VIII (1911), 279; *Phys. Rev.*, XXXIII (1911), 107.

of Table XIII, there results for the weighted mean value which represents an average of 1,735 displacements, $\sqrt{Ne} = 1.698 \times 10^7$ or $Ne = 2.88 \times 10^{14}$ *electrostatic units*, *as against* 2.896×10^{14}, the *value found in electrolysis*. The agreement between theory and experiment is then in this case about as good as one-half of 1 per cent, which is well within the limits of observational error.

This work seemed to demonstrate, with considerably greater precision than had been attained in earlier Brownian-movement work and with a minimum of assumptions, the correctness of the Einstein equation, which is in essence merely the assumption that a particle in a gas, no matter how big or how little it is or out of what it is made, is moving about with a mean translatory kinetic energy which is a universal constant dependent only on temperature. To show how well this conclusion has been established I shall refer briefly to a few later researches.

In 1914 Dr. Fletcher, assuming the value of K which I had published[1] for oil drops moving through air, made new and improved Brownian-movement measurements in this medium and solved for N the original Einstein equation, which, when modified precisely as above by replacing $\overline{\Delta x}^2$ by $\dfrac{2}{\pi}(\overline{\Delta x})^2$ and $(\overline{\Delta x})^2 = v_1^2(\overline{\Delta t})^2$ becomes

$$N = \frac{4}{\pi} \frac{RTtg}{Kv_1^2(\overline{\Delta t})^2} \quad \dots \dots \dots \dots \dots (30)$$

He took, all told, as many as 18,837 Δt's, not less than 5,900 on a single drop, and obtained $N = 60.3 \times 10^{22} \pm 1.2$. This cannot be regarded as an altogether independent determination of N, since it involves my value

[1] *Phys. Rev.*, I (1913), 218.

of K. Agreeing, however, as well as it does with my value of N, it does show with much conclusiveness that both Einstein's equation and my corrected form of Stokes's equation apply accurately to the motion of oil drops of the size here used, namely, those of radius from 2.79×10^{-5} cm. to 4.1×10^{-5} cm. $(280 - 400 \ \mu\mu)$.

In 1915 Mr. Carl Eyring tested by equation (29) the value of Ne on oil drops, of about the same size, in hydrogen and came out within .6 per cent of the value found in electrolysis, the probable error being, however, some 2 per cent.

Precisely similar tests on substances other than oils were made by Dr. E. Weiss[1] and Dr. Karl Przibram.[2] The former worked with silver particles only half as large as the oil particles mentioned above, namely, of radii between 1 and 2.3×10^{-5} cm. and obtained $Ne = 10{,}700$ electromagnetic units instead of 9,650, as in electrolysis. This is indeed 11 per cent too high, but the limits of error in Weiss's experiments were in his judgment quite as large as this. K. Przibram worked on suspensions in air of five or six different substances, the radii varying from 200 $\mu\mu$ to 600 $\mu\mu$, and though his results varied among themselves by as much as 100 per cent, his mean value came within 6 per cent of 9,650. Both of the last two observers took too few displacements on a given drop to obtain a reliable mean displacement, but they used so many drops that their mean Ne still has some significance.

It would seem, therefore, that the validity of Einstein's Brownian-movement equation had been pretty

[1] *Sitzungsber. d. k. Akad. d. Wiss. in Wien*, CXX (1911), II, 1021.

[2] *Ibid.*, CXXI (1912), II, 950.

thoroughly established in gases. In liquids too it has recently been subjected to much more precise test than had formerly been attained. Nordlund,[3] in 1914, using minute mercury particles in water and assuming Stokes's Law of fall and Einstein's equations, obtained $N = 59.1 \times 10^{22}$. While in 1915 Westgren at Stockholm[4] by a very large number of measurements on colloidal gold, silver, and selenium particles, of diameter from 65 $\mu\mu$ to 130 $\mu\mu$ (6.5 to 13×10^{-6} cm.), obtained a result which he thinks is correct to one-half of 1 per cent, this value is $N = 60.5 \times 10^{22} \pm .3 \times 10^{22}$, which agrees perfectly with the value which I obtained from the measurements on the isolation and measurement of the electron.

It has been because of such agreements as the foregoing that the last trace of opposition to the kinetic and atomic hypotheses of matter has disappeared from the scientific world, and that even Ostwald has been willing to make such a statement as that quoted on p. 10 above.

[3] *Ztschr. f. Phys. Chem.*, LXXXVII (1914), 40.

[4] *Die Brown'sche Bewegung besonders als Mittel zur Bestimmung der Avogadroschen Konstante*, inaugural dissertation. Upsala: Almquist & Wiksells Boktryckeri, 1915.

CHAPTER VIII

THE EXISTENCE OF A SUB-ELECTRON?

It would not be in keeping with the method of modern science to make any dogmatic assertion as to the indivisibility of the electron. Such assertions used to be made in high-school classes with respect to the atoms of the elements, but the far-seeing among physicists, like Faraday, were always careful to disclaim any belief in the necessary ultimateness of the atoms of chemistry, and that simply because there existed until recently no basis for asserting anything about the insides of the atom. We knew that there was a smallest thing which took part in chemical reactions and we named that thing the atom, leaving its insides entirely to the future.

Precisely similarly the electron was defined as the smallest quantity of electricity which ever was found to appear in electrolysis, and nothing was then said or is now said about its necessary ultimateness. Our experiments have, however, now shown that this quantity is capable of isolation and exact measurement, and that all the kinds of charges which we have been able to investigate are exact multiples of it. Its value is 4.774×10^{-10} electrostatic units.

I. A SECOND METHOD OF OBTAINING e

I have presented one way of measuring this charge, but there is an indirect method of arriving at it which was worked out independently by Rutherford and Geiger[1]

[1] *Proc. Roy. Soc.*, A LXXXI (1908), 141, 161.

and Regener.[1]   The unique feature in this method consists in actually counting the number of α-particles shot
off per second by a small speck of radium or polonium
through a given solid angle and computing from this the
number of these particles emitted per second by one gram
of the radium or polonium.   Regener made his determination by counting the scintillations produced on a dia-
mond screen in the focal plane of his observing microscope.
He then caught in a condenser all the α-particles emitted
per second by a known quantity of his polonium and
determined the total quantity of electricity delivered to
the condenser by them.   This quantity of electricity
divided by the number of particles emitted per second
gave the charge on each particle.   Because the α-particles
had been definitely proved to be helium atoms[2] and the
value of $\dfrac{e}{m}$ found for them showed that if they were
helium they ought to carry double the electronic charge,
Regener divided his result by 2 and obtained

$$e = 4.79 \times 10^{-10}.$$

He estimated his error at 3 per cent.   Rutherford and
Geiger made their count by letting the α-particles from
a speck of radium C shoot into a chamber and produce
therein sufficient ionization by collision to cause an
electrometer needle to jump every time one of them
entered.   These authors measured the total charge as
Regener did and, dividing by 2 the charge on each
α-particle, they obtained

$$e = 4.65 \times 10^{-10}.$$

---

[1] *Sitzungsber. d. k. Preuss. Akad.*, XXXVIII (1909), 948.

[2] Rutherford and Royds, *Phil. Mag.*, XVII (1909), 281.

All determinations of e from radioactive data involve one or the other of these two counts, namely, that of Rutherford and Geiger or that of Regener. Thus, Boltwood and Rutherford[1] measured the total weight of helium produced in a second by a known weight of radium. Dividing this by the number of α-particles (helium atoms) obtained from Rutherford and Geiger's count, they obtain the mass of one atom of helium from which the number in a given weight, or volume since the gas density is known, is at once obtained. They published for the number n of molecules in a gas per cubic centimeter at $0°.76$ cm., $n = 2.69 \times 10^{19}$, which corresponds to

$$e = 4.81 \times 10^{-10}.$$

This last method, like that of the Brownian movement, is actually a determination of N, rather than of e, since e is obtained from it only through the relation $Ne = 9,650$ electromagnetic units. Indeed, this is true of all methods of estimating e, so far as I am aware, except the oil-drop method and the Rutherford-Geiger-Regener method, and of these two the latter represents the measurement of the *mean* charge on an immense number of α-particles.

Thus a person who wished to contend that the unit charge appearing in electrolysis is only a mean charge which may be made up of individual charges which vary widely among themselves, in much the same way in which the atomic weight assigned to *neon* has recently been shown to be a mean of the weights of at least two different elements inseparable chemically, could not be gainsaid, save on the basis of the evidence contained in

[1] *Phil. Mag.* (6), XXII (1911), 599.

the oil-drop experiments; for these constitute the only method which has been found of measuring directly the charge on each individual ion. It is of interest and significance for the present discussion, however, that the mean charge on an α-particle has been directly measured and that it comes out, within the limits of error of the measurement, at exactly two electrons—as it should according to the evidence furnished by $\frac{e}{m}$ measurements on the α-particles.

II. THE EVIDENCE FOR THE EXISTENCE OF A SUB-ELECTRON

Now, the foregoing contention has actually been made recently, and evidence has been presented which purports to show that electric charges exist which are much smaller than the electron. Since this raises what may properly be called the most fundamental question of modern physics, the evidence needs very careful consideration. This evidence can best be appreciated through a brief historical review of its origin.

The first measurements on the mobilities in electric fields of swarms of charged particles of microscopically visible sizes were made by H. A. Wilson[1] in 1903, as detailed in chap. iii. These measurements were repeated with modifications by other observers, including ourselves, during the years immediately following. De Broglie's modification, published in· 1908,[2] consisted in sucking the metallic clouds discovered by Hemsalech and De Watteville,[3] produced by sparks or arcs between

[1] *Phil. Mag.* (6), V (1903), 429.

[2] *Comptes rendus*, CXLVI (1908), 624, 1010.

[3] *Ibid.*, CXLIV (1907), 1338.

metal electrodes, into the focal plane of an ultra-microscope and observing the motions of the individual particles in this cloud *in a horizontal electrical field produced by applying a potential difference to two vertical parallel plates* in front of the objective of his microscope. In this paper De Broglie first commented upon the fact that some of these particles were charged positively, some negatively, and some not at all, and upon the further fact that holding radium near the chamber caused changes in the charges of the particles. He promised quantitative measurements of the charges themselves. One year later he fulfilled the promise,[1] and at practically the same time Ehrenhaft[2] published similar measurements made with precisely the arrangement described by De Broglie a year before. Both men, as Ehrenhaft clearly pointed out,[3] while *observing* individual particles, obtained only a mean charge, since the different measurements entering into the evaluation of e were made on different particles. So far as concerns e, these measurements, as everyone agrees, were essentially cloud measurements like Wilson's.

In the spring and summer of 1909 I isolated individual water droplets and determined the charges carried by each one,[4] and in April, 1910, I read before the American Physical Society the full report on the oil-drop work in which the multiple relations between charges were established, Stokes's Law corrected, and e accurately

---

[1] *Ibid.*, CXLVIII (1909), 1316.

[2] *Phys. Zeitschr.*, X (1909), 308.

[3] *Ibid.*, XI (1910), 619.

[4] This paper was published in abstract in *Phys. Rev.*, XXX (1909), 560, and *Phil. Mag.*, XIX (1910), 209.

determined.[1] In the following month (May, 1910) Ehrenhaft,[2] having seen that a vertical condenser arrangement made possible, as shown theoretically and experimentally in the 1909 papers mentioned above, the independent determination of the charge on each individual particle, read the first paper in which he had used this arrangement in place of the De Broglie arrangement which he had used theretofore. He reported results identical in all essential particulars with those which I had published on water drops the year before, save that where I obtained consistent and simple multiple relations between charges carried by different particles he found no such consistency in these relations. The absolute values of these charges obtained on the assumption of Stokes's Law fluctuated about values considerably lower than 4.6×10^{-10}. Instead, however, of throwing the burden upon Stokes's Law or upon wrong assumptions as to the density of his particles, he remarked in a footnote that Cunningham's theoretical correction to Stokes's Law,[3] which he (Ehrenhaft) had just seen, would make his values come still lower, and hence that no failure of Stokes's Law could be responsible for his low values. He considered his results therefore as opposed to the atomic theory of electricity altogether, and in any case as proving the existence of charges much smaller than that of the electron.[4]

[1] This paper was published in abstract in *Phys. Rev.*, XXXI (1910), 92; *Science*, XXXII (1910), 436; *Phys. Zeitschr.*, XI (1910), 1097.

[2] *Wien. Ber.*, CXIX (1910), II, 809. This publication was apparently not issued before December, 1910, for it is not noted in *Naturae Novitates* before this date.

[3] *Proc. Roy. Soc.*, LXXXIII (1910), 360.

[4] These results were presented and discussed at great length in the fall of 1910; see *Phys. Zeitschr.*, XI (1910), 619, 940.

The apparent contradiction between these results and mine was explained when Mr. Fletcher and myself showed[1] experimentally that Brownian movements produced just such apparent fluctuations as Ehrenhaft observed when the e is computed, as had been done in his work, from one single observation of a speed under gravity and a corresponding one in an electric field. We further showed that the fact that his values fluctuated about too low an average value meant simply that his particles of gold, silver, and mercury were less dense because of surface impurities, oxides or the like, than he had assumed. The correctness of this explanation would be well-nigh demonstrated if the values of Ne computed by equations (28) or (29) in chap. vii from a large number of observations on Brownian movements always came out as in electrolysis, for in these equations no assumption has to be made as to the density of the particles. As a matter of fact, all of the nine particles studied by us and computed by Mr. Fletcher[2] showed the correct value of Ne, while only six of them as computed by me fell on, or close to, the line which pictures the law of fall of an oil drop through air (Fig. 5, p. 104). This last fact was not published in 1911 because it took me until 1913 to determine with certainty the complete law of fall of a droplet through air; in other words, to extend curves of the sort given in Fig. 5 to as large values of $\dfrac{l}{a}$ as correspond to particles small enough to show large Brownian movements. As soon as I had done this I computed all the nine drops which gave cor-

---

[1] *Phys. Zeitschr.*, XII (1911), 161; *Phys. Rev.*, XXXII (1911), 394.

[2] *Le Radium*, VIII (1911), 279; *Phys. Rev.*, XXXIII (1911), 107.

rect values of Ne and found that two of them fell way below the line, one more fell somewhat below, while one fell considerably above it. This meant obviously that these four particles were not spheres of oil alone, two of them falling much too slowly to be so constituted and one considerably too rapidly. There was nothing at all surprising about this result, since I had explained fully in my first paper on oil drops[1] that until I had taken great precaution to obtain dust-free air "the values of e_1 came out differently, even for drops showing the same velocity under gravity." In the Brownian-movement work no such precautions to obtain dust-free air had been taken because we wished to test the general validity of equations (28) and (29). That we actually used in this test two particles which had a mean density very much smaller than that of oil and one which was considerably too heavy, was fortunate since it indicated that our result was indeed independent of the material used.

It is worthy of remark that in general, even with oil drops, almost all of those behaving abnormally fall too slowly, that is, they fall below the line of Fig. 5 and only rarely does one fall above it. This is because the dust particles which one is likely to observe, that is, those which remain long in suspension in the air, are either in general lighter than oil or else expose more surface and hence act as though they were lighter. When one works with particles made of dense metals this behavior will be still more marked, since all surface impurities of whatever sort will diminish the density. The possibility, however, of freeing oil-drop experiments from all such sources of error is shown by the fact that although during

[1] *Phys. Rev.*, XXXIII (1911), 366, 367.

the past year I have studied altogether as many as three hundred drops, there has not been a single case that I can recall which did not fall within less than 1 per cent of the line of Fig. 5. It will be shown, too, in this chapter, that in spite of the failure of the Vienna experimenters, it is possible to obtain mercury drops which behave, even as to law of fall, in practically all cases with perfect consistency and normality.

When E. Weiss in Prag and K. Przibram in the Vienna laboratory itself, as explained in chap. vii, had found that Ne for all the substances which they worked with, including silver particles like those used by Ehrenhaft, gave about the right value of Ne, although yielding much too low values of e when the latter was computed from the law of fall of *silver* particles, the scientific world practically universally accepted our explanation of Ehrenhaft's results and ceased to concern itself with the idea of a sub-electron.[1]

In 1914 and 1915, however, Professor Ehrenhaft[2] and two of his pupils, F. Zerner[3] and D. Konstantinowsky,[4] published new evidence for the existence of such a sub-electron. This evidence appears to be but little understood and therefore calls for some comment. These authors make three contentions. The first is essentially that they have now determined Ne for their particles by equation (29); and although in many instances it comes out as in electrolysis, in some instances it comes out from

[1] See R. Pohl, *Jahrbuch der Radioactivität und Elektronik*, VIII (1912), 431.

[2] *Wien. Sitzungsber.*, CXXIII (1914), 53–155; *Ann. d. Phys.*, XLIV (1914), 657.

[3] *Phys. Zeitschr.*, XVI (1915), 10.

[4] *Ann. d. Phys.*, XLVI (1915), 261.

20 per cent to 50 per cent too low, while in a few cases it is as low as one-fourth or one-fifth of the electrolytic value. Their procedure is in general to publish, not the value of Ne, but, instead, the value of e obtained from Ne by inserting Perrin's value of N (70×10^{22}) in (29) and then solving for e. This is their method of determining e "from the Brownian movements."

Their second contention is the same as that originally advanced, namely, that, in some instances, when e is determined with the aid of Stokes's Law of fall (equation 12, p. 89), even when Cunningham's correction or my own (equation 15, p. 99) is employed, the result comes out very much lower than 4.77×10^{-10}. Their third claim is that the value of e, determined as just explained from the Brownian movements, is in general higher than the value computed from the law of fall, and that the departures become greater and greater the smaller the particle. These observers conclude therefore that we at the Ryerson Laboratory failed to detect sub-electrons because our droplets were too big to be able to reveal their existence. The minuter particles which they study, however, seem to them to bring these sub-electrons to light. *In other words, they think the value of the smallest charge which can be caught from the air actually is a function of the radius of the drop on which it is caught, being smaller for small drops than for large ones.*

Ehrenhaft and Zerner even analyze our reports on oil droplets and find that these also show in certain instances indications of sub-electrons, for they yield in these observers' hands too low values of e, whether computed from the Brownian movements or from the law of fall.

When the computations are made in the latter way e is found, according to them, to decrease with decreasing radius, as is the case in their experiments on particles of mercury and gold.

III. CAUSES OF THE DISCREPANCIES

Now, the single low value of Ne which these authors find in the oil-drop work is obtained by computing Ne from some twenty-five observations on the times of fall, and an equal number on the times of rise, of a particle which, before we had made any Ne computations at all, we reported upon[1] for the sake of showing that the Brownian movements would produce just such fluctuations as Ehrenhaft had observed when the conditions were those under which he worked. When I compute Ne by equation (29), using merely the twenty-five times of fall, I find the value of Ne comes out 26 per cent low, just as Zerner finds it to do. If, however, I omit the first reading it comes out but 11 per cent low. In other words, the omission of one single reading changes the result by 15 per cent. Furthermore, Fletcher[2] has just shown that these same data, though treated entirely legitimately, but with a slightly different grouping than that used by Zerner, can be made to yield exactly the right value of Ne. This brings out clearly the futility of attempting to test a statistical theorem by so few observations as twenty-five, which is nevertheless more than Ehrenhaft usually uses on his drops. Furthermore, I shall presently show that unless one observes under carefully chosen conditions, his own errors of observation

[1] *Phys. Zeitschr.*, XII (1911), 162.

[2] *Ibid.*, XVI (1915), 316.

and the slow evaporation of the drop tend to make Ne obtained from equation (29) come out too low, and these errors may easily be enough to vitiate the result entirely. *There is, then, not the slightest indication in any work which we have thus far done on oil drops that Ne comes out too small.*

Next consider the apparent *variation in e* when it is computed from the law of fall. Zerner computes e from my law of fall in the case of the nine drops published by Fletcher, in which Ne came out as in electrolysis, and finds that one of them yields $e = 6.66 \times 10^{-10}$, one $e = 3.97 \times 10^{-10}$, one $e = 1.32 \times 10^{-10}$, one $e = 1.7 \times 10^{-10}$, while the other five yield about the right value, namely, 4.8×10^{-10}. In other words (as stated on p. 162 above), five of these drops fall exactly on my curve (Fig. 5), one falls somewhat above it, one somewhat below, while two are entirely off and very much too low. These two, therefore, I concluded were not oil at all, but dust particles. Since Zerner computes the radius from the rate of fall, these two dust particles which fall much too slowly, and therefore yield too low values of e, must, of course, yield correspondingly low values of a. Since they are found to do so, Zerner concludes that our oil drops, as well as Ehrenhaft's mercury particles, yield decreasing values of e with decreasing radius. His own tabulation does not show this. It merely shows three erratic values of e, two of which are very low and one rather high. But a glance at all the other data which I have published on oil drops shows the complete falsity of this position,[1] *for these data show that after I had eliminated dust all of my particles yielded exactly the same value of "e" whatever their*

[1] *Phys. Rev.*, II (1913), 138.

size.[1] The only possible interpretation then which could be put on these two particles which yielded correct values of Ne, but too slow rates of fall, was that which I put upon them, namely, that they were not spheres of oil.

As to the Vienna data on mercury and gold, Ehrenhaft publishes, all told, data on just sixteen particles and takes for his Brownian-movement calculations on the average *fifteen times of fall and fifteen of rise on each, the smallest number being 6 and the largest 27.* He then computes his statistical average $(\overline{\Delta t})^2$ from observations of this sort. Next he assumes Perrin's value of N, namely, 70×10^{22}, which corresponds to $e = 4.1$, and obtains instead by the Brownian-movement method, i.e., the Ne method, the following values of e, the exponential term being omitted for the sake of brevity: 1.43, 2.13, 1.38, 3.04, 3.5, 6.92, 4.42, 3.28, .84. Barring the first three and the last of these, the mean value of e is just about what it should be, namely, 4.22 instead of 4.1. Further, the first three particles are the heaviest ones, the first one falling between his cross-hairs in 3.6 seconds, and its fluctuations in time of fall are from 3.2 to 3.85 seconds, that is, three-tenths of a second on either side of the mean value. *Now, these fluctuations are only slightly greater than those which the average observer will make in timing the passage of a uniformly moving body across equally spaced cross-hairs.* This means that in these observations two nearly equally potent causes were operating to produce fluctuations. The observed Δt's were, of course, then, larger than those due to Brownian movements alone, and might easily, with but a few observations, be two or three times as large. Since

[1] See *Phys. Rev.*, II (1913), 134–35.

$(\overline{\Delta t})^2$ appears in the denominator of equation (29), it will be seen at once that because of the observer's timing errors a series of observed Δt's will always tend to be larger than the Δt due to Brownian movements alone, and hence that the Brownian-movement method always tends to yield too low a value of Ne, and accordingly too low a value of e. *It is only when the observer's mean error is wholly negligible in comparison with the Brownian-movement fluctuations that this method will not yield too low a value of e.* The overlooking of this fact is, in my judgment, one of the causes of the low values of e recorded by Ehrenhaft.

Again, in the original work on mercury droplets which I produced both by atomizing liquid mercury and by condensing the vapor from boiling mercury,[1] I noticed that such droplets evaporated for a time even more rapidly than oil, and other observers who have since worked with mercury have reported the same behavior.[2] The amount of this effect may be judged from the fact that one particular droplet of mercury recently under observation in this laboratory had at first a speed of 1 cm. in 20 seconds, which changed in half an hour to 1 cm. in 56 seconds. The slow cessation, however, of this evaporation indicates that the drop slowly becomes coated with some sort of protecting film. Now, if any evaporation whatever is going on while successive times of fall are being observed—and as a matter of fact changes due to evaporation or condensation are always taking place to some extent—the apparent $(\overline{\Delta t})^2$ will be larger than that due to Brownian movements, even

---

[1] *Phys. Rev.*, XXXII (1911), 389.

[2] See Schidlof et Karpowicz, *Comptes rendus*, CLVIII (1914), 1912.

though these movements are large enough to prevent the observer from noticing, in taking twenty or thirty readings, that the drop is continually changing. These changes combined with the fluctuations in t due to the observer's error are sufficient, I think, to explain all of the low values of e obtained by Ehrenhaft by the Brownian-movement method. Indeed, I have myself repeatedly found Ne coming out less than half of its proper value *until I corrected for the evaporation of the drop*, and this was true when the evaporation was so slow that its rate of fall changed but 1 or 2 per cent in a half-hour. But it is not merely evaporation which introduces an error of this sort. The running down of the batteries, the drifting of the drop out of focus, or anything which causes changes in the times of passage across the equally spaced cross-hairs tends to decrease the apparent value of Ne. There is, then, so far as I can see, no evidence at all in any of the data published to date that the Brownian-movement method actually does yield too low a value of e, and very much positive evidence that it does not was given in the preceding chapter.

Konstantinowsky's data are very much like Ehrenhaft's in the possibility which they permit of too low values of Ne due to observational error, evaporation, and drifting out of focus, but they emphasize one further source of error which apparently leads the author entirely astray. He publishes Ne observations on only 11 particles,[1] five of which yield values of e between 3.3 and 4.2×10^{-10}, or roughly correct values when the fact is considered that his chosen value of N is 70×10^{22}; three of the others yield about 2×10^{-10}, two more about

[1] *Ann. d. Phys.*, XLVI (1915), 292.

1×10^{-10}, while one yields $.5 \times 10^{-10}$. His determination of the series of multiple relationships by which he gets the greatest common divisor $(v_1 + v_2)_0$ (see equation (29)) is however so unreliable that he raises a question as to whether there is any greatest common divisor at all, in spite of the fact that all other observers, a dozen of us now at least, including Ehrenhaft himself, now find these exact multiple relations invariably to hold. But an uncertainty in $(v_1 + v_2)_0$ (see equation (29)) means an equal uncertainty in Ne. Konstantinowsky's very low values of Ne (one-tenth of the normal value) are, then, in my judgment, due to the fact that he chooses the wrong value of $(v_1 + v_2)_0$. But with apparatus of his dimensions and particles as minute as he uses it is not at all surprising that he cannot find the greatest common divisor of the series of speeds. *It would take more observations than he usually makes on a particle to locate it with certainty where the Brownian movements are as large as those which his particles ought to show, and where the field strengths are as small as those which he uses* (nine volts only in some cases on condenser plates 2 mm. apart), and hence where the drops are relatively heavily charged.

That e and a computed from the law of fall become farther and farther removed from the values of e and a computed from the Brownian movements, the smaller these particles appear to be, is just what would be expected if the particles under consideration have surface impurities or non-spherical shapes or else are not mercury at all. Again, the fact that these data are all taken when the observers are working with the exceedingly dense substances, mercury and gold, *volatilized in an electric arc*, and when, therefore, anything not mercury or

gold, but assumed to be, would yield very low values of
e and a, is in itself a very suspicious circumstance. The
further fact that Ehrenhaft implies that normal values
of e very frequently appear in his work,[1] while these
low erratic drops represent only a part of the data taken,
is suggestive. When one considers, too, that in place of
the beautiful consistency and duplicability shown in the
oil-drop work, Ehrenhaft and his pupils never publish
data on any two particles which yield the same value
of e, but instead find only irregularities and erratic
behavior,[2] just as they would expect to do with non-
uniform particles, or with particles having dust specks
attached to them, one wonders why any explanation
other than the foreign-material one, which explains all
the difficulties, has ever been thought of. As a matter
of fact, in our work with mercury droplets at the Ryerson
Laboratory, we have found that the initial rapid evaporation gradually ceases, just as though the droplets had
become coated with some foreign film which prevents
further loss. Schidlof and Karpowicz find that the
behavior of their mercury drops as regards evaporation
is the same in the purest nitrogen as it is in air. Ehrenhaft himself, in speaking of the Brownian movements of
his metal particles, comments on the fact that they seem
at first to show large movements which grow smaller with

[1] "Die bei grösseren Partikeln unter gewissen Umständen bei
gleicher Art der Erzeugung haufig wiederkehrenden hoheren Quanten
waren dann etwa als stabilere raumliche Gleichgewichtsverteilungen
dieser Sub-electron anzusehen, die sich unter gewissen Umstanden
ergeben."—*Wien. Ber.*, CXXIII, 59.

[2] Their whole case is summarized in the tables in *Ann. d. Phys.*,
XLIV (1914), 693, and XLVI (1915), 292, and it is recommended that
all interested in this discussion take the time to glance at the data on
these pages, for the data themselves are so erratic as to render discussion needless.

time.[1]   This is just what would happen if the radius were increased by the growth of a foreign film.

Now what does Ehrenhaft say to these very obvious suggestions as to the cause of his troubles?   Merely that he has avoided all oxygen, and hence that an oxide film is impossible.   *Yet he makes his metal particle by striking an electric arc between metal electrodes.*   This, as everyone knows, brings out all sorts of occluded gases.   Besides, chemical activity in the electric arc is tremendously intense, so that there is opportunity for the formation of all sorts of higher nitrites, the existence of which in the gases coming from electric arcs has many times actually been proved.   Ehrenhaft says further that he photographs big mercury droplets and finds them spherical and free from oxides.   But the fact that some drops are pure mercury is no reason for assuming that all of them are, and it is only the data on those which are not which he publishes. Further, because big drops which he can see and measure are of mercury is no justification at all for assuming that sub-microscopic particles are necessarily also spheres of pure mercury.   In a word, Ehrenhaft's tests as to sphericity and purity are all absolutely worthless as applied to the particles in question, which according to him have radii of the order 10^{-6} cm.—a figure a hundred times below the limit of sharp resolution.

IV.   THE BEARING OF THE VIENNA WORK ON THE QUES-
TION OF THE EXISTENCE OF A SUB-ELECTRON

But let us suppose that these observers do actually work with particles of pure mercury and gold, as they

[1] "Wie ich in meinen früheren Publikationen erwahnt habe zeigen die ultramikroskopischen Metallpartikel, unmittelbar nach der Erzeugung beobachtet eine viel lebhaftere Brownsche Bewegung als nach einer halben Stunde."—*Phys. Zeitschr.*, XII, 98.

think they do, and that the observational and evaporational errors do not account for the low values of Ne. Then what conclusion could legitimately be drawn from their data? Merely this and nothing more, that (1) Einstein's Brownian-movement equation is not universally applicable, and (2) that the law of motion of their very minute charged particles through air is not yet fully known. So long as they find exact multiple relationships, as Ehrenhaft now does, between the charges carried by a given particle when its charge is changed by the capture of ions or the direct loss of electrons, the charges on these ions must be the same as the ionic charges which I have accurately and consistently measured and found equal to 4.77×10^{-10} electrostatic units; for they, in their experiments, capture exactly the same sort of ions, produced in exactly the same way as those which I captured and measured in my experiments. That these same ions have one sort of a charge when captured by a big drop and another sort when captured by a little drop is obviously absurd. *If they are not the same ions which are caught, then in order to reconcile the results with the existence of the exact multiple relationship found by Ehrenhaft as well as ourselves, it would be necessary to assume that there exist in the air an infinite number of different kinds of ionic charges corresponding to the infinite number of possible radii of drops, and that when a powerful electric field drives all of these ions toward a given drop this drop selects in each instance just the charge which corresponds to its particular radius.* Such an assumption is not only too grotesque for serious consideration, but it is directly contradicted by my experiments, for I have repeatedly pointed out that with a given value of $\dfrac{l}{a}$ I obtain exactly the same value of e_1, whether I work with big drops or with little ones.

V.   NEW PROOF OF THE CONSTANCY OF e

For the sake of subjecting the constancy of e to the most searching test, I have recently made new measurements of the same kind as those heretofore reported, but using now a range of sizes which overlaps that in which Ehrenhaft works. I have also varied through wide limits the nature and density of both the gas and the drops. Fig. 13 (I) contains new oil-drop data taken in air; Fig. 13 (II) similar data taken in hydrogen. The radii of these drops, computed by the very exact method given in the *Physical Review*,[1] vary tenfold, namely, from .000025 cm. to .00023 cm. Ehrenhaft's range is from .000008 cm. to .000025 cm. It will be seen that these drops fall in every instance on the lines of Fig. 13, I and II, and hence that they all yield exactly the same value of $e^{\frac{2}{3}}$, namely, 61.1×10^{-8}. The details of the measurements, which are just like those previously given, will be entirely omitted, but sample data on four of the drops in hydrogen are given in Tables I, II, III, and IV, above. There is here *not a trace of an indication that the value of "e" becomes smaller as "a" decreases.* The points on these two curves represent consecutive series of observations, not a single drop being omitted in the case of either the air or the hydrogen. This shows the complete uniformity and consistency which we have succeeded in obtaining in the work with oil drops.

That mercury drops show a similar behavior was somewhat imperfectly shown in the original observations

[1] II (1913), 117.

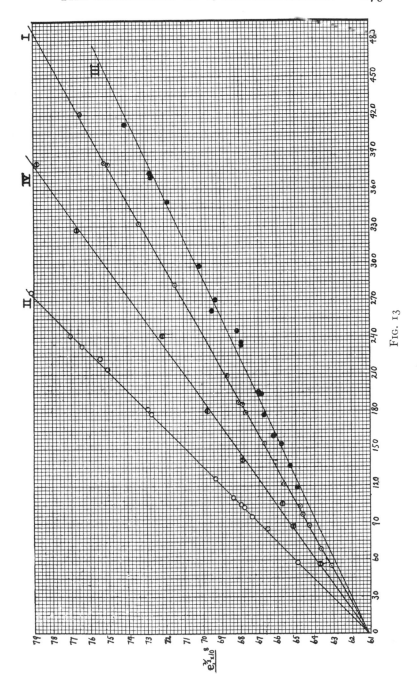

FIG. 13

which I published on mercury.[1] I have since fully confirmed the conclusions there reached. That mercury drops can with suitable precautions be made to behave practically as consistently as oil is shown in Fig. 13 (III), which represents data obtained by blowing into the observing chamber above the pinhole in the upper plate a cloud of mercury droplets formed by the condensation of the vapor arising from boiling mercury. These results have been obtained in the Ryerson Laboratory with my apparatus by Mr. John B. Derieux. Since the pressure was here always atmospheric, the drops progress in the order of size from left to right, the largest having a diameter about three times that of the smallest, the radius of which is .00003244 cm. The original data may be found in the *Physical Review*, December, 1916. In Fig. 13 (IV) is found precisely similar data taken with my apparatus by Dr. J. Y. Lee on solid spheres of shellac falling in air.[2]

These results establish with absolute conclusiveness the correctness of the assertion that the apparent value of the electron is not in general a function of the gas in which the particle falls, of the materials used, or of the radius of the drop on which it is caught, even when that drop is of mercury, and even when it is as small as some of those with which Ehrenhaft obtained his erratic results. If it appears to

[1] *Phys. Rev.*, CCC (1911), 389–90.

[2] The results shown in Fig. 13 do not lay claim to the precision reached in those recorded in Table X and Fig. 10. No elaborate precautions were here taken in the calibration of the Hipp chronoscope and the voltmeter, and it is due to slight errors discovered later in these calibrations that the slope of line I in Fig. 13 is not quite in agreement with the slope in Fig. 10.

be so with his drops, the cause cannot possibly be found in actual fluctuations in the charge of the electron without denying completely the validity of my results. But these results have now been checked, in their essential aspects, by scores of observers, including Professor Ehrenhaft himself. Furthermore, it is not my results alone with which Ehrenhaft's contention clashes. The latter is at variance also with all experiments like those of Rutherford and Geiger and Regener on the measurement of the charges carried by α- and β-particles, for these are infinitely smaller than any particles used by Ehrenhaft; and if, as he contends, the value of the unit out of which a charge is built up is smaller and smaller the smaller the capacity of the body on which it is found, then these α-particle charges ought to be extraordinarily minute in comparison with the charges on our oil drops. Instead of this, the charge on the α-particle comes out exactly twice the charge which I measure in my oil-drop experiments.

While then it would not be in keeping with the spirit or with the method of modern science to make any dogmatic assertion about the existence or non-existence of a sub-electron, it can be asserted with entire confidence that there is not in Ehrenhaft's experiments a scrap of evidence for the existence of charges smaller than the electron. If all of his assumptions as to the nature of his particles are correct, then his experiments mean simply that Einstein's Brownian-movement equation is not of universal validity and that the law of motion of minute charged particles is quite different from that which he has assumed. It is very unlikely that either of these results can be drawn from his experiments, for

Nordlund[1] and Westgren[2] have apparently verified the Einstein equation in liquids with very much smaller particles than Ehrenhaft uses; and, on the other hand, while I have worked with particles as small as 2×10^{-5} cm. and with values of $\dfrac{l}{a}$ as large as 135, which is very much larger than any which appear in the work of Ehrenhaft and his pupils, I have thus far found no evidence of a law of motion essentially different from that which I published in 1913.

There has then appeared up to the present time no evidence whatever of the existence of a sub-electron.

[1] *Zeit. für Phys. Chem.*, LXXXVII (1914), 40.

[2] Inaugural Dissertation von Arne Westgren, *Untersuchungen über Brownsche Bewegung*, Stockholm, 1915.

CHAPTER IX

THE STRUCTURE OF THE ATOM

We have shown in the preceding chapters how within the last two decades there has been discovered beneath the nineteenth-century world of molecules and atoms a wholly new world of electrons, the very existence of which was undreamed of twenty years ago. We have seen that these electrons, since they can be detached by X-rays from all kinds of neutral atoms, must be constitutents of all atoms. Whether or not they are the sole constituents we have thus far made no attempt to determine. We have concerned ourselves with studying the properties of these electrons themselves and have found that they are of two kinds, negative and positive, which are, however, exactly alike in strength of charge but wholly different in inertia or mass, the negative being commonly associated with a mass which is but $1/1,845$ of that of the lightest known atom, that of hydrogen, while the positive appears never to be associated with a mass smaller than that of the hydrogen atom. We have found how to isolate and measure accurately the electronic charge and have found that this was the key which unlocked the door to many another otherwise inaccessible physical magnitude. It is the purpose of this chapter to consider certain other fields of exact knowledge which have been opened up through the measurement of the electron, and in particular to discuss what the physicist, as he has peered with his newly discovered agencies, X-rays, radioactivity, ultra-violet light, etc., into the insides of atoms, has been able to discover regarding the numbers and sizes and relative positions of these electronic constituents, and to show how far he has gone in answering the question as to whether the electrons are the sole building-stones of the atoms.

I.   THE SIZES OF ATOMS

One of the results of the measurement of the electronic charge was to make it possible to find the quantity which is called the diameter of an atom with a definiteness and precision theretofore altogether unattained.

It was shown in chap. v that the determination of e gave us at once a knowledge of the exact number of molecules in a cubic centimeter of a gas. Before this was known we had fairly satisfactory information as to the relative diameters of different molecules, for we have known for a hundred years that different gases when at the same temperature and pressure possess the same number of molecules per cubic centimeter (Avogadro's rule). From this it is at once evident that, as the molecules of gases eternally dart hither and thither and ricochet against one another and the walls of the containing vessel, the average distance through which one of them will go between collisions with its neighbors will depend upon how big it is. The larger the diameter the less will be the mean distance between collisions—a quantity which is technically called "the mean free path." Indeed, it is not difficult to see that in different gases the mean free path l is an inverse measure of the molecular cross-section. The exact relation is easily deduced (see Appendix E). It is

$$l = \frac{1}{\pi n d^2 \sqrt{2}} \quad \ldots\ldots\ldots\ldots\ldots (31)$$

in which d is the molecular diameter and n is the number of molecules per cubic centimeter of the gas. Now, we have long had methods of measuring l, for it is upon this that the coefficient of viscosity of the gas largely depends. When, therefore, we have measured the viscosities of different gases we can compute the corresponding l's, and then from equation (31) the relative diameters d, since n is the same for all gases at the same temperature and pressure. But the absolute value of d can be found only after the absolute value of n is known. If we insert in equation (31) the value of n found from e by the method presented in chap. v, it is found that the average diameter of the atom of the monatomic gas helium is 2×10^{-8} cm., that of the diatomic hydrogen molecule is a trifle more, while the diameters of the molecules of the diatomic gases, oxygen and nitrogen, are 50 per cent larger.[1] This would make the diameter of a single atom of hydrogen a trifle smaller, and that of a single atom of oxygen or nitrogen a trifle larger than that of helium. By the average molecular diameter we mean the average distance to which the centers of two molecules approach one another in such impacts as are continually occurring in connection with the motions of thermal agitation of gas molecules—this and nothing more.

As will presently appear, the reason that two molecules thus rebound from one another when in their motion of thermal agitation their centers of gravity approach to a distance of about 2×10^{-8} cm. is presumably that the atom is a system with negative electrons in its outer regions. When these negative electrons in two

[1] R. A. Millikan, *Phys. Rev.*, XXXII (1911), 397.

different systems which are coming into collision approach to about this distance, the repulsions between these similarly charged bodies begin to be felt, although at a distance the atoms are forceless. With decreasing distance this repulsion increases very rapidly until it becomes so great as to overcome the inertias of the systems and drive them asunder.

II. THE RADIUS OF THE ELECTRON FROM THE ELECTRO-MAGNETIC THEORY OF THE ORIGIN OF MASS

The first estimates of the volume occupied by a single one of the electronic constituents of an atom were obtained from the electromagnetic theory of the origin of mass, and were therefore to a pretty large degree speculative, but since these estimates are strikingly in accord with results which follow from direct experiments and are independent of any theory, and since, further, they are of extraordinary philosophic as well as historic interest, they will briefly be presented here.

Since Rowland proved that an electrically charged body in motion is an electrical current the magnitude of which is proportional to the speed of motion of the charge, and since an electric current, by virtue of the property called its self-induction, opposes any attempt to increase or diminish its magnitude, it is clear that an electrical charge, as such, possesses the property of inertia. But inertia is the only invariable property of matter. It is the quantitative measure of matter, and matter quantitatively considered is called *mass*. It is clear, then, theoretically, that an electrically charged pith ball must possess more mass than the same pith ball when uncharged. But when we compute how much the mass of a pith ball is increased by any charge which we can actually get it to hold, we find that the increase is so extraordinarily minute as to be hopelessly beyond the possibility of experimental detection. However, the method of making this computation, which was first pointed out by Sir J. J. Thomson in 1881,[1] is of unquestioned validity, so that we may feel quite sure of the correctness of the result. Further, when we combine the discovery that an electric charge possesses the distinguishing property of matter, namely, inertia, with the discovery that all electric charges are built up out of electrical specks all alike in charge, we have made it entirely legitimate to consider an electric current as *the passage of a definite, material, granular substance along the conductor.* In other words, the two entities, electricity and matter, which the nineteenth century tried to keep distinct, begin to look like different aspects of one and the same thing.

But, though we have thus justified the statement that electricity is material, have we any evidence as yet that all matter is electrical—that is, that all inertia is of the same origin as that of an electrical charge? The answer is that we have *evidence*, but as yet no *proof.* The theory that this is the case is still a speculation, but one which rests upon certain very significant facts. These facts are as follows:

If a pith ball is spherical and of radius a, then the mass m due to a charge E spread uniformly over its surface is given, as is shown in Appendix D by,

$$m = \frac{2}{3} \frac{E^2}{a} \quad \dots \dots \dots \dots \dots \dots (32)$$

[1] J. J. Thomson, *Phil. Mag.*, XI (1881), 229.

The point of especial interest in this result is that the mass is inversely proportional to the radius, so that the smaller the sphere upon which we can condense a given charge E the larger the mass of that charge. If, then, we had any means of measuring the minute increase in mass of a pith ball when we charge it electrically with a known quantity of electricity E, we could compute from equation (32) the size of this pith ball, even if we could not see it or measure it in any other way. This is much the sort of a position in which we find ourselves with respect to the negative electron. We can measure its mass, and it is found to be accurately $1/1,845$ of that of the hydrogen atom. We have measured accurately its charge and hence can compute the radius a of the equivalent sphere, that is, the sphere over which e would have to be uniformly distributed to have the observed mass, provided we assume that the observed mass of the electron is all due to its charge.

The justification for such an assumption is of two kinds. First, since we have found that electrons are constituents of all atoms and that mass is a property of an electrical charge, it is of course in the interests of simplicity to assume that all the mass of an atom is due to its contained electrical charges, rather than that there are two wholly different kinds of mass, one of electrical origin and the other of some other sort of an origin. Secondly, if the mass of a negative electron is all of electrical origin, then we can show from electromagnetic theory that this mass ought to be independent of the speed with which the electron may chance to be moving unless that speed approaches close to the speed of light. But from one-tenth the speed of light up to that speed the mass ought to vary with speed in a definitely predictable way.

Now, it is a piece of rare good fortune for the testing of this theory that radium actually does eject negative electrons with speeds which can be accurately measured and which do vary from three-tenths up to ninety-eight hundredths of that of light. *It is further one of the capital discoveries of the twentieth century[1] that within these limits the observed rate of variation of the mass of the negative electron with speed agrees accurately with the rate of variation computed on the assumption that this mass is all of electrical origin.* This leaves no room for a mass of any other kind to be associated with the free negative electron. Such is the experimental argument for the electrical origin of mass.

Solving then equation (32) for *a*, we find that the radius of the sphere over which the charge *e* of the negative electron would have to be distributed to have the observed mass is but 2×10^{-13} cm., or but one fifty-thousandth of the radius of the atom (10^{-8} cm.). From this point of view, then, the negative electron represents a charge of electricity which is condensed into an exceedingly minute volume. In fact, its radius cannot be larger in comparison with the radius of the atom than is the radius of the earth in comparison with the radius of her orbit about the sun.

In the case of the positive electron there is no direct experimental justification for the assumption that the mass is also wholly of electrical origin, for we cannot impart to the positive electrons speeds which approach the speed of light, nor have we as yet found in nature

[1] Bucherer, *Annalen der Physik*, XXVIII (1909), 513.

any of them which are endowed with speeds greater than about one-tenth that of light. But in view of the experimental results obtained with the negative electron, the carrying over of the same assumption to the positive electron is at least natural. Further, if this step be taken, it is clear from equation (32), since m for the positive is nearly two thousand times larger than m for the negative, that a for the positive can be only $1/2,000$ of what it is for the negative. In other words, the size of the positive electron would be to the size of the negative as a sphere having a two-mile radius would be to the size of the earth. From the standpoint, then, of the electromagnetic theory of the origin of mass, the dimensions of the negative and positive constitutents of atoms in comparison with the dimensions of the atoms themselves are like the dimensions of the planets and asteroids in comparison with the size of the solar system. All of these computations, whatever their value, are rendered possible by the fact that e is now known.

Now we know from methods which have nothing to do with the electromagnetic theory of the origin of mass, that the excessive minuteness predicted by that theory for both the positive and the negative constituents of atoms is in fact correct, though we have no evidence as to whether the foregoing ratio is right.

III. DIRECT EXPERIMENTAL PROOF OF THE EXCESSIVE MINUTENESS OF THE ELECTRONIC CONSTITUENTS OF ATOMS

For more than ten years we have had direct experimental proof[1] that the fastest of the α-particles, or

[1] Bragg, *Phil. Mag.*, VIII (1904), 719, 726; X (1905), 318; XI (1906), 617.

Fig. 14   Fig. 15

Photographs of the Tracks of α-Particles
Shooting through Air

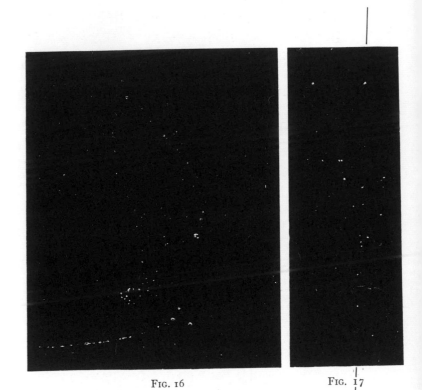

FIG. 16   FIG. 17

PHOTOGRAPHS OF THE TRACKS OF β-PARTICLES
SHOOTING THROUGH AIR

helium atoms, which are ejected by radium, shoot in practically straight lines through as much as 7 cm. of air at atmospheric pressure before being brought to rest. Some α-particles which have a range of 11.3 cm. have just been found.[1]   Figs. 14 and 15 show actual photographs of the tracks of such particles. We know too, for the reasons given on p. 138, that these α-particles do not penetrate the air after the manner of a bullet, namely, by pushing the molecules of air aside, but rather that they actually shoot through all the molecules of air which they encounter.   The number of such passages through molecules which an α-particle would have to make in traversing seven centimeters of air would be about half a million.

Further, the very rapid β-particles, or negative electrons, which are shot out by radium have been known for a still longer time to shoot in straight lines through much greater distances in air than 7 cm., and even to pass practically undeflected through appreciable thicknesses of glass or metal.

We saw in chap. vi that the tracks of both the α- and the β-particles through air could be photographed because they ionize some of the molecules through which they pass.   These ions then have the property of condensing water vapor about themselves, so that water droplets are formed which can be photographed by virtue of the light which they reflect.   Fig. 17 shows the track of a very high-speed β-ray.   A little to the right of the middle of the photograph a straight line can be drawn from bottom to top which will pass through a dozen or so of pairs of specks.   These specks are the

[1] Rutherford and Wood, *Phil. Mag.*, XXXI (1916), 379.

water droplets formed about the ions which were produced at these points.   Since we know the size of a
molecule and the number of molecules per cubic centimeter, we can compute, as in the case of the α-particle,
the number of molecules through which a β-particle
must pass in going a given distance.   The extraordinary
situation revealed by this photograph is that this particular particle shot through on an average as many as
10,000 atoms before it came near enough to an electronic constituent of any one of these atoms to detach
it from its system and form an ion.   *This shows conclusively that the electronic or other constituents of atoms
can occupy but an exceedingly small fraction of the space
inclosed within the atomic system.   Practically the whole
of this space must be empty to an electron going with
this speed.*

The left panel in the lower half of the plate (Fig. 16)
shows the track of a negative electron of much slower
speed, and it will be seen, first, that it ionizes much
more frequently, and, secondly, that instead of continu-
ing in a straight line it is deflected at certain points
from its original direction.   The reason for both of these
facts can readily be seen from the considerations on
p. 138, which it may be worth while to extend to the case
in hand as follows.

If a new planet or other relatively small body were
to shoot with stupendous speed through our solar system, the time which it spent within our system might
be so small that the force between it and the earth or
any other member of the solar system would not have
time either to deflect the stranger from its path or to
pull the earth out of its orbit.   If the speed of the strange

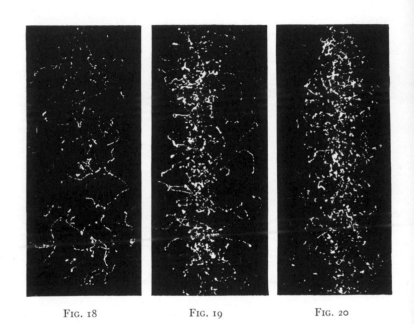

FIG. 18   FIG. 19   FIG. 20

PHOTOGRAPHS OF THE TRACKS OF β-PARTICLES EJECTED
BY X-RAYS FROM MOLECULES OF AIR

body were smaller, however, the effect would be more disastrous both to the constituents of our solar system and to the path of the strange body, for the latter would then have a much better chance of pulling one of the planets out of our solar system and also a much better chance of being deflected from a straight path itself. The slower a negative electron moves, then, the more is it liable to deflection and the more frequently does it ionize the molecules through which it passes.

This conclusion finds beautiful experimental confirmation in the three panels of the plate opposite this page, for the speed with which X-rays hurl out negative electrons from atoms has long been known to be much less than the speed of β-rays from radium, and the zigzag tracks in these photographs are the paths of these corpuscles. It will be seen that they bend much more often and ionize much more frequently than do the rays shown in Figs. 16 and 17.

But the study of the tracks of the α-particles (Figs. 14 and 15, opposite p. 187) is even more illuminating as to the structure of the atom. For the α-particle, being an atom of helium eight thousand times more massive than a negative electron, could no more be deflected by one of the latter in an atom through which it passes than a cannon ball could be deflected by a pea. Yet Figs. 14 and 15 show that toward the end of its path the α-particle does in general suffer several sudden deflections. Such deflections could be produced only by a very powerful center of force within the atom whose mass is at least comparable with the mass of the helium atom.

These sharp deflections, which occasionally amount to as much as 150° to 180°, lend the strongest of support to the view that the atom consists of a heavy positively charged nucleus about which are grouped enough electrons to render the whole atom neutral. But the fact that in these experiments the α-particle goes through 500,000 atoms without approaching near enough to this central nucleus to suffer appreciable deflection more than two or three times constitutes the most convincing evidence that this central nucleus which holds the negative electrons within the atomic system occupies an excessively minute volume, just as we computed from the electromagnetic theory of the origin of mass that the positive electron ought to do. Indeed, knowing as he did by direct measurement the speed of the α-particle, Rutherford, who is largely responsible for the nucleus-atom theory, first computed,[1] with the aid of the inverse square law, which we know to hold between charged bodies of dimensions which are small compared with their distances apart, how close the α-particle would approach to the nucleus of a given atom like that of gold before it would be turned back upon its course (see Appendix F). The result was in the case of gold, one of the heaviest atoms, about 10^{-12} cm., and in the case of hydrogen, the lightest atom, about 10^{-13} cm. These are merely upper limits for the dimensions of the nuclei.

However uncertain, then, we may feel about the sizes of positive and negative electrons computed from the electromagnetic theory of the origin of the mass, we may regard it as fairly well established by such direct experiments as these that the electronic constituents

[1] *Phil. Mag.*, XXI (1911), 669.

of atoms are as small, in comparison with the dimensions of the atomic systems, as are the sun and planets in comparison with the dimensions of the solar system. Indeed, when we reflect that we can shoot helium atoms by the billion through a thin-walled highly evacuated glass tube without leaving any holes behind, i.e., without impairing in the slightest degree the vacuum or perceptibly weakening the glass, we see from this alone that the atom itself must consist mostly of "hole"; in other words, that an atom, like a solar system, must be an exceedingly loose structure whose impenetrable portions must be extraordinarily minute in comparison with the penetrable portions. The notion that an atom can appropriate to itself all the space within its boundaries to the exclusion of all others is then altogether exploded by these experiments. A particular atom can certainly occupy the same space at the same time as any other atom if it is only endowed with sufficient kinetic energy. Such energies as correspond to the motions of thermal agitation of molecules are not, however, sufficient to enable one atom to penetrate the boundaries of another, hence the seeming impenetrability of atoms in ordinary experiments in mechanics. That there is, however, a portion of the atom which is wholly impenetrable to the alpha particles is definitely proved by experiments of the sort we have been considering; for it occasionally happens that an alpha particle hits this nucleus "head on," and, when it does so, it is turned straight back upon its course. As indicated above, the size of this impenetrable portion, which may be defined as the size of the nucleus, is in no case larger than 1/10,000 the diameter of the atom.

IV.   THE NUMBER OF ELECTRONS IN AN ATOM

If it be considered as fairly conclusively established by the experiments just described that an atom consists of a heavy but very minute positively charged nucleus which holds light negative electrons in some sort of a configuration about it, then the number of negative electrons outside the nucleus must be such as to have a total charge equal to the free positive charge of the nucleus, since otherwise the atom could not be neutral.

But the positive charge on the nucleus has been approximately determined as follows: With the aid of the knowledge, already obtained through the determination of e, of the exact number of atoms in a given weight of a given substance, Sir Ernest Rutherford[1] first computed the chance that a single helium atom in being shot with a known speed through a sheet of gold foil containing a known number of atoms per unit of area of the sheet would suffer a deflection through a given angle. This computation can easily be made in terms of the known kinetic energy and charge of the α-particle, the known number of atoms in the gold foil, and the unknown charge on the nucleus of the gold atom (see Appendix F).   Geiger and Marsden[2] then actually counted in Rutherford's laboratory, by means of the scintillations produced on a zinc-sulphide screen, what fraction of, say, a thousand α-particles, which shot normally into the gold foil, were deflected through a given angle, and from this observed number and Rutherford's theory they obtained the number of free positive charges on the nucleus of the gold atom.

[1] *Phil. Mag.*, XXI (1911), 669–88.
[2] *Ibid.*, XXV (1913), 604.

Repeating the experiment and the computations with foils made from a considerable number of other metals, they found that in every case *the number of free positive charges on the atoms of different substances was approximately equal to half its atomic weight.* This means that the aluminum atom, for example, has a nucleus containing about thirteen free positive charges and that the nucleus of the atom of gold contains in the neighborhood of a hundred. This result was in excellent agreement with the conclusion reached independently by Barkla[1] from experiments of a wholly different kind, namely, experiments on the scattering of X-rays. These indicated that the number of scattering centers in an atom—that is, its number of free negative electrons—was equal to about half the atomic weight. But this number must, of course, equal the number of free positive electrons in the nucleus.

V.   MOSELEY'S REMARKABLE DISCOVERY

The foregoing result was only approximate. Indeed, there was internal evidence in Geiger and Marsden's work itself that a half was somewhat too high. The answer has recently been made very definite and very precise through the extraordinary work of a brilliant young Englishman, Moseley, who, at the age of twenty-seven, had accomplished as notable a piece of research in physics as has appeared during the last fifty years. Such a mind has recently fallen a victim to the most ghastly crime in history, the present European war. He was shot and killed instantly in the trenches in the summer of 1915.

[1] Barkla, *Phil. Mag.*, XXI (1911), 648.

Laue in Munich had suggested in 1912 the use of the regular spacing of the molecules of a crystal for the analysis, according to the principle of the grating, of ether waves of very short wave-length, such as X-rays were supposed to be, and the Braggs[1] had not only perfected an X-ray spectrometer which utilized this principle, but had determined accurately the wavelengths of the X-rays which are characteristic of certain metals. The accuracy with which this can be done is limited simply by the accuracy in the determination of e, so that the whole new field of exact X-ray spectrometry is made available through our exact knowledge of e. Moseley's discovery,[2] made as a result of an elaborate and difficult study of the wave-lengths of the characteristic X-rays which were excited when cathode rays were made to impinge in succession upon anticathodes embracing most of the known elements, was that these characteristic wave-lengths of the different elements, or, better, their characteristic frequencies, are related in a very simple but a very significant way. *These frequencies were found to constitute the same sort of an arithmetical progression as do the charges which we found to exist on our oil drops.* It was the square root of the frequencies rather than the frequencies themselves which showed this beautifully simple relationship, but this is an unimportant detail. The significant fact is that, *arranged in the order of increasing frequency of their characteristic X-ray spectra, all the known elements which have been examined constitute a simple arithmetical series each member of which is obtained from its predecessor by adding always the same quantity.*

[1] Bragg, *X-Rays and Crystal Structure*, 1915.
[2] *Phil. Mag.*, XXVI. (1912), 1024; XXVII (1914), 703.

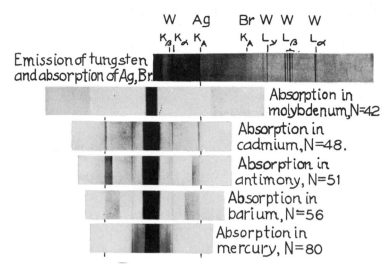

FIG. 22.—X-RAY ABSORPTION SPECTRA, K SERIES

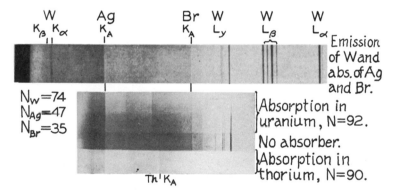

FIG. 23—X-RAY ABSORPTION SPECTRA, L SERIES

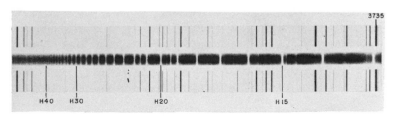

FIG. 24.—HYDROGEN SPECTRUM FROM A NEBULA

The plate opposite this page shows photographs of the X-ray spectra of a number of elements whose atomic numbers—that is, the numbers assigned them in Moseley's arrangement of the elements on the basis of increasing X-ray frequency—are given on the left. These photographs were taken by Siegbahn.[1] The distance from the "central image"—in this case the black line on the left—to a given line of the line spectrum on the right is approximately proportional to the wave-length of the rays producing this line. The photographs show beautifully, first, how the atoms of all the elements produce spectra of just the same type, and, secondly, how the wave-lengths of corresponding lines decrease, or the frequencies increase, with increasing atomic number. The photograph on the left shows this progression for the highest frequency rays which the atoms produce, the so-called K series, while the one on the right shows the same sort of a progression for the next lower frequency rays, namely, those of the so-called L series, which have uniformly from seven to eight times the wave-length of the K series. The plate opposite p. 197 shows some very beautiful photographs taken by De Broglie in Paris[2] in October, 1916. The upper one is the X-ray emission spectrum of tungsten. It consists of general radiations, corresponding to white light, scattered throughout the whole length of the spectrum as a background and superposed upon this two groups of lines. The two K lines are here close to the central image, for the K wave-lengths are here very short, since tungsten has a high atomic number (74). Farther to the right

[1] *Jahrbuch der Radioaktivität u. Elektronik*, XIII (1916), 326.

[2] *Comptes rendus*, CLXV (1916), 87, 352.

is the L series of tungsten lines which will be recognized because of its similarity to the L series in the plate opposite p. 195. Between the K and the L lines are two absorption edges marked $\frac{Ag}{K_A}$ and $\frac{Br}{K_A}$. The former represents the frequency above which the silver absorbs all the general radiation of tungsten but below which it lets it all through. The latter is the corresponding line for bromine. In a print from a photograph absorption in the plate itself obviously appears as a darkening, transmission as a lightening. Just below is the spectrum obtained by inserting a sheet of molybdenum in the path of the beam, i.e., before the slit of the spectrometer. Absorption in the molybdenum will obviously appear as a lightening, transmission as a darkening. It will be seen that the molybdenum absorbs all the frequencies in the X-ray emission of tungsten higher than a particular frequency and lets through all frequencies lower than this value. This remarkable characteristic of the absorption of X-rays was discovered by Barkla in 1909.[1] The absorption edge at which, with increasing frequency, absorption suddenly begins is very sharply marked. This edge coincides, as will presently be shown, with the highest emission frequency of which molybdenum is capable. De Broglie has measured accurately these critical absorption frequencies for all the heavy elements up to thorium, thus extending the K series from atomic number $N = 60$ where he found it, to $N = 90$, a notable advance. The two absorption edges characteristic of the silver and the bromine in the photographic plate appear in the same place on all the photographs in

[1] Barkla and Sadler, *Phil. Mag.*, XVII (May, 1909), 749.

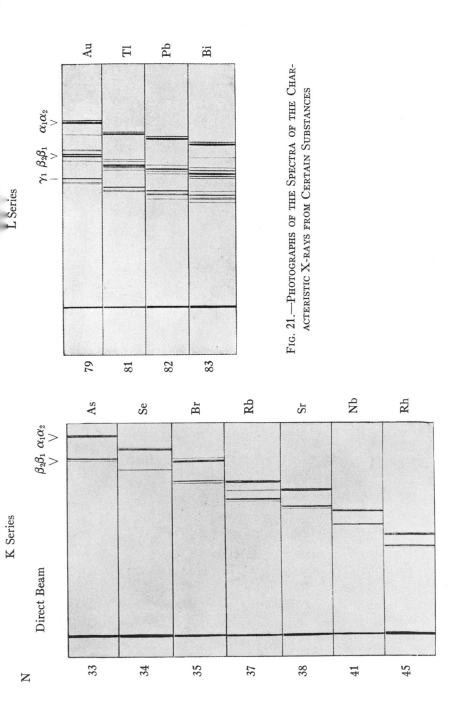

FIG. 21.—PHOTOGRAPHS OF THE SPECTRA OF THE CHAR-
ACTERISTIC X-RAYS FROM CERTAIN SUBSTANCES

which they could appear.   The other absorption edges vary from element to element and are characteristic each of its particular element.   The way in which this critical absorption edge moves toward the central image as the atomic number increases in the steps Br 35, Mo 42, Ag 47, Cd 48, Sb 51, Ba 56, W 74, Hg 80, is very beautifully shown in De Broglie's photographs all the way up to mercury, where the absorption edge is somewhat inside the shortest of the characteristic K radiations of tungsten.   There must be twelve more of these edges between mercury ($N = 80$) and uranium ($N = 92$) and De Broglie has measured them up to thorium ($N = 90$).   They become, however, very difficult to locate in this K region of frequencies on account of their extreme closeness to the central image.   But the L radiations, which are of seven times longer wave-length, may then be used, and Fig. 23 of the plate opposite this page shows the L-ray absorption edge as obtained by De Broglie in both uranium and thorium, so that the position in the Moseley table of each element all the way to the heaviest one, uranium, is fixed in this way by direct experiment.   Fig. 25 shows the progression of square-root frequencies as it appears from measurements made on De Broglie's photographs.   It will be noticed that, in going from bromine (35) to uranium (92), the length of the step does change by a few percent. The probable cause of this will be considered later.

The data given in Table XIV show that the absorption edge for the K-rays coincides exceedingly closely in every case with the shortest emission K line of the absorbing substance, while in the case of the L series one of the two absorption edges coincides in every case

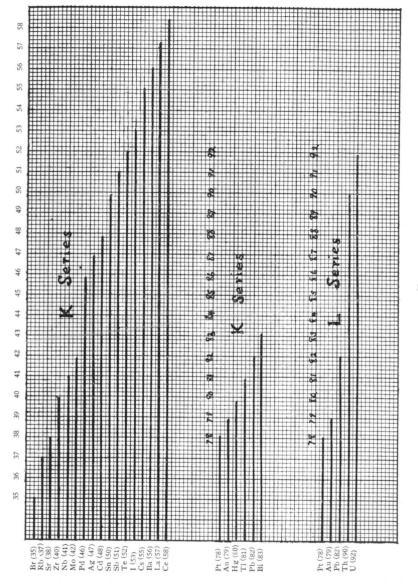

FIG. 25

with the shortest beta line of this L series. The other absorption edge in the L region also coincides in every case with an emission line, though the data are as yet too meager to permit of any general statement as to what this line is.

TABLE XIV

COMPARISON OF K_A AND K_β

N	Element	K_A	K_β	N	Element	K_A	K_β
35	Br	.914	.914	53	I	.367	(.380)
37	Rb	.810	.813	55	Cs	.338	(.345)
38	Sr	.764	.767	56	Ba	.325	(.333)
40	Zr	.681	(.695)	57	La	.310	(.319)
41	Nb	.645	.657	58	Ce	.298	(.304)
42	Mo	.611	(.620)	78	Pt	.150	......
46	Pd	.503	.503	79	Au	.147	......
47	Ag	.479	.488	80	Hg	.143	......
48	Cd	.458	(.466)	81	Tl	.139	......
50	Sn	.419	(.419)	82	Pb	.135	......
51	Sb	.399	.408	83	Bi	.130	......
52	Te	.383	(.396)	90	Th	.098 about	......

COMPARISON OF L_A AND L_β

N	Element	L_A	L_β	N	Element	L_A	L_β
78	Pt	1.067	1.072	90	Th	.756	.750
79	Au	1.037	1.035	92	U	.719	.702
82	Pb	.945	.948				

Since these enormously high X-ray frequencies are presumably due to the vibrations arising from electrons which are in extraordinarily powerful fields of force, such as might be expected to exist in the inner regions of the atom close to the nucleus, Moseley's discovery strongly suggests that the charge on this nucleus is produced in the case of each atom by adding some particular invariable charge to the nucleus of the atom next below it in Moseley's table. This suggestion gains added weight when it is found that with one or two trifling exceptions, to be considered later, *Moseley's series of increasing X-ray frequencies is exactly the series of increasing atomic weights*. It also receives powerful support from the following recent discovery.

Mendeleéff's periodic table shows that the progression of chemical properties among the elements coincides in general with the progression of atomic weights. Now it has recently been pointed out that whenever a radioactive substance loses a doubly charged α-particle it moves two places to the left in the periodic table, while whenever it loses a singly charged β-particle it moves one place to the right,[1] thus showing that the chemical character of a substance depends upon the number of free positive charges in its nucleus.

One of the most interesting and striking characteristics of Moseley's table is that all the known elements between sodium (atomic number 11, atomic weight 23) and lead (atomic number 82, atomic weight, 207.2) have been fitted into it and there are left but four vacancies within this range. Below sodium there are just 10 known elements, and the X-ray spectra of these have not as yet been obtained, but the progression of atomic weights and of chemical properties is here altogether definite and unambiguous. It seems highly probable then from Moseley's work that we have already found all except four of the complete series of different types of atoms from hydrogen to lead, i.e., from 1 to 82, of which the physical world is built. From 82 to 92 comes

[1] Soddy, *The Chemistry of the Radioelements*, Part II, 1914.

the group of radioactive elements which are continually transmuting themselves into one another, and above 92 (uranium) it is not likely that any elements exist.

That hydrogen is indeed the base of the Moseley series is rendered well-nigh certain by the following computation. If we write Moseley's discovery that the square roots of the highest frequencies, n_1, n_2, etc., emitted by different atoms are proportional to the nuclear charges, E_1, E_2, etc., in the following form:

$$\sqrt{\frac{n_1}{n_2}} = \frac{E_1}{E_2} \text{ or } \frac{\lambda_2}{\lambda_1} = \frac{E_1^2}{E_2^2} \dots \dots \dots \dots (33)$$

and substitute for λ_2 the observed wave-length of the highest frequency line emitted by tungsten—a wave-length which has been found by Hull to be 0.185×10^{-8} cm.; and, further, if we substitute for E_2, 74, the atomic number of tungsten, and for E_1, 1, we should obtain, by solving for λ_1, the wave-length of the highest frequency line which can be emitted by the element whose nucleus contains but one single positive electron. The result of this substitution is $\lambda_1 = 101.3 \ \mu\mu$ (millionths millimeters). Now the wave-length corresponding to the highest frequency in the ultra-violet series of hydrogen lines recently discovered by Lyman is $91.2 \ \mu\mu$ and there is every reason to believe from the form of the Balmer series of which this is the convergence wave-length that it corresponds to the highest frequency of which the hydrogen atom is capable. The agreement is only approximate, but it is as close as could be expected in view of the lack of exact equality in the Moseley steps. *It is well-nigh certain, then, that this Lyman ultra-violet series of hydrogen lines is nothing but the K X-ray series of hydrogen.* Similarly, it is equally certain that the L X-ray series of hydrogen is the ordinary Balmer series in the visible region, the head of which is at $\lambda = 365 \,\mu\mu$. In other words, hydrogen's ordinary radiations are its X-rays and nothing more.

There is also an M series for hydrogen discovered by Paschen in the ultra-red, which in itself would make it probable that there are series for all the elements of longer wave-length than the L series, and that the complicated optical series observed with metallic arcs are parts of these longer wave-length series. As a matter of fact, an M series has been found for six of the elements of high atomic number.

Thus the Moseley experiments have gone a long way toward solving the mystery of spectral lines. They reveal to us clearly and certainly the whole series of elements from hydrogen to uranium, all producing spectra of remarkable similarity, at least so far as the K and L radiations are concerned, but scattered regularly through the whole frequency region, from the ultra-violet, where the K lines for hydrogen are found, all the way up to frequencies $(92)^2$ or 8,464 times as high. There can scarcely be a doubt that this whole field will soon be open to exploration. How brilliantly, then, have these recent studies justified the predictions of the spectroscopists that the key to atomic structure lay in the study of spectral lines!

Moseley's work is, in brief, evidence from a wholly new quarter that all these elements constitute a family, each member of which is related to every other member in a perfectly definite and simple way. It looks as if the dream of Thales of Miletus had actually come true and that we have not only found a primordial element out of which all substances are made, but that that primordial element is hydrogen itself. It is well known that this result was suggested by Prout just one hundred years ago, arguing as he did from the fact that most of the atomic weights of all the elements are very nearly exact multiples of the weight of hydrogen. Prout's theory failed of general acceptance because the multiple relationships are not found to be exact. These departures from exactness in the case of the atomic weights must, of course, be explained somehow, but if mass is electromagnetic in its origin, it is not impossible to explain them on the basis of the overlapping of the electric fields of the electronic constituents of the atoms. Thus, if a positive and negative charge could be brought into exact coincidence, their fields would entirely disappear, and with them their masses also, provided mass is merely a property of an electric field. If, then, when the positive nucleus of the hydrogen atom enters into the nucleus of a heavier atom, it is packed very close to negative electrons, the mass of that nucleus would be somewhat less than the sum of the masses of the hydrogen atoms which it contains, as it is found in fact to be. This explanation on the basis of close "packing" of the lack of exactness in the multiple relations between the atomic weights of the elements was suggested about 1901, as soon as the Kaufmann[1] experiments had given an experimental basis for the electromagnetic theory of the origin of mass. It has been discussed by Lorenz, by

---

[1] Kaufmann, *Göttinger Nachrichten*, November 8, 1901.

Rutherford,[1] and later by Harkins.[2] With its aid we
can account for the lack of exact coincidence between
the progression of atomic weights, and that found in
Moseley's table.   (See Appendix H.)

Whether or not hydrogen is the building-stone of all
the 92 elements of Moseley's table, we may at least feel
fairly sure that the number of free positive electrons in
the nucleus of an atom is exactly the number assigned to
that atom in Moseley's table.   This is, in general, a
little less than half the atomic weight, since the highest
number in the table is 92, while the atomic weight of the
corresponding heaviest known element, uranium, is
238.5.   It is the positive charge on this nucleus which
obviously determines the number of negative electrons
which are distributed around the nucleus in the outer
regions of the atom, and there is just now an increasing
weight of evidence that this number determines the
chemical affinity of the atom, and, indeed, all its chemical and physical properties except its weight.   It is for
this reason that we now think there can be no more
different kinds of elements between hydrogen and uranium than those which correspond to the 92 numbers in
Moseley's table.

How these free positive charges in the nucleus varying from 1 to 92 are held together we do not know.   The
experimental evidence at present stops with the fact
that a number of free positive electrons equal to the
atomic number exist in the nucleus and that a corresponding number of free negative electrons are held in

---

[1] Rutherford, *Phil. Mag.*, XXI (1911), 669.

[2] Harkins, *Phil. Mag.*, XXX (1915), 723.

equilibrium in the outer regions of the atom. We may imagine that there are some negative electrons also inside the nucleus, for they seem to be shot out from it in radioactive changes. Further, to take the case of the lightest of the composite atoms, helium, of atomic number 2, since its nucleus has but two free positive charges, while its atomic weight is 4, we may imagine that its nucleus is actually made up of 4 positive electrons which are held together by 2 negative electrons. In like manner, from this point of view, each nucleus would have a number of binding negative electrons equal to its atomic number, and the number of positive electrons bound by them in the nucleus would be twice the atomic number, each negative binding two positives. This would leave, as it should, an equal number of negative electrons to be held in the outer regions of each atom.

But plausible as this point of view may be, it is as yet speculative. This much, however, is known with certainty, namely, that inside all the atoms there are a definite number of two fundamental entities, namely, positive and negative electrons, which are known not to differ from one another at all in charge, but which do seem to differ both in mass and in volume. The electron then in its two forms is, according to the physicists' present view, the building-stone of the sub-atomic world. Someone has called it the "ultim-atom" of twentieth-century science.

VI. THE BOHR ATOM

Thus far nothing has been said as to whether the electrons within the atom are at rest or in motion, or, if they are in motion, as to the character of these motions.

In the hydrogen atom, however, which contains, according to the foregoing evidence, but one positive and one negative electron, there is no known way of preventing the latter from falling into the positive nucleus unless centrifugal forces are called upon to balance attractions, as they do in the case of the earth and moon. Accordingly it seems to be necessary to assume that the negative electron is rotating in an orbit about the positive. But such an orbit would normally be accompanied by a continuous radiation of energy of continuously increasing frequency as the electron, by virtue of its loss of energy, approached closer and closer to the nucleus. Yet experiment reveals no such behavior, for, so far as we know, hydrogen does not radiate at all unless it is ionized, and, when it does radiate, it gives rise, not to a continuous spectrum, as the foregoing picture would demand, but rather to a line spectrum in which the frequencies corresponding to the various lines are related to one another in the very significant way shown in the photograph of Fig. 24 and represented by the so-called Balmer equation, which has the form

$$\nu = N\left(\frac{1}{n_1^2} - \frac{1}{n_2^2}\right) \dots\dots\dots\dots (34)$$

In this formula ν represents frequency, N a constant, and n_1, for all the lines in the visible region, has the value 2, while n_2 takes for the successive lines the values 3, 4, 5, 6, etc. In the hydrogen series in the infra-red discovered by Paschen[1] $n_1 = 3$ and n_2 takes the successive values 4, 5, 6, etc. It is since the development of the

[1] Paschen, *Annalen der Physik*, XXVII (1908), 565.

Bohr theory that Lyman[1] discovered his hydrogen series in the ultra-violet in which $n_1 = 1$ and $n_2 = 2, 3, 4,$ etc. Since 1 is the smallest whole number, this series should correspond, as indicated heretofore, to the highest frequencies of which hydrogen is capable, the upper limit toward which these frequencies tend being reached when $n_1 = 1$ and $n_2 = \infty$, that is, when $\nu = N$.

Guided by all of these facts except the last, N. Bohr, a young mathematical physicist of Copenhagen, has recently devised[2] an atomic model which has had some very remarkable successes. This model was originally designed to cover only the simplest possible case of one single electron revolving around a positive nucleus. In order to account for the large number of lines which the spectrum of such a system reveals (Fig. 24, taken by Professor Wright of the Lick Observatory, shows all of the Balmer series given by the spectrum of a nebula except the longest wave-length line called H_a, which is beyond the left edge of the plate), Bohr's first assumption was that the electron may rotate about the nucleus in a whole series of different orbits and that each of these orbits is governed by the well-known Newtonian law, which when mathematically stated takes the form:

$$\frac{eE}{a^2} = (2\pi n)^2 ma \dots\dots\dots\dots\dots (35)$$

in which e is the change of the electron, E that of the nucleus, a the radius of the orbit, n the orbital frequency, and m the mass of the electron. This is merely the

[1] *Spectroscopy of the Extreme Ultraviolet*, p. 78.

[2] N. Bohr, *Phil. Mag.*, XXVI (1913), 1 and 476 and 857; XXIX (1915), 332; XXX (1915), 394.

assumption that the electron rotates in a circular orbit which is governed by the laws which are known, from the work on the scattering of the alpha particles, to hold inside as well as outside the atom. The radical element in it is that it permits the negative electron to maintain this orbit without radiating energy even though this appears to conflict with ordinary electromagnetic theory. But, on the other hand, the facts of magnetism[1] and of optics, in addition to the successes of the Bohr theory which are to be detailed, appear at present to lend experimental justification to such an assumption.

Bohr's second assumption is that radiation takes place only when an electron jumps from one to another of these orbits. If A_2 represents the energy of the electron in one orbit and A_1 that in any other orbit, then it is clear from considerations of energy alone that when the electron passes from the one orbit to the other the amount of energy radiated must be $A_2 - A_1$; further, this radiated energy obviously must have some frequency ν, and, in view of the experimental work presented in the next chapter, Bohr placed it proportional to ν, and wrote:

$$h\nu = A_2 - A_1 \dots\dots\dots\dots\dots\dots (36)$$

h being the so-called Planck constant to be discussed later. It is to be emphasized that this assumption gives no physical picture of the way in which the radiation takes place. It merely states the energy relations which must be satisfied when it occurs.

[1] Einstein and De Haas, *Verh. der deutsch. phys. Ges.*, XVII (1915), 152; also Barnett, *Phys. Rev.*, VI (1915), 239.

Bohr's third assumption is that the various possible circular orbits are determined by assigning to each orbit a kinetic energy T such that

$$T = \tfrac{1}{2}\tau hn \dots\dots\dots\dots\dots (37)$$

in which τ is a whole number, n the orbital frequency, and h is again Planck's constant. This value of T is assigned so as to make the series of frequencies agree with that actually observed, namely, that represented by the Balmer series of hydrogen.

It is to be noticed that, if circular electronic orbits exist at all, no one of these assumptions is arbitrary. Each of them is merely the statement of the existing *experimental* situation. It is not surprising, therefore, that they predict the sequence of frequencies found in the hydrogen series. They have been purposely made to do so. But they have not been made with any reference whatever to the exact numerical values of these frequencies.

The evidence for the soundness of the conception of non-radiating electronic orbits is to be looked for, then, first, in the success of the constants involved, and, second, in the physical significance, if any, which attaches to the third assumption. If these constants come out right within the limits of experimental error, then the theory of non-radiating electronic orbits has been given the most crucial imaginable of tests, especially if these constants are accurately determinable.

What are the facts? The constant of the Balmer series in hydrogen, that is, the value of N in equation (34), is known with the great precision attained in all wave-length determinations and is equal to 3.290×10^{15}. From the Bohr theory it is given by the simplest algebra (Appendix G) as

$$N = \frac{2\pi^2 e^4 m}{h^3} = \frac{2\pi^2 e^5}{h^3 \dfrac{e}{m}} \quad \ldots \ldots \ldots \ldots (38)$$

As already indicated, I have recently redetermined[1] e with an estimated accuracy of one part in 1,000 and obtained for it the value $4,774 \times 10^{-10}$. As will be shown in the next chapter, I have also determined h photo-electrically[2] with an error, in the case of sodium, of no more than one-half of 1 per cent, the value for sodium being 6.56×10^{-27}. The value found by Webster[3] by a method recently discovered by Duane and Hunt[4] is 6.53×10^{-27}. Taking the mean of these two results, viz. $6,545 \times 10^{-27}$, as the most probable value, we get with the aid of Bucherer's value of $\dfrac{e}{m}$ (1.767×10^7) which is probably correct to 0.1 per cent, $N = 3.294 \times 10^{15}$, *which agrees within a tenth of 1 per cent with the observed value.* This agreement constitutes most extraordinary justification of the theory of non-radiating electronic orbits. It demonstrates that the behavior of the negative electron in the hydrogen atom is at least correctly described by the *equation* of a circular non-radiating orbit. If this equation can be obtained from some other physical condition than that of an actual orbit,

[1] R. A. Millikan, *Proc. Nat. Acad.*, April, 1917.

[2] R. A. Millikan, *Phys. Rev.*, VII (1916), 362.

[3] *Phys. Rev.*, VII (1916), 599.

[4] *Ibid.*, VI (1915), 168.

it is obviously incumbent upon those who so hold to show what that condition is. Until this is done, it is justifiable to suppose that the equation of an orbit means an actual orbit.

Again, the radii of the stable orbits for hydrogen are easily found from Bohr's assumptions to take the mathematical form (Appendix G)

$$a = \frac{\tau^2 h^2}{4\pi^2 m e^4} \quad \cdots \cdots \cdots \cdots \cdots \cdots (39)$$

In other words, since τ is a whole number, the radii of these orbits bear the ratios 1, 4, 9, 16, 25. If normal hydrogen is assumed to be that in which the electron is in the inmost possible orbit, namely, that for which $\tau = 1$, $2a$, the diameter of the normal hydrogen *atom*, comes out 1.1×10^{-8}. The best determination for the diameter of the hydrogen *molecule* yields 2.2×10^{-8}, in extraordinarily close agreement with the prediction from Bohr's theory. Further, the fact that normal hydrogen does not absorb at all the Balmer series lines which it emits is beautifully explained by the foregoing theory, since, according to it, normal hydrogen has no electrons in the orbits corresponding to the lines of the Balmer series. Again, the fact that *hydrogen emits its characteristic radiations only when it is ionized* favors the theory that the process of emission is a process of settling down to a normal condition through a series of possible intermediate states, and is therefore in line with the view that a change in orbit is necessary to the act of radiation. Similarly, the fact that in the stars there are 33 lines in the Balmer series, while in the

laboratory we never get more than 12, is easily explicable
from the Bohr theory, but no other theory has offered
even a suggestion of an explanation.

Another triumph of the theory is that the third
assumption, devised to fit a purely empirical situation,
viz., the observed relations between the frequencies
of the Balmer series, is found to have a very simple
and illuminating physical meaning. It is that all the
possible values of the angular momentum of the electron
rotating about the positive nucleus are exact multiples
of a particular value of this angular momentum. Angular momentum then has in the hydrogen atom the
property of *atomicity*. Such relationships do not in
general drop out of *empirical* formulae. When they do,
we usually see in them real interpretations of the
formulae—not merely coincidences.

Again, the success of a theory is often tested as much
by its adaptability to the explanation of deviations from
the behavior predicted by its most elementary form
as by the exactness of the fit between calculated and
observed results. The theory of electronic orbits has
had remarkable successes of this sort. Thus it predicts
the Moseley law (33). But this law, discovered after-
ward, was found inexact, and it should be inexact when
there is more than one electron in the atom, as is the
case save for H atoms and for such He atoms as have
lost one negative charge, and that because of the way
in which the electrons influence one another's fields.
It will probably be found to break down completely
for very light atoms like those of lithium. The more
powerful the nucleus, however, and the closer to it the
inner orbit the smaller should this effect be. Now

precisely this result is observed. The Moseley law holds most accurately when tested for hydrogen and the elements of highest atomic number, and much less accurately when tested for hydrogen and aluminum or magnesium. Similarly the ratio between the frequencies of the α and β lines of the K series approaches closer to the theoretical value (that for hydrogen) the higher the atomic number of the element.

Again, it is shown in the photographs opposite p. 195 that the various lines in the characteristic X-ray spectra are not single lines as required by the simple theory. Accordingly Sommerfeld[1] extended Bohr equations in the endeavor to account for this structure on the basis of ellipticity in some of the orbits, and Paschen,[2] by measurements on the structure of the complex helium lines, has obtained such extraordinary checks upon this theory that $\frac{e}{m}$ comes out from his measurements to within a tenth of 1 per cent of the accepted value.

A further prediction made by the theory and dis- covered as soon as looked for was a relation between the frequencies of the lines of two succeeding series like the K and the L series. This relation is expressed in the equation:

$$\nu_{K\beta} - \nu_{K\alpha} = \nu_{L\alpha} \dots\dots\dots\dots\dots (40)$$

Thus, according to Bohr, the longest wave-length line of the K series, the α line, is due to jumping from orbit 2 (Fig. 26) to orbit 1 with a change in energy $A_2 - A_1$; the next longest wave-length line, the β line is due to

[1] *Annalen der Physik*, LI (1916), 1.

[2] *Ibid.*, October, 1916.

jumping from 3 to 1 with a change in energy $A_3 - A_1$; while the longest wave-length line of the L series, the α line, is due to jumping from 3 to 2, with a change in energy $A_3 - A_2$. Hence if the frequency ν is in every case proportional to the change in energy, equation (40) follows at once, and, further, it should hold accurately from the energy relations between the orbits *whether there be one or many electrons in the atoms. I have been able to find no case of its failure*, though the data upon which it may be tested are now considerable. I have also recently pointed out[1] that it is equivalent to the well-known Rydberg-Schuster law,[2] which has been found to hold quite generally among optical series.

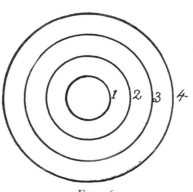

Fig. 26

If then the test of truth in a physical theory is large success both in the prediction of new relationships and in correctly and exactly accounting for old ones, the theory of non-radiating orbits is one of the well-established truths of modern physics. For the present at least it is truth, and no other theory of atomic structure need be considered until it has shown itself able to approach it in fertility. I know of no competitor which is as yet even in sight.

[1] *Phys. Rev.*, May, 1917, presented before the American Physical Society, December 1, 1916.

[2] Baly's *Spectroscopy*, p. 488.

I am well aware that the facts of organic chemistry seem to demand that the valence electrons be grouped in certain definite equilibrium positions about the periphery of the atom, and that at first sight this demand appears difficult to reconcile with the theory of electronic orbits. As yet, however, there is no necessary clash. Hydrogen and helium present no difficulties, since the former has but one valency, and the latter none. It is to these atoms alone that the unmodified Bohr theory applies, for it treats only the case of a single negative electron rotating about a positive nucleus. That the K radiations of the heavy elements are so accurately predictable from those of hydrogen indicates, indeed, that close to the nucleus of these elements there lie electrons to which the Bohr theory applies fairly accurately, but the radiations give us no information about the conditions or behaviors of the external electrons which have to do with the phenomena of valency, and we have investigated but little the radiating properties of the atoms which possess but few electrons. A further study of the behavior with respect to X-rays of the elements from lithium, atomic number 3, to magnesium, atomic number 11, may be expected to throw new light on this problem.

It has been objected, too, that the Bohr theory is not a radiation theory because it gives us no picture of the mechanism of the production of the frequency ν. This is true, and therein lies its strength, just as the strength of the first and second laws of thermodynamics lies in the fact that they are true irrespective of a mechanism. The Bohr theory is a theory of atomic structure; it is not a theory of radiation, for it merely states what energy relations must exist when radiation, whatever its mechanism, takes place. It is the first attempt to determine in the light of well-established experimental facts what the electrons inside the atom are doing, and as such a first attempt it must be regarded as, thus far, a success, though it has by no means got beyond the hypothetical stage. Its chief difficulty arises from the apparent contradiction involved in a non-radiating electronic orbit—a contradiction which would disappear, however, if the negative electron itself, when inside the atom, were a ring of some sort, capable of expanding to various radii, and capable, only when freed from the atom, of assuming essentially the properties of a point charge, such as we find it endowed with in experiments upon cathode rays, β-rays, and ionization in gases. That it actually does possess certain properties not in the past always associated with electrical charges will appear in the next chapter.

CHAPTER X

THE NATURE OF RADIANT ENERGY

The problems thus far discussed have all been in the domain of molecular physics, but the discovery and measurement of the electron have also exerted a powerful influence upon recent developments in the domain of ether physics. These developments are of extraordinary interest and suggestiveness, but they lead into regions in which the physicist sees as yet but dimly—indeed even more dimly than he thought he saw twenty years ago.

But while the beauty of a problem solved excites the admiration and yields a certain sort of satisfaction, it is after all the unsolved problem, the quest of the unknown, the struggle for the unattained, which is of most universal and most thrilling interest. I make no apologies, therefore, for introducing in this chapter one of the great unsolved problems of modern physics, nor for leaving it with but the vaguest of suggestions toward a solution.

I. THE CORPUSCULAR AND THE ETHER THEORIES OF RADIATION

The newest of the problems of physics is at the same time the oldest. For nothing is earlier in the experiences either of the child or of the race than the sensation of receiving light and heat from the sun. But how does light get to us from the sun and the stars through the empty interstellar spaces? The Greeks answered this query very simply and very satisfactorily from the standpoint of people who were content with plausible explanations but had not yet learned perpetually to question nature experimentally as to the validity or invalidity of a conclusion. They said that the sun and all radiators of light and heat must shoot off minute corpuscles whose impact upon the eye or skin produces the sensations of light and warmth.

This corpuscular theory was the generally accepted one up to 1800 A.D. It was challenged, it is true, about 1680 by the Dutch physicist Huygens, who, starting with the observed phenomena of the transmission of water waves over the surface of a pond or of sound waves through the air, argued that light might be some vibratory disturbance transmitted by some medium which fills all interstellar space. He postulated the existence of such a medium, which was called the luminiferous or light-bearing ether.

Partly no doubt because of Newton's espousal of the corpuscular theory, the ether or wave theory gained few adherents until some facts of interference began to appear about 1800 which baffled explanation from the standpoint of the corpuscular theory, but which were easily handled by its rival. During the nineteenth century the evidence became stronger and stronger, until by its close the corpuscular theory had been permanently eliminated for four different reasons: (1) The facts of interference were not only found inexplicable in terms of it, but they were completely predicted by the wave theory. (2) The fact that the speed of propagation of light was experimentally found to be greater in air than in water was in accord with the demands of the ether theory, but directly contrary to the demands of the corpuscular theory. (3) Wireless waves had appeared and had been shown to be just like light waves save for wave-length, and they had been found to pass over continuously, with increasing wave-length, into static electrical fields such as could not possibly be explained from a corpuscular point of view.   (4) The speed of light had been shown to be independent of the speed of the source as demanded by the ether theory and denied by the corpuscular theory.

By 1900, then, the ether theory had become apparently impregnably intrenched.   A couple of years later it met with some opposition of a rather ill-considered sort, as it seems to me, from a group of extreme advocates of the relativity theory, but this theory is now commonly regarded, I think, as having no bearing whatever upon the question of the existence or non-existence of a luminiferous ether.   For such an ether was called into being solely for the sake of furnishing a carrier for electromagnetic waves, and it obviously stands or falls with the existence of such waves *in vacuo*, and this has never been questioned by anyone so far as I am aware.

II.   DIFFICULTIES CONFRONTING THE WAVE THEORY

Up to 1903, then, the theory which looked upon an electromagnetic wave as a disturbance which originated at some point in the ether at which an electric charge was undergoing a change in speed, and was propagated from that point outward as a spherical wave or pulse, the total energy of the disturbance being always spread uniformly over the wave front, had met with no serious question from any source.   Indeed, it had been extraordinarily successful, not only in accounting for all the known facts, but in more than one instance in predicting new ones. The first difficulty appeared after the discovery of the electron and in connection with the relations of the electron to the absorption or emission of such electromagnetic waves. It was first pointed out in 1903 by Sir J. J. Thomson in his Silliman lectures at Yale. It may be stated thus:

X-rays unquestionably pass over or pass all but an exceedingly minute fraction, say one in a thousand billion, of the atoms contained in the space traversed without spending any energy upon them or influencing them in any observable way. But here and there they find an atom from which, as is shown in the photographs opposite p. 189, they hurl a negative electron with enormous speed. This is the most interesting and most significant characteristic of X-rays, and one which distinguishes them from the α- and β-rays just as sharply as does the property of non-deviability in a magnetic field; for Figs. 14 and 15 and the plate opposite p. 189 show that neither α- nor β-rays ever eject electrons from the atoms through which they pass, with speeds comparable with those produced by X-rays, else there would be new zigzag lines branching out from points all along the paths of the α- and β-particles shown in these photographs.

But this property of X-rays introduces a serious difficulty into the ether theory. For if the electric intensity in the wave front of the X-ray is sufficient thus to hurl a corpuscle with huge energy from one particular atom, why does it not at least detach corpuscles from all of the atoms over which it passes?

Again when ultra-violet light falls on a metal it, too, like X-rays, is found to eject negative electrons. This phenomenon of the emission of corpuscles under the influence of light is called the photo-electric effect. Lenard[1] first made the astonishing discovery that the energy of ejection of the corpuscle is altogether independent of the intensity of the light which causes the ejection, no matter whether this intensity is varied by varying the distance of the light or by introducing absorbing screens. I have myself[2] subjected this relation to a very precise test and found it to hold accurately. Furthermore, this sort of independence has also been established for the negative electrons emitted by both X- and γ-rays.

Facts of this sort are evidently difficult to account for on any sort of a spreading-wave theory. But it will be seen that they lend themselves to easy interpretation in terms of a corpuscular theory, for if the energy of an escaping electron comes from the absorption of a light-corpuscle, then the energy of emission of the ejected electron ought to be independent of the distance of the source, as it is found to be, and furthermore corpuscular rays would hit but a very minute fraction of the atoms contained in the space traversed by them. This would explain, then, both the independence of the energy of emission upon intensity and the smallness of the number of atoms ionized.

In view, however, of the four sets of facts mentioned above, Thomson found it altogether impossible to go back to the old and exploded form of corpuscular theory for an explanation of the new facts as to the emission of electrons under the influence of ether waves. He accordingly attempted to reconcile these troublesome new facts with the wave theory by assuming a fibrous

[1] *Ann. d. Phys.* (4), VIII (1902), 149.
[2] *Phys. Rev.*, I (1913), 73.

structure in the ether and picturing all electromagnetic energy as traveling along Faraday lines of force conceived of as actual strings extending through all space. Although this concept, which we shall call the ether-string theory, is like the corpuscular theory in that the energy, after it leaves the emitting body, remains localized in space, and, when absorbed, is absorbed as a whole, yet it is after all essentially an ether theory. For in it the speed of propagation is determined by the properties of the medium and has nothing to do with the nature or condition of the source. Thus the last three of the fatal objections to a corpuscular theory are not here encountered. As to the first one, no one has yet shown that Thomson's suggestion is reconcilable with the facts of interference, though so far as I know neither has its irreconcilability been as yet absolutely demonstrated.

But interference aside, all is not simple and easy for Thomson's theory. For one encounters serious difficulties when he attempts to visualize the universe as an infinite cobweb whose threads never become tangled or broken however swiftly the electrical charges to which they are attached may be flying about.

III.   EINSTEIN'S QUANTUM THEORY OF RADIATION

Yet the boldness and the difficulties of Thomson's "ether-string" theory did not deter Einstein[1] in 1905 from making it even more radical. In order to connect it up with some results to which Planck of Berlin had been led in studying the facts of black-body radiation, Einstein assumed that the energy emitted by any radiator not only kept together in bunches or quanta as it traveled

[1] *Ann. d. Phys.* (4), XVII (1905), 132; XX (1906), 199.

through space, as Thomson had assumed it to do, but that a given source could emit and absorb radiant energy only in units which are all exactly equal to $h\nu$, ν being the natural frequency of the emitter and h a constant which is the same for all emitters.

I shall not attempt to present the basis for such an assumption, for, as a matter of fact, it had almost none at the time. But whatever its basis, it enabled Einstein to predict at once that the energy of emission of corpuscles under the influence of light would be governed by the equation

$$\tfrac{1}{2}mv^2 = Ve = h\nu - p \ \dots\dots\dots\dots\dots (41)$$

in which $h\nu$ is the energy absorbed by the electron from the light wave or light quantum, for, according to the assumption it was the whole energy contained in that quantum, p is the work necessary to get the electron out of the metal, and $\tfrac{1}{2}mv^2$ is the energy with which it leaves the surface—an energy evidently measured by the product of its charge e by the potential difference V against which it is just able to drive·itself before being brought to rest.

At the time at which it was made this prediction was as bold as the hypothesis which suggested it, for at that time there were available no experiments whatever for determining anything about how the positive potential V necessary to apply to the illuminated electrode to stop the discharge of negative electrons from it under the influence of monochromatic light varied with the frequency ν of the light, or whether the quantity h to which Planck had already assigned a numerical value appeared at all in connection with photo-electric discharge. We are confronted, however, by the astonishing situation that after ten years of work at the Ryerson Laboratory and elsewhere upon the discharge of electrons by light this equation of Einstein's seems to us to predict accurately all of the facts which have been observed.

IV. THE TESTING OF EINSTEIN'S EQUATION

The method which has been adopted in the Ryerson Laboratory for testing the correctness of Einstein's equation has involved the performance of so many operations upon the highly inflammable alkali metals in a vessel which was freed from the presence of all gases that it is not inappropriate to describe the present experimental arrangement as a machine-shop *in vacuo*. Fig. 27 shows a photograph of the apparatus, and Fig. 28 is a drawing of a section which should make the necessary operations intelligible.

One of the most vital assertions made in Einstein's theory is that the kinetic energy with which monochromatic light ejects electrons from any metal is proportional to the frequency of the light, i.e., if violet light is of half the wave-length of red light, then the violet light should throw out the electron with twice the energy imparted to it by the red light. In order to test whether any such linear relation exists between the energy of the escaping electron and the light which throws it out it was necessary to use as wide a range of frequencies as possible. This made it necessary to use the alkali metals, sodium, potassium, and lithium, for electrons are thrown from the ordinary metals only by ultra-violet light, while the alkali metals respond in this way to any waves shorter than those of the red, that is, they respond throughout practically the whole visible spectrum as well as the ultra-violet spectrum. Cast cylinders of these metals were therefore placed on the wheel W (Fig. 28) and fresh clean surfaces were obtained by cutting shavings from each metal in an excellent vacuum with the aid of the knife K, which was operated

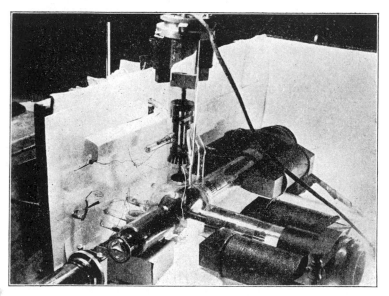

FIG. 27

by an electromagnet F outside the tube. After this the freshly cut surface was turned around by another electromagnet until it was opposite the point O of Fig. 28 and a beam of monochromatic light from a spectrometer was let in through O and allowed to fall on the new surface. The energy of the electrons ejected by it was measured by applying to the surface a positive potential just strong enough to prevent any of the discharged electrons from

reaching the gauze cylinder opposite (shown in dotted
lines) and thus communicating an observable negative

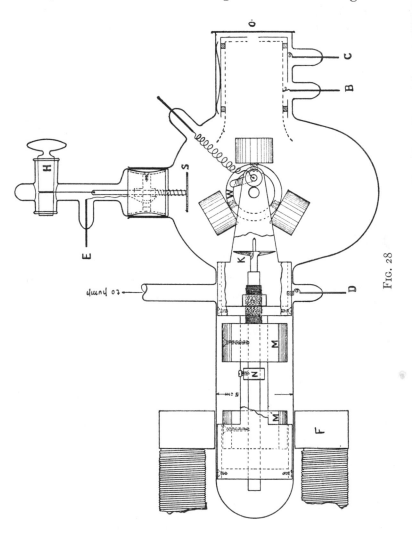

FIG. 28

charge to the quadrant electrometer which was attached
to this gauze cylinder. For a complete test of the

equation it was necessary also to measure the contact-electromotive force between the new surface and a test plate S. This was done by another electromagnetic device shown in Fig. 27, but for further details the original paper may be consulted.[1] Suffice it here to say that Einstein's equation demands a linear relation between the applied positive volts and the frequency of the light, and it also demands that the slope of this line should be exactly equal to $\dfrac{h}{e}$. Hence from this slope, since e is known, it should be possible to obtain h. How perfect a linear relation is found may be seen from Fig. 29, which also shows that from the slope of this line h is found to be 6.26×10^{-27}, which is as close to the value obtained by Planck from the radiation laws as is to be expected from the accuracy with which the experiments in radiation can be made. The most reliable value of h obtained from a consideration of the whole of this work is

$$h = 6.56 \times 10^{-27}.$$

In the original paper will be found other tests of the Einstein equation, but the net result of all this work is to confirm in a very complete way the equation which Einstein first set up on the basis of his semi-corpuscular theory of radiant energy. And if this equation is of general validity it must certainly be regarded as one of the most fundamental and far-reaching of the equations of physics, and one which is destined to play in the future a scarcely less important rôle than Maxwell's equations have played in the past, for it must govern the trans-

[1] *Phys. Rev.*, VII (1916), 362.

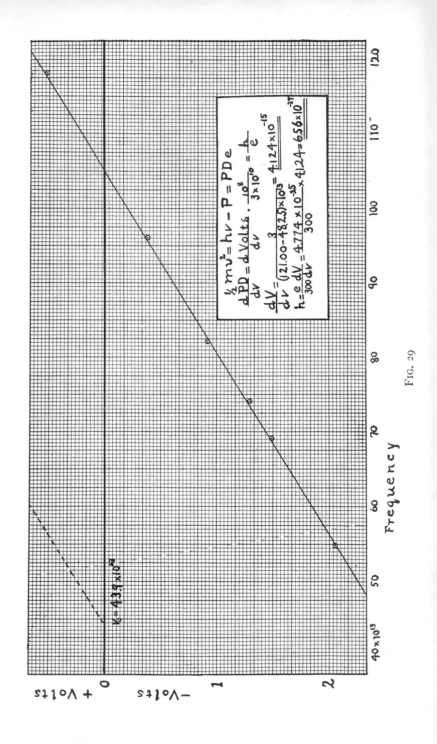

$\frac{1}{2}mv^2 = h\nu - P = PDe$

$\frac{dPD}{d\nu} = dVolts \cdot \frac{10^8}{3\times10^{10}} = \frac{h}{e}$

$\frac{dV}{d\nu} = \frac{3}{(121.00 - 48.25)\times10^{13}} = \frac{4.124\times10^{-15}}{}$

$h = \frac{e}{300}\frac{dV}{d\nu} = \frac{4.774\times10^{-25}}{300}\times4.124 = 656\times10^{-29}$

$V_0 = 43.9\times10^{13}$

Frequency

40×10^{13} 50   60   70   80   90   100   110   120$^-$

−Volts   0   + Volts

1

2

Fig. 29

formation of all short-wave-length electromagnetic energy into heat energy.

v. OBJECTIONS TO AN ETHER-STRING THEORY

In spite of the credentials which have just been presented for Einstein's equation, we are confronted with the extraordinary situation that the semi-corpuscular theory out of which Einstein got his equation seems to be wholly untenable and has in fact been pretty generally abandoned, though Sir J. J. Thomson[1] and a few others[2] seem still to adhere to some form of ether-string theory, that is, to some form of theory in which the energy remains localized in space instead of spreading over the entire wave front.

Two very potent objections, however, may be urged against all forms of ether-string theory, of which Einstein's is a particular modification. The first is that no one has ever yet been able to show that such a theory can predict any one of the facts of interference. The second is that there is direct positive evidence against the view that the ether possesses a fibrous structure. For if a static electrical field has a fibrous structure, as postulated by any form of ether-string theory, "each unit of positive electricity being the origin and each unit of negative electricity the termination of a Faraday tube,"[3] then the force acting on one single electron between the plates of an air condenser cannot possibly vary *continuously* with the potential difference

---

[1] *Proc. Phys. Soc. of London*, XXVII (December 15, 1914), 105.

[2] *Modern Electrical Theory*, Cambridge, University Press, 1913, p. 248.

[3] J. J. Thomson, *Electricity and Matter*, p. 9.

between the plates. Now in the oil-drop experiments[1] we actually study the behavior in such an electric field of one single, isolated electron and we find, over the widest limits, exact proportionality between the field strength and the force acting on the electron as measured by the velocity with which the oil drop to which it is attached is dragged through the air.

When we maintain the field constant and vary the charge on the drop, the granular structure of electricity is proved by the discontinuous changes in the velocity, but when we maintain the charge constant and vary the field the lack of discontinuous change in the velocity disproves the contention of a fibrous structure in the field, unless the assumption be made that there are an enormous number of ether strings ending in one electron. Such an assumption takes all the virtue out of an ether-string theory.

Despite then the apparently complete success of the Einstein equation, the physical theory of which it was designed to be the symbolic expression is found so untenable that Einstein himself, I believe, no longer holds to it, and we are in the position of having built a very perfect structure and then knocked out entirely the underpinning without causing the building to fall. It stands complete and apparently well tested, but without any visible means of support. These supports must obviously exist, and the most fascinating problem of modern physics is to find them. Experiment has outrun theory, or, better, guided by erroneous theory, it has discovered relationships which seem to be of the greatest interest and importance, but the reasons for them are as yet not at all understood.

[1] *Phys. Rev.*, II (1913), 109.

VI.   ATTEMPTS TOWARD A SOLUTION

It is possible, however, to go a certain distance toward a solution and to indicate some conditions which must be satisfied by the solution when it is found.   For the energy $h\nu$ with which the electron is found by experiment to escape from the atom must have come either from the energy stored up inside of the atom or else from the light.   There is no third possibility.   Now the fact that the energy of emission is the same, whether the body from which it is emitted is held within an inch of the source, where the light is very intense, or a mile away, where it is very weak, would seem to indicate that the light simply pulls a trigger in the atom which itself furnishes all the energy with which the electron escapes, as was originally suggested by Lenard in 1902,[1] or else, if the light furnishes the energy, that light itself must consist of bundles of energy which keep together as they travel through space, as suggested in the Thomson-Einstein theory.

Yet the fact that the energy of emission is directly proportional to the frequency ν of the incident light spoils Lenard's form of trigger theory, since, if the atom furnishes the energy, it ought to make no difference what kind of a wave-length pulls the trigger, while it ought to make a difference what kind of a gun, that is, what kind of an atom, is shot off.   But both of these expectations are the exact opposite of the observed facts.   *The energy of the escaping corpuscle must come then, in some way or other, from the incident light.*

When, however, we attempt to compute on the basis of a spreading-wave theory how much energy a corpuscle

[1] *Ann. d. Phys.* (4), VIII (1902), 149.

can receive from a given source of light, we find it difficult to find anything more than a very minute fraction of the amount which the corpuscle actually acquires.

Thus, the total luminous energy falling per second from a standard candle on a square centimeter at a distance of 3 m. is 1 erg.[1] Hence the amount falling per second on a body of the size of an atom, i.e., of cross-section 10^{-15} cm., is 10^{-15} ergs, but the energy $h\nu$ with which a corpuscle is ejected by light of wave-length 500 $\mu\mu$ (millionths millimeter) is 4×10^{-12} ergs, or 4,000 times as much. Since not a third of the incident energy is in wave-lengths shorter than 500 $\mu\mu$, a surface of sodium or lithium which is sensitive up to 500 $\mu\mu$ should require, even if all this energy were in one wave-length, which it is not, at least 12,000 seconds or 4 hours of illumination by a candle 3 m. away before any of its atoms could have received, all told, enough energy to discharge a corpuscle. Yet the corpuscle is observed to shoot out the instant the light is turned on. It is true that Lord Rayleigh has recently shown[2] that an atom may conceivably absorb wave-energy from a region of the order of magnitude of the square of a wave-length of the incident light rather than of the order of its own cross-section. This in no way weakens, however, the cogency of the type of argument just presented, for it is only necessary to apply the same sort of analysis to the case of γ-rays, the wavelength of which is of the order of magnitude of an atomic diameter (10^{-8} cm.), and the difficulty is found still more pronounced. Thus Rutherford[3] estimates that

---

[1] Drude, *Lehrbuch der Optik*, 1906, p. 472.

[2] *Phil. Mag.*, XXXII (1916), 188.

[3] *Radioactive Substances and the Radiations*, p. 288.

the total γ-ray energy radiated per second by one gram of radium cannot possibly be more than 4.7×10^4 ergs. Hence at a distance of 100 meters, where the γ-rays from a gram of radium would be easily detectable, the total γ-ray energy falling per second on a square millimeter of surface, the area of which is ten-thousand billion times greater than that either of an atom or of a disk whose radius is a wave-length, would be $4.7 \times 10^4 \div 4\pi \times 10^{10} = 4 \times 10^{-7}$ ergs. This is very close to the energy with which β-rays are actually observed to be ejected by these γ-rays, the velocity of ejection being about nine-tenths that of light. Although, then, it should take ten thousand billion seconds for the atom to gather in this much energy from the γ-rays, on the basis of classical theory, the β-ray is observed to be ejected with this energy as soon as the radium is put in place. This shows that if we are going to abandon the Thomson-Einstein hypothesis of localized energy, which is of course competent to satisfy these energy relations, there is no alternative but to assume that at some previous time the corpuscle had absorbed and stored up from light of this or other wave-length enough energy so that it needed but a minute addition at the time of the experiment to be able to be ejected from the atom with the energy $h\nu$.

Now the corpuscle which is thus ejected by the light cannot possibly be one of the free corpuscles of the metal, for such a corpuscle, when set in motion within a metal, constitutes an electric current, and we know that such a current at once dissipates its energy into heat. In other words, a *free* corpuscle can have no mechanism for storing up energy and then *jerking* itself up "by its boot straps" until it has the huge speed of emission observed.

The ejected corpuscle must then have come *from the inside of the atom*, in which case it is necessary to assume, if the Thomson-Einstein theory is rejected, that within the atom there exists some mechanism which will permit a corpuscle continually to absorb and load itself up with energy of a given frequency until a value at least as large as $h\nu$ is reached. What sort of a mechanism this is we have at present no idea. Further, if the absorption is due to resonance—and we have as yet no other way in which to conceive it—it is difficult to see how there can be, in the atoms of a solid body, corpuscles having all kinds of natural frequencies so that some are always found to absorb and ultimately be ejected by impressed light of any particular frequency. But apart from these difficulties, the thing itself is impossible if these absorbing corpuscles, when not exposed to radiation, are emitting any energy at all; for if they did so, they would in time lose all their store and we should be able, by keeping bodies in the dark, to put them into a condition in which they should show no emission of corpuscles whatever until after hours or years of illumination with a given wave-length. Since this is contrary to experiment, we are forced, even when we discard the Thomson-Einstein theory of localized energy, to postulate electronic absorbers which, during the process of absorbing, do not radiate at all until the absorbed energy has reached a certain critical value when explosive emission occurs.

However, then, we may interpret the phenomenon of the emission of corpuscles under the influence of ether waves, whether upon the basis of the Thomson-Einstein assumption of bundles of localized energy traveling through the ether, or upon the basis of a peculiar property of the inside of an atom which enables it to absorb continuously incident energy and emit only explosively, *the observed characteristics of the effect seem to furnish proof that the emission of energy by an atom is a discontinuous or explosive process.* This was the fundamental assumption of Planck's so-called quantum theory of radiation. The Thomson-Einstein theory makes both the absorption and the emission sudden or explosive, while the loading theory first suggested by Planck, though from another view-point, makes the absorption continuous and only the emission explosive.

The *h* determined above with not more than one-half of 1 per cent of uncertainty is the explosive constant, i.e., it is the unchanging ratio between the energy of emission and the frequency of the incident light. It is a constant the existence of which was first discovered by Planck by an analysis of the facts of black-body radiation, though the physical assumptions underlying Planck's analysis do not seem to be longer tenable. For the American physicists Duane and Hunt[1] and Hull[2] have recently shown that the same quantity *h* appears in connection with the impact of corpuscles against any kind of a target, the observation here being that the highest frequency in the general or white-light X-radiation emitted when corpuscles impinge upon a target is found by dividing the kinetic energy of the impinging corpuscle by *h*. Since black-body radiation is presumably due to the impact of the *free* corpuscles within a metal upon the atoms, it is probable that the

[1] *Phys. Rev.*, VI (1915), 166.   [2] *Ibid.*, VII (1916), 157.

appearance of h in black-body radiation and in general X-radiation is due to the same cause, so that, contrary to Planck's assumption, there need not be, in either of these cases, any coincidence between natural and impressed periods at all. The $h\nu$ which here appears is not a characteristic of the atom, but merely a property of the ether pulse which is generated by the stopping of a moving electron. Why this ether pulse should be resolvable into a continuous, or white-light spectrum which, however, has the peculiar property of being chopped off sharply at a particular limiting frequency given by $h\nu = PD \times e$ is thus far a complete mystery. All that we can say is that experiment seems to demand a sufficient modification of the ether-pulse theory of white-light and of general X-radiation to take this experimental fact into account.

On the other hand, the appearance of h in connection with the absorption and emission of *monochromatic* light (photo-electric effect and Bohr atom) seems to demand some hitherto unknown type of absorbing and emitting mechanism within the atom. This demand is strikingly emphasized by the remarkable absorbing property of matter for X-rays, discovered by Barkla[1] and beautifully exhibited in De Broglie's photographs opposite p. 197. It will be seen from these photographs that *the atoms of each particular substance transmit the general X-radiation up to a certain critical frequency and then absorbs all radiations of higher frequency than this critical value.* The extraordinary significance of this discovery lies in the fact that it indicates that there is a type of absorption which is not due either to resonance or

[1] *Phil. Mag.*, XVII (1909), 749.

to free electrons. But these are the only types of absorption which are recognized in the structure of modern optics. We have as yet no way of conceiving of this new type of absorption in terms of a mechanical model.

There is one result, however, which seems to be definitely established by all of this experimental work. Whether the radiation is produced by the stopping of a free electron, as in Duane and Hunt's experiments, and presumably also in black-body experiments, or by the absorption and re-emission of energy by bound electrons, as in photo-electric and spectroscopic work, Planck's h seems to be always tied up in some way with the emission and absorption of energy by the electron. *h may therefore be considered as one of the properties of the electron.*

The new facts in the field of radiation which have been discovered through the study of the properties of the electron seem, then, to require in any case a very fundamental revision or extension of classical theories of absorption and emission of radiant energy. The Thomson-Einstein theory throws the whole burden of accounting for the new facts upon the unknown nature of the ether and makes radical assumptions about its structure. The loading theory leaves the ether as it was and puts the burden of an explanation upon the unknown conditions and laws which exist inside the atom, and have to do with the nature of the electron. I have already given reasons for discrediting the first type of theory. The second type, though as yet very incomplete, seems to me to be the only possible one, and it has already met with some notable successes, as in the case of the Bohr atom. Yet the theory is at present woefully incomplete and hazy. About all that we can say now is that we seem to be driven by newly discovered relations in the field of radiation either to the Thomson-Einstein semi-corpuscular theory, or else to a theory which is equally subversive of the established order of things in physics. For either one of these alternatives brings us to a very revolutionary quantum theory of radiation. To be living in a period which faces such a complete reconstruction of our notions as to the way in which ether waves are absorbed and emitted by matter is an inspiring prospect. The atomic and electronic worlds have revealed themselves with beautiful definiteness and wonderful consistency to the eye of the modern physicist, but their relation to the world of ether waves is still to him a profound mystery for which the coming generation has the incomparable opportunity of finding a solution.

In conclusion there is given a summary of the most important physical constants the values of which it has become possible to fix,[1] within about the limits indicated, through the isolation and measurement of the electron.

The electron.................... $e = (4.774 \pm 0.005) \times 10^{-10}$

The Avogadro constant.......... $N = (6.062 \pm 0.006) \times 10^{23}$

Number of gas molecules per cc. at
   0°C. 76 cm................. $n = (2.705 \pm 0.003) \times 10^{19}$

Kinetic energy of translation of a
   molecule at 0°C............. $E_0 = (5.621 \pm 0.006) \times 10^{-14}$

Change of translational molecular
   energy per °C............... $\epsilon = (2.058 \pm 0.002) \times 10^{-16}$

Mass of an atom of hydrogen in grams $m = (1.662 \pm 0.002) \times 10^{-24}$

Planck's element of action... .... $h = (6.547 \pm 0.013) \times 10^{-27}$

Wien constant of spectral radiation $C_2 = 1.4312 \pm 0.0030$

Stefan-Boltzmann constant of total
   radiation .... $\sigma = (5.72 \pm 0.034) \times 10^{-12}$

Grating spacing in calcite........ $d = 3.030 \pm 0.001 Å$

[1] See *Proc. Nat. Acad. Sci.*, III (1917), 236; also *Phil. Mag.*, July, 1917.

APPENDIX A

ne FROM MOBILITIES AND DIFFUSION COEFFICIENTS

If we assume that gaseous ions, which are merely charged molecules or clusters of molecules, act exactly like the uncharged molecules about them, they will tend to diffuse just as other molecules do and will exert a partial gas pressure of exactly the same amount as would an equal number of molecules of any gas. Imagine then the lower part of the vessel of Fig. 30 to be filled with gas through which ions are distributed and imagine that these ions are slowly diffusing upward. Let n' be the ionic concentration, i.e., the number of ions per cubic centimeter at any distance x from the bottom of the vessel. Then the number N of ions which pass per second through 1 sq. cm. taken perpendicular to x at a distance x from the bottom must be directly proportional to the concentration gradient $\dfrac{dn'}{dx}$ and the factor of proportionality in a given gas is by definition the diffusion coefficient D of the ions through this gas, i.e.,

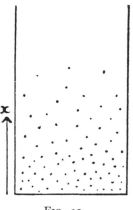

Fig. 30

$$N = D\frac{dn'}{dx} \dots\dots\dots\dots\dots (42)$$

But since N is also equal to the product of the average velocity V with which the ions are streaming upward at

x by the number of ions per cubic centimeter at x, i.e., since $N = n'V$, we have from equation (42)

$$V = \frac{D}{n'}\frac{dn'}{dx}.$$

The force which is acting on these n'-ions to cause this upward motion is the difference in the partial pressure of the ions at the top and bottom of a centimeter cube at the point x. It is, therefore, equal to $\frac{dp}{dx}$ dynes, and the ratio between the force acting and the velocity produced by it is

$$\frac{\dfrac{dp}{dx}}{\dfrac{D}{n'}\dfrac{dn'}{dx}}.$$

Now this ratio must be independent of the particular type of force which is causing the motion. Imagine then the same n'-ions set in motion, not by the process of diffusion, but by an electric field of strength F. The total force acting on the n'-ions would then be Fen', and if we take v as the velocity produced, then the ratio between the force acting and the velocity produced will now be $\frac{Fen'}{v}$. By virtue then of the fact that this ratio is constant, whatever kind of force it be which is causing the motion, we have

$$\frac{Fen'}{v} = \frac{\dfrac{dp}{dx}}{\dfrac{D}{n'}\dfrac{dn'}{dx}} \quad \cdots\cdots\cdots\cdots\cdots (43)$$

Now if v_0 denote the velocity in unit field, a quantity which is technically called the "ionic mobility," $\dfrac{v}{F} = v_0$. Again since the partial pressure p is proportional to n', i.e., since $p = Kn'$, it follows that $\dfrac{dp}{p} = \dfrac{dn'}{n'}$. Hence equation (43) reduces to

$$\frac{en'}{v_0} = \frac{1}{\dfrac{D}{p}}$$

or

$$v_0 = De\frac{n'}{p} \dotfill (44)$$

But if we assume that, so far as all pressure relations are concerned, the ions act like uncharged molecules (this was perhaps an uncertain assumption at the time, though it has since been shown to be correct), we have $\dfrac{n'}{p} = \dfrac{n}{P}$ in which n is the number of molecules per cubic centimeter in the air and P is the pressure produced by them, i.e., P is atmospheric pressure. We have then from equation (44)

$$ne = \frac{v_0 P}{D} \dotfill (45)$$

APPENDIX B

TOWNSEND'S FIRST ATTEMPT AT A DETER-MINATION OF e

Fig. 31 shows the arrangement of apparatus used. The oxygen rising from the electrode E is first bubbled through potassium iodide in A to remove ozone, then through water in B to enable the ions to form a cloud. This cloud-laden air then passes through a channel in an electrical insulator—a paraffin block P—into the tubes

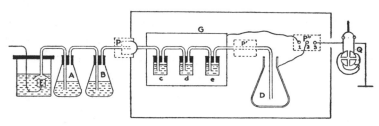

FIG. 31

c, d, e, which contain concentrated sulphuric acid. These drying tubes remove all the moisture from the air and also such part of the charge as is held on ions which in the process of bubbling through c, d, e have actually touched the sulphuric acid. The dry air containing the rest of the charge passes out through a channel in the paraffin block P' into the flask D. (If the gas being studied was lighter than air, e.g., hydrogen, D was of course inverted.) The outside of D is covered with tin foil which is connected to one of the three mercury cups held by the paraffin block P''. If the air in D contained at first no charge, then an electrical charge exactly equal to the quantity of electricity which enters the flask D will appear by induction on the tin-foil coating which covers this flask and this quantity q_1 can be measured by connecting the mercury cup 2 to cup 3 which is connected to the quadrant electrometer Q, and observing the deflection per minute. Precisely similarly the total quantity of electricity which is left per minute in the drying tubes c, d, e is exactly equal to the quantity which appears by induction on the outer walls of the hollow metal vessel G, which surrounds the tubes c, d, e. This quantity q_2 can be measured by connecting mercury cup 1 to cup 3 and observing the deflection per minute of the quadrant electrometer. The number of cubic centimeters of gas which pass through the apparatus per minute is easily found from the number of amperes of current which are used in the electrolysis apparatus E and the electro-chemical equivalent of the gas. By dividing the quantities of electricity appearing per minute in D and G by the number of cubic centimeters of gas generated per minute we obtain the total charge per cubic centimeter carried by the cloud.

The increase in weight of the drying tubes c, d, e per cubic centimeter of gas passing, minus the weight per cubic centimeter of saturated water vapor, gives the weight of the cloud per cubic centimeter. This completes the measurements involved in (2) and (3), p. 45.

As to (4), p. 46, the average size of the droplets of water Townsend found by passing the cloud emerging from B into a flask and observing how long it took for the top of the cloud to settle a measured number of centimeters. The radius of the drops could then be obtained from a purely theoretical investigation made by Sir George Stokes,[1] according to which the velocity v_I of fall of a spherical droplet through a gas whose co-efficient of viscosity was η is given by

$$v_\mathrm{I} = \frac{2}{9}\frac{ga^2}{\eta}\sigma$$

in which σ is the density of the droplet. From this Townsend got the average radius a of the droplets and computed their average weight m by the familiar formula $m = \frac{4}{3}\pi a^3\sigma$. He was then ready to proceed as in (5), see p. 46.

[1] Lamb, *Hydronamics*, 1895, p. 533.

APPENDIX C

THE BROWNIAN-MOVEMENT EQUATION

A very simple derivation of this equation of Einstein has been given by Langevin of Paris[1] essentially as follows: From the kinetic theory of gases we have $PV = RT = \frac{1}{3}Nm\overline{c^2}$ in which $\overline{c^2}$ is the average of the squares of the velocities of the molecules, N the number of molecules in a gram molecule, and m the mass of each. Hence the *mean* kinetic energy of agitation E of each molecule is given by $E = \frac{1}{2}m\overline{c^2} = \frac{3}{2}\frac{RT}{N}$.

Since in observations on Brownian movements we record only motions along one axis, we shall divide the total energy of agitation into three parts, each part corresponding to motion along one of the three axes, and, placing the velocity along the x-axis equal to $\frac{dx}{dt}$, we have

$$\frac{E}{3} = \frac{1}{2}m\left(\overline{\frac{dx}{dt}}\right)^2 = \frac{1}{2}\frac{RT}{N} \quad \ldots\ldots\ldots\ldots (46)$$

Every Brownian particle is then moving about, according to Einstein's assumption, with a mean energy of motion along each axis equal to $\frac{1}{2}\frac{RT}{N}$. This motion is due to molecular bombardment, and in order to write an equation for the motion at any instant of a particle subjected to such forces we need only to know (1) the

[1] *Comptes Rendus*, CXLVI (1908), 530.

value X of the x-component of all the blows struck by the molecules at that instant, and (2) the resistance offered by the medium to the motion of the particle through it. This last quantity we have set equal to Kv and have found that in the case of the motion of oil droplets through a gas K has the value $6\pi\eta a\left(1+A\dfrac{l}{a}\right)^{-1}$. We may then write the equation of motion of the particle at any instant under molecular bombardment in the form

$$m\frac{d^2x}{dt^2} = -K\frac{dx}{dt}+X \ldots\ldots\ldots\ldots\ldots (47)$$

Since in the Brownian movements we are interested only in the absolute values of displacements without regard to their sign, it is desirable to change the form of this equation so as to involve x^2 and $\left(\dfrac{dx}{dt}\right)^2$. This can be done by multiplying through by x. We thus obtain, after substituting for $x\dfrac{d^2x}{dt^2}$ its value $\frac{1}{2}\dfrac{d^2(x^2)}{dt^2}-\left(\dfrac{dx}{dt}\right)^2$,

$$\frac{m}{2}\frac{d^2(x^2)}{dt^2} - m\left(\frac{dx}{dt}\right)^2 = -\frac{K}{2}\frac{d(x^2)}{dt}+Xx\ldots\ldots\ldots (48)$$

Langevin now considers the *mean* result arising from applying this equation at a given instant to a large number of different particles all just alike.

Writing then z for $\dfrac{d\overline{(x^2)}}{dt}$ in which $\overline{x^2}$ denotes the mean of all the large number of different values of x^2, he gets after substituting $\dfrac{RT}{N}$ for $m\left(\dfrac{dx}{dt}\right)^2$, and remembering that in taking the mean, since the X in the last term is as likely to be positive as negative and hence that $\overline{Xx}=0$,

$$\frac{m}{2}\frac{dz}{dt}-\frac{RT}{N}=-\frac{Kz}{2}.$$

Separating the variables this becomes

$$\frac{dz}{\left(z-\dfrac{2RT}{NK}\right)}=-\frac{K}{m}dt,$$

which yields upon integration between the limits o and τ

$$z=\frac{2RT}{NK}+Ce^{-\frac{K}{m}\tau}\dots\dots\dots\dots(49)$$

For any interval of time τ long enough to measure this takes the value of the first term. For when Brownian movements are at all observable, a is 10^{-4} cm. or less, and since K is roughly equal to $6\pi\eta a$ we see that, taking the density of the particle equal to unity,

$$\frac{m}{K}=\frac{\frac{4}{3}\pi(10^{-4})^3}{6\pi.00018\times10^{-4}}=10^{-5}.$$

Hence when τ is taken greater than about 10^{-5} seconds, $e^{-\frac{K}{m}\tau}$ rapidly approaches zero, so that for any measurable time intervals

$$z=\frac{2RT}{NK}$$

or

$$\frac{d(\overline{x^2})}{dt}=\frac{2RT}{NK}$$

and, letting $\overline{\Delta x^2}$ represent the change in $\overline{x^2}$ in the time τ

$$\overline{\Delta x^2} = \frac{2RT}{NK}\tau \dots\dots\dots\dots (50)$$

This equation means that if we could observe a large number n of exactly similar particles through a time τ, square the displacement which each undergoes along the x-axis in that time, and average all these squared displacements, we should get the quantity $\frac{2RT}{NK}\tau$. But we must obviously obtain the same result if we observe the same identical particle through n-intervals each of length τ and average these n-displacements. The latter procedure is evidently the more reliable, since the former must assume the exact identity of the particles.

APPENDIX D

THE INERTIA OR MASS OF AN ELECTRICAL CHARGE ON A SPHERE OF RADIUS a

If Fig. 32 represents a magnet of pole area A, whose two poles are d cm. apart, and have a total magnetization M, a density of magnetization σ, and a field strength between them of H, then the work necessary to carry a unit pole from M to M' is Hd, and the work necessary to create the poles M and M', i.e., to carry M units of magnetism across against a mean field strength $\dfrac{H}{2}$ is $\dfrac{HMd}{2}$. Hence the total energy E_1 of the magnetic field is given by

$$E_1 = \frac{HMd}{2} = \frac{HA\sigma d}{2},$$

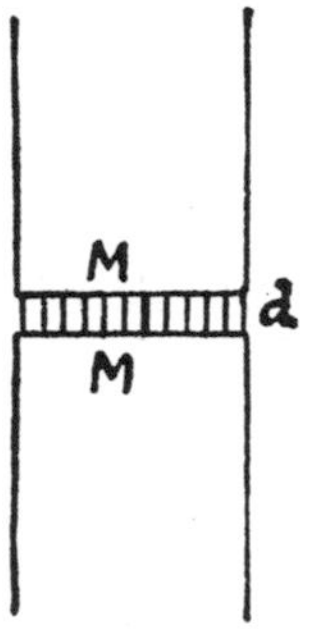

but since $H = 4\pi\sigma$

$$E_1 = \frac{H^2 A d}{8\pi},$$

FIG. 32

or since Ad is the volume of the field the energy E per unit volume of the magnetic field is given by

$$E = \frac{H^2}{8\pi} \dots\dots\dots\dots\dots (51)$$

Now the strength of the magnetic field at a distance r from a moving charge in the plane of the charge is $\dfrac{ev}{r^2}$, if e is the charge and v its speed. Also the magnetic field strength at a point distant $r\theta$ from the charge, θ being the angle between r and the direction of motion, is given by

$$H = \frac{ev}{r^2}\sin\theta .$$

Hence the total energy of the magnetic field created by the moving charge is

$$\int E d\tau = \int \frac{H^2}{8\pi} d\tau$$

in which τ is an element of volume and the integration is extended over all space. But in terms of v, θ, and ϕ.

$$d\tau = rd\theta, \, dr, \, r\sin\theta d\phi$$

$\therefore$ Total energy$=$

$$\frac{e^2v^2}{8\pi}\int \frac{\sin^2\theta}{r^4}d\tau = \frac{e^2v^2}{8\pi}\int_a^\infty \frac{dr}{r^2}\int_0^{2\pi} d\phi \int_0^\pi \sin^3\theta d\theta = \frac{e^2v^2}{3a} .$$

Since kinetic energy $= \frac{1}{2}mv^2$, the mass-equivalent m of the moving charge is given by setting

$$\frac{1}{2}mv^2 = \frac{e^2v^2}{3a}$$

$$\therefore \quad m = \frac{2}{3}\frac{e^2}{a} \dots\dots\dots\dots\dots (52)$$

The radius of the spherical charge which would have a mass equal to the observed mass of the negative electron is found by inserting in the last equation $e = 4.774 \times 10^{-10}$

electrostatic units $= 1.591 \times 10^{-20}$ electromagnetic units and $\dfrac{e}{m} = 1.767 \times 10^7$ electromagnetic units. This gives $a = 1.9 \times 10^{-13}$ cm.

The expression just obtained for m obviously holds only so long as the magnetic field is symmetrically distributed about the moving charge, as assumed in the integration, that is, so long as v is small compared with the velocity of light. When v exceeds .1 the speed of light c, the mass of the charge begins to increase measurably and becomes infinite at the speed of light. According to the theory developed by Lorenz, if the mass for slow speeds is called m_0 and the mass at any speed v is called m, then

$$\frac{m}{m_0} = \frac{1}{\sqrt{1 - \dfrac{v^2}{c^2}}} \quad\dots\dots\dots\dots\dots\dots (53)$$

This was the formula which Bucherer found to hold accurately for the masses of negative electrons whose speeds ranged from .3 to .8 that of light.

APPENDIX E

MOLECULAR CROSS-SECTION AND MEAN FREE PATH

If there is one single molecule at rest in a cubical space 1 cm. on a side, the chance that another molecule which is shot through the cube will impinge upon the one contained is clearly $\frac{\pi d^2}{1}$ in which d is the mean diameter of the two molecules. If there are n contained molecules the chance is multiplied by n, that is, it becomes $\frac{n\pi d^2}{1}$. But on the average the chance of an impact in going a centimeter is the number of impacts actually made in traversing this distance. The mean free path l is the distance traversed divided by the number of impacts made in going that distance. Hence

$$l = \frac{1}{n\pi d^2} \quad \dots\dots\dots\dots\dots\dots (54)$$

This would be the correct expression for the mean free path of a molecule which is moving through a group of molecules at rest. If, however, the molecules are all in motion they will sometimes move into a collision which would otherwise be avoided, so that the collisions will be more numerous when the molecules are in motion than when at rest—how much more numerous will depend upon the law of distribution of the speeds of the molecules. It is through a consideration of the Maxwell distribution law that the factor $\sqrt{2}$ is introduced into the denominator (see Jeans, *Dynamical Theory of Gases*) so that equation (54) becomes

$$l = \frac{1}{\sqrt{2}n\pi d^2} \quad \dots\dots\dots\dots\dots\dots (55)$$

APPENDIX F

NUMBER OF FREE POSITIVE ELECTRONS IN THE NUCLEUS OF AN ATOM BY RUTHERFORD'S METHOD

If N represents the number of free positive electrons in the nucleus, e the electronic charge, E the known charge on the α-particle, namely $2e$, and $\frac{1}{2}mV^2$ the known kinetic energy of the α-particle, then, since the inertias of the negative electrons are quite negligible in comparison with that of the α-particle, if the latter suffers an appreciable change in direction in passing through an atom it will be due to the action of the nuclear charge. If b represents the closest possible approach of the α-particle to the center of the nucleus, namely, that occurring when the collision is "head on," and the α-particle is thrown straight back upon its course, then the original kinetic energy $\frac{1}{2}mV^2$ must equal the work done against the electric field in approaching to the distance b, i.e.,

$$\tfrac{1}{2}mV^2 = \frac{NeE}{b} \quad \dots\dots\dots\dots\dots (56)$$

Suppose, however, that the collision is not "head on," but that the original direction of the α-particle is such that, if its direction were maintained, its nearest distance of approach to the nucleus would be p (Fig. 33). The deflection of the α-particle will now be, not 180°, as before, but some other angle ϕ. It follows simply from the geometrical properties of the hyperbola and the elementary principles of mechanics that

$$p = \frac{b}{2} \cot \frac{\phi}{2} \quad \dots \dots \dots \dots \dots \dots (57)$$

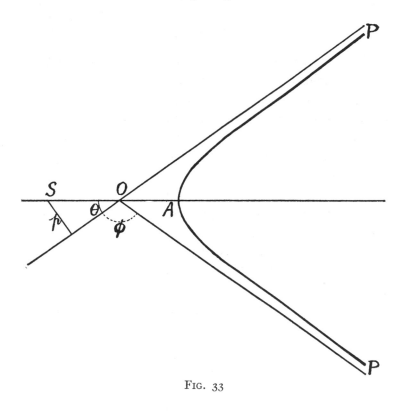

Fig. 33

For let PAP' represent the path of the particle and let $POA = \theta$. Also let $V =$ velocity of the particle on entering the atom and v its velocity at A. Then from the conservation of angular momentum

$$pV = SA \cdot v \dots \dots \dots \dots \dots \dots (58)$$

and from conservation of energy

$$\tfrac{1}{2}mV^2 = \tfrac{1}{2}mv^2 + \frac{NeE}{SA}$$

$$\therefore \quad v^2 = V^2\left(1 - \frac{b}{SA}\right) \dots\dots\dots\dots (59)$$

Since the eccentricity $\epsilon = \sec\theta$, and for any conic the focal distance is the eccentricity times one-half the major axis, i.e., $SO = OA \cdot \epsilon$, it follows that

$$SA = SO + OA = SO\left(1 + \frac{1}{\epsilon}\right) = p \; csc \; \theta(1 + \cos\theta) = p\cot\frac{\theta}{2}.$$

But from equations (58) and (59)

$$p^2 = SA(SA - b) = p\cot\frac{\theta}{2}\left(p\cot\frac{\theta}{2} - b\right)$$

$$\therefore \quad b = 2p\cot\theta \dots\dots\dots\dots (60)$$

and since the angle of deviation ϕ is $\pi - 2\theta$, it follows that

$$\cot\frac{\phi}{2} = \frac{2p}{b} \dots\dots\dots (61) \quad \text{Q.E.D.}$$

Now it is evident from the method used in Appendix E that if there are n atoms per cubic centimeter of a metal foil of thickness t, and if each atom has a radius R, then the probability M that a particle of size small in comparison with R will pass through one of these atoms in shooting through the foil is given by

$$M = \pi R^2 nt.$$

Similarly the probability m that it will pass within a distance p of the center of an atom is

$$m = \pi p^2 nt.$$

If this probability is small in comparison with unity, it represents the fraction ρ of any given number of particles shooting through the foil which will actually come within a distance p of the nucleus of an atom of the foil.

The fraction of the total number which will strike within radii p and $p+dp$ is given by differentiation as

$$dm = 2\pi pnt \cdot dp$$

but from equation (57)

$$dp = -\frac{b}{2}\frac{1}{2}csc^2\frac{\phi}{2}d\phi$$

$$\therefore \quad dm = -\frac{\pi}{4}ntb^2 \cot\frac{\phi}{2} \, csc^2\frac{\phi}{2}d\phi.$$

Therefore the fraction ρ which is deflected between the angles ϕ_1 and ϕ_2 is given by integration as

$$\rho = \frac{\pi}{4}ntb^2\left(\cot^2\frac{\phi_1}{2} - \cot^2\frac{\phi_2}{2}\right)$$

It was this fraction of a given number of α-particles shot into the foil which Geiger and Marsden found by direct count by the scintillation method to be deflected through the angles included between any assigned limits ϕ_1 and ϕ_2. Since n and t are known, b could be at once obtained. It was found to vary with the nature of the atom, being larger for the heavy atoms than for the lighter ones, and having a value for gold of 3.4×10^{-12} cm. This is then an upper limit for the size of the nucleus of the gold atom.

As soon as b has thus been found for any atom, equation (56) can be solved for N, since E, e, and $\frac{1}{2}mV^2$ are all known. It is thus that the number of free positive electrons in the nucleus is found to be roughly half the atomic weight of the atom, and that the size of the nucleus is found to be very minute in comparison with the size of the atom.

APPENDIX G

BOHR'S THEORETICAL DERIVATION OF THE VALUE OF THE RYDBERG CONSTANT

The Newtonian equation of a circular orbit of an electron e rotating about a central attracting charge E, at a distance a, with a rotational frequency n, is

$$\frac{eE}{a^2} = (2\pi n)^2 ma \dots \dots \dots \dots \dots (62)$$

The kinetic energy of the electron is $\frac{1}{2}m(2\pi na)^2 = \frac{1}{2}\frac{eE}{a}$. The work required to move the electron from its orbit to a position at rest at infinity is $\frac{eE}{a} - \frac{1}{2}m(2\pi na)^2 = \frac{1}{2}\frac{eE}{a}$. If we denote this quantity of energy by T, it is seen at once that

$$2a = \frac{eE}{T}$$

and

$$n = \frac{\sqrt{2}T^{\frac{3}{2}}}{\pi eE\sqrt{m}} \dots \dots \Bigg\} \dots \dots \dots (63)$$

If we combine this with (37), p. 209, there results at once

$$T = \frac{2\pi^2 me^2 E^2}{\tau^2 h^2} \qquad 2a = \frac{\tau^2 h^2}{2\pi^2 meE} \qquad n = \frac{4\pi^2 me^2 E^2}{\tau^3 h^3} \dots (64)$$

Upon change in orbit the radiated energy must be

$$T_{\tau_1} - T_{\tau_2} = \frac{2\pi^2 me^2 E^2}{h^2}\left(\frac{1}{\tau_1^2} - \frac{1}{\tau_2^2}\right),$$

and, if we place this equal to $h\nu$, there results the Balmer formula (34), p. 206,

$$\nu = N\left(\frac{1}{\tau_1^2} - \frac{1}{\tau_2^2}\right)$$

in which

$$N = \frac{2\pi^2 e^2 E^2}{h^3}.$$

Since for hydrogen $E = e$, we have

$$N = \frac{2\pi^2 m e^4}{h^3}$$

and from (60)

$$a = \frac{\tau^2 h^3}{4\pi^2 m e^4}.$$

APPENDIX H

THE ELEMENTS, THEIR ATOMIC NUMBERS, ATOMIC WEIGHTS, AND CHEMICAL POSITIONS

1 H
1.008

0	I	II	III	IV	V	VI	VII	VIII
2 He 3.99	3 Li 6.94	4 Be 9.1	5 B 11.0	6 C 12.00	7 N 14.01	8 O 16.00	9 F 19.0	
10 Ne 20.2	11 Na 23.00	12 Mg 24.32	13 Al 27.1	14 Si 28.3	15 P 31.04	16 S 32.06	17 Cl 35.46	
18 A 39.88	19 K 39.10	20 Ca 40.07	21 Sc 44.1	22 Ti 48.1	23 V 51.0	24 Cr 52.0	25 Mn 54.93	26 Fe 55.84 27 Co 58.97 28 Ni 58.68
....	29 Cu 63.57	30 Zn 65.37	31 Ga 69.9	32 Ge 72.5	33 As 74.96	34 Se 79.2	35 Br 79.92	
36 Kr 82.92	37 Rb 85.45	38 Sr 87.63	39 Y 88.7	40 Zr 90.6	41 Nb 93.5	42 Mo 96.0	43 —	44 Ru 101.7 45 Rh 102.9 46 Pd 106.7
....	47 Ag 107.88	48 Cd 112.40	49 In 114.8	50 Sn 118.7	51 Sb 120.2	52 Te 127.5	53 J 126.92	
54 X 130.2	55 Cs 132.81	56 Ba 137.37	57 La 139.0	58 Ce 140.25	59 Pr 140.6	60 Nd 144.3	61– 62 Sm 150.4	63 Eu 152 64 Gd 157.3 65 Tb 159.2 66 Ds 162.5
67 Ho 163.5	68 Ev 167.7	69 Tu 168.5	70 Yb 173.5	71 Lu 175.0 72 —	73 Ta 181.5	74 W 184.0	75 —	76 Os 190.9 77 Ir 193.1 78 Pt 195.2
....	79 Au 197.2	80 Hg 200.6	81 Tl 204.0	82 Pb 207.20	83 Bi 208.0	84 Po (210.0)	85 —	
86 Em (222.0)	87 —	88 Ra 226.0	89 Ac (227)	90 Th 232.15	UrX$_2$ (234)	92 Ur 238.2	....	....

Elements, the atomic numbers of which are not in the order of atomic weights, are in italics. The numbers corresponding to missing elements are in bold-faced type.

1 Hydrogen
2 Helium
3 Lithium
4 Beryllium
5 Boron
6 Carbon
7 Nitrogen
8 Oxygen
9 Fluorine
10 Neon
11 Sodium
12 Magnesium
13 Aluminium
14 Silicon
15 Phosphorus
16 Sulphur
17 Chlorine
18 Argon
19 Potassium
20 Calcium
21 Scandium
22 Titanium
23 Vanadium
24 Chromium
25 Manganese
26 Iron
27 Cobalt
28 Nickel
29 Copper
30 Zinc
31 Gallium
32 Germanium
33 Arsenic
34 Selenium
35 Bromine
36 Krypton
37 Rubidium
38 Strontium
39 Yttrium
40 Zirconium
41 Niobium
42 Molybdenum
43 ———
44 Rhuthenium
45 Rhodium
46 Paladium
47 Silver
48 Cadmium
49 Indium
50 Tin
51 Antimony
52 Tellurium
53 Iodine
54 Xenon
55 Caesium
56 Barium
57 Lanthanum
58 Cerium
59 Praseodymium
60 Neodymium
61 ———
62 Samarium
63 Europium
64 Gadolinium
65 Terbium
66 Dyprosium
67 Holmium
68 Erbium
69 Thulium
70 Ytterbium
71 Lutecium
72 ———
73 Tantalum
74 Tungsten
75 ———
76 Osmium
77 Iridium
78 Platinum
79 Gold
80 Mercury
81 Thallium
82 Lead
83 Bismuth
84 Polonium
85 ———
86 Emanation
87 ———
88 Radium
89 Actinium
90 Thorium
91 Uranium X$_2$
92 Uranium

INDEXES

AUTHOR INDEX

SUBJECT INDEX